GAMES

American Boxed Games
and Their Makers 1822–1992

with values

CHIVALRY

Copyright 1888
BY GEO. S. PARKER & CO. — SALEM, MASS.

CHIVALRY.

Easily Learned and conceded to be the
most Pleasing Modern Board
Game of Skill.

Entered according to Act of Congress in the year 1888, by
GEO. S. PARKER & CO.,
in the office of the Librarian of Congress, at Washington, D. C.

CHIVALRY.
A GAME OF SKILL.

DIRECTIONS FOR TWO PLAYERS.

THE PIECES.

Each player's force consists of twenty pieces ;
one player taking the 12 yellow MEN and 8
yellow KNIGHTS with black tips, the other player
taking the 12 red MEN and 8 red KNIGHTS tipped
with black.

Place the board so that each player has two
gold-starred squares directly in front of him.

Each player should place his twenty pieces
in two straight ranks on the squares having
round gold spots in the centre, *with four knights*
on each flank on the gold spots marked with a
small letter "K."

THE OBJECT OF THE GAME.

In order to *win the game* a player must get

(3)

GAMES

American Boxed Games and Their Makers 1822–1992

with values

Bruce Whitehill

Wallace-Homestead Book Company
RADNOR, PENNSYLVANIA

Published in Radnor, Pennsylvania 19089, by
Wallace-Homestead, a division of Chilton Book Company

Unless otherwise indicated, all black and white photographs are by the author and all games pictured are from the author's collection.
Color photography by Jim Conroy

Front cover: RAMBLES THROUGH OUR COUNTRY, American Publishing; GAME OF PLAYING DEPARTMENT STORE, McLoughlin Bros.; BUSTER BROWN AT THE CIRCUS, Selchow & Righter. *Back cover:* THE FOUR DARE-DEVILS, Marx, Hess & Lee; DIM THOSE LIGHTS, Alderman-Fairchild; THE BIG GAME HUNT, Wilder; THE GAME OF TOM SAWYER, Milton Bradley; JACKIE GLEASON'S "AND AWA-A-A-A-Y WE GO" TV FUN GAME, Transogram; MARLIN PERKINS' ZOO PARADE, Cadaco-Ellis; LITTLE SHOPPERS, Gibson Game Co.

Title page photo courtesy of Pat Mautner.

Designed by Adrianne Onderdonk Dudden
Manufactured in the United States of America

Library of Congress Cataloging in Publication Data
Whitehill, Bruce.
Games : American boxed games and their makers, 1822–1992, with values / Bruce Whitehill.
p. cm.
Includes bibliographical references and indexes.
ISBN 0-87069-583-5
1. Board games—United States—History. 2. Board games—Collectors and collecting—United States. I. Title.
GV1312.W48 1992
794—dc20 91-50683
CIP

1 2 3 4 5 6 7 8 9 0 1 0 9 8 7 6 5 4 3 2

The author is engaged in continuing research on the history of American games and game companies and would be interested in hearing from other collectors and researchers. Please send any information, including additions, corrections, and comments on this book, to Bruce Whitehill, 620 Park Ave., #202, Rochester, NY 14607-2994.

This book is dedicated to

John Mautner (1929–87),

Frank Simon (1941–91),

and **George Sanborn** (1943–91),

ardent collectors whose enthusiasm and knowledge were appreciated and enjoyed by many. The information about games and collecting they shared with me has made a significant contribution to this book.

As per his last request, the back of John Mautner's tombstone pays tribute to his love for games with an engraving of "Mr. Pennybags," the character that adorned many a Monopoly game.

Contents

Acknowledgments

First and foremost I would like to thank those special friends and fellow collectors who provided considerable information for this book, who allowed me to photograph games from their collections, and who helped with the evaluations of the games listed in Part Three and the proofreading of the manuscript: Paul Fink, Debby and Marty Krim, Pat McFarland and Nancy Boyea, and David Oglesby and Susan Stock. (Information about their collecting expertise follows this section.)

I would like to acknowledge the people in the game industry and their descendants who provided information about company histories or particular games. They include Barbara Allen, Ralph Anspach, Benjamin Bain, Jim Becker and Jonathan Becker (of Anjar), Les Berger, Babette Bole, Darwin Bromley, Alfred Butts, Robert Butts, William Cass, Jr., Jeff Conrad, Julie Cooper, Evelyn Cuoco, William Hill, Ralph Kaufman, Ken Kolsbun, Mike Meyers, Phyllis Opolko, Philip Orbanes (author of *The Monopoly Companion*), Stephen Peek (author of *Gameplan: The Game Inventor's Handbook*), Jim Prentice, Jim Pressman, Lynn Pressman, Sandy Shellhase, Marvin Silverman, and Ron Weingartner (co-author of *Inside Santa's Workshop*).

Special thanks to fellow collectors and researchers who contributed specific material or information, especially Bill Alexander, Herb Levy, Steve Olin (who assisted with pricing and proofreading the listings), Alex Malloy, Sid Sackson (author of *A Gamut of Games* and other works), Herb Siegel, and Ann Williams (author of *Jigsaw Puzzles*). Thanks also to Joe Angiolillo, Richard Bueschel (author of books on bagatelle games), Lee Dennis (author of *Antique American Games*), Steve Fadem (descendant of Transogram founder, Charles Raizen), David Galt, Ted Hake (author of *Hake's Guide to TV Collectibles*), John and Wendy Overall (owners of the home of Henry Dutton Degen, partner in the game-producing company of Degen & Estes), Harry Rinker (columnist and author/editor of books on antiques and collectibles), Richard Russack, and Blair Whitton (author of books on R. Bliss, among others).

I would also like to thank the antique and collectible dealers who, in saving "Bruce" games over the years, have helped me build the collection that eventually prompted the writing of this book. These dealers include Richard Sternfeld, Mary Donaldson and Roberta Sackin (of Pekl), Gary Darrow (Darrow's Fun Antiques), Ken Farrell (Just Kids), Peter Boody (The Paper Tiger), and Betty Messenger.

Thanks to Pat Mautner, Allan Petretti, Dr. Stephen M. Sheppard, Robert Bruce, Patti Becker, and the American Antiquarian Society; to the people with answers to my research questions who phoned me from The Connecticut Trolley Museum, The National Railway Museum in Wisconsin, Dow Chemical Information Services, and the U.S. Post Office Communication Support Division; to R.C. Bell, whose books boosted my enthusiasm; and to Chris Kitchell for the processing and printing of the black and white photos. Also, I greatly appreciate the help of the research volunteers and staff at the Public Libraries of Princeton (NJ), New York City, Great Neck (NY), and West Springfield (MA), and to Gail Kolglazier of the Connecticut Valley Historical Museum.

Special thanks go to the members of the American Game Collectors Association who have provided not only moral support but information about games and game collecting. Some of the many AGCA members who have been especially helpful over time in providing data for this book include Bill and Betty Barnard, Bill and Debby Boyd, Mark and Sharon Carron, Arlan Coffman, Bert Cohen, Bob DeCenzo, John and Anna Ellerbe, William and Mary Furnish, Elayne Heitner, Robert Henry, Dale Kelley, Pat Laffin, Joyce Magee, Jan McDerment, Gary Medeiros, Carol Monica, Roy and Grace Olson, Rick Polizzi, Wayne Saunders, Michael Shor, Will Shortz, Jerry Slocum, Alfonzo Smith, Bill Smith, John and Mildred Spear, Diana Tillson, Lindy and Jim Van Fleet, and Les Zakarin.

I would also like to thank a number of people for various contributions or for their long-term advice, support, and interest: Judy Emerson, Barbara Niman, Sue Whitehill ("the Big Game Hunter's mother," according to her tee-shirt, who provided the special kind of support every writer needs), and Ruth Steinman and Hy Whitehill. So many people have been of assistance that it is impossible to mention them all; I apologize to anyone whose name I have inadvertently left out—thank you!

Contributors and Resources

The best resources for information on games are the individuals who collect them and research them. Many dedicated collectors, dealers, and historians have assisted me in the writing of this book. The individuals listed here have been particularly helpful in furnishing material and providing information and suggestions; these knowledge-

An appreciative smile (as shown in Wilder's STAR FLIGHT, 1920s) goes out to all those who assisted in making this book possible.

able collectors and researchers welcome correspondence from readers about games and the game industry. Each listing provides details about the individual's *special collecting or historical interests.* (**Important:** When writing, please include a self-addressed stamped envelope; however, please understand that because of the volume of mail received, not all inquiries can receive responses. When telephoning, please make sure you're calling between 10 a.m. and 9 p.m. in *their* time zone. Note that, since the value of a game is subjective, controlled by many factors, and subject to fluctuating market conditions, collectors usually will *not* answer inquiries over the phone or by mail regarding what a game is worth.).

Paul Fink Box 266, Kent, CT 06757; (203) 927-4001
Transportation games, Art Deco-style games, and the "streamline" look; also black character games, radio games, and games by All-Fair.

Debby and Marty Krim P.O. Box 2273, West Peabody, MA 01960; (508) 535-3140
Wide range of games from early McLoughlin to television and character collectible games; also sports games. Owners of the New England Auction Gallery.

Pat McFarland and Nancy Boyea Box 161, Averill Park, NY 12018; (518) 674-8390
Specializing in games by Elizabeth Magie Phillips (THE LANDLORD'S GAME, BARGAIN DAY, MOCK TRIAL, KING'S MEN, and BUSINESS); researching Phillips and the origins of MONOPOLY and other financial games,

such as FORTUNE, FINANCE, and the first EASY MONEY; also a wide range of games from the late 1800s through the 1950s.

Susan Stock and David Oglesby (Wizard of Os), 57 Lakeshore Drive, Marlboro, MA 01752; (508) 481-1087
Diversified collection ranging from the earliest board games to television and character collectible games.

Bill Alexander 4628 S.E. Barlow Drive, Bartlesville, OK 74006
Games from the West and Midwest, especially Oklahoma; primarily card games, especially from small companies. In addition, Bill Alexander over the years has researched and compiled material on game companies and the games they produced. Bill is past editor of the American Game Collector's Association's *Game Times* and editor of *Game Researcher's Notes* and "The Game Directory."

Bruce Whitehill (The Big Game Hunter)
620 Park Ave., #202, Rochester, NY 14607-2994
Specializing in small American game companies, unusual games, and all catalogs, advertising premiums, and paper ephemera relating to games; continuously researching the history of games and game companies and the relationship between games and American culture; especially interested in information on and games by Cadaco (California only), H.B. Chaffee and Chaffee & Selchow, Einson-Freeman, E.G. Selchow and Selchow & Righter, J.C. Singer, Stoll & Edwards, Stoll & Einson, and W.G. Young, and all games from 1937.

Introduction

Games: A Mirror to the Past

Games are an art form as well as symbols of our cultural history. People collect games for many reasons: the play value, the historical significance, the love of the art and design, and for nostalgia. A more recent phenomenon shows people collecting games also for the investment potential.

Game playing has always been an important part of our culture, though in the nineteenth century a game was as likely to be educational or morally instructive as it was to be fun. Strategy games from ancient times have evolved over centuries to become some of the classics that we still play today. Inventors of modern games understand that games should reflect the balance of luck and skill that is

The setting, the clothing, and the theme of the GAME OF CROQUET (McLoughlin, 1870) give us a glimpse of American culture over a century ago. (Krim collection)

THE GREAT AMERICAN WAR GAME by J.H. Hunter (1899) is about the Civil War. (Mautner collection)

a part of life, and the better, more recent entries to the market leave less to the throw of the dice and demand more thought and imagination from the player.

Many collectors revel in the way a game records and reflects a part of America's past. Researchers are intrigued at how much the study of antique American games can tell us about our customs and traditions. Historical collectors look for games about America's personalities and politics, games about social periods, from peacetime through war, and games that served as the tools that helped educate Americans before the era of mass communication.

Collectors of early games are awed by the beautiful box cover illustrations or the exceptional designs of the colorful gameboards. Many are intrigued by the game implements—intricate metal tokens, tiny dice made of wood, bone, or even metal, carved wooden playing pieces, unusual cards, and other paraphernalia. The art, the graphic design, the construction, the materials are all important, as is the way these elements fit together to make the complete game.

Games from the 1960s and 1970s, and even some from the 1980s, are already collectible—out-of-print games that help freeze a time in recent social history. Collectors of newer games such as character collectibles or TV-related games are often caught up in the sentimental appeal

McLoughlin's LOST IN THE WOODS (± 1895) is as much a work of art as any painting from the period. (Mautner collection)

THE CAPTIVE PRINCESS from 1875 captures
McLoughlin's artistic style both in the gameboard and the
intricate paper-on-wood playing pieces.

of the game. Some see collecting the games from their
childhood as a connection with their past. Unlike their
counterparts in search of earlier games, these collectors
are not trying to "discover" as much as to "remember."

Whatever the reason for collecting games, and whatever era the games come from, people have begun to see
collecting games as an enjoyable pastime, *and* as an investment. As interest in the hobby grows, so do the prices of
games, and there is every reason to think this escalation
in the value of games will continue.

Game Manufacturing in the United States

The games played in the United States prior to the middle
of the nineteenth century were imported from other countries, mostly Britain. Simpler games were drawn on slate,
carved into wood, put on parchment, or even drawn in
the dirt or sand. The gameboards that have survived from
earlier times, usually carved or painted wood, are considered folk art today.

American playing cards date back to the colonial era,
but card *games* (different from the four-suit, thirteen-card-
per-suit decks) were probably not manufactured commercially until the early 1800s. The first known copy of an
American-manufactured board game is dated 1822, but
the industry didn't take hold until the 1840s, when W. &
S.B. Ives started publishing card and board games.

Ives did well, especially in a business with minimal
competition. John McLoughlin began producing games in
the 1850s, and his success led to the formation of
McLoughlin Brothers in 1858. The McLoughlin name has
become the most important name for collectors of early
games.

Innovations in printing allowed for the mass production of games by 1860, and the work of the hand-coloring
artist all but disappeared. During the 1880s and 1890s,
rebounding from the depression of the 1870s, companies
such as McLoughlin Brothers, R. Bliss, E.I. Horsman, and
J.H. Singer produced well-made games with exceptional
lithography, along with two companies whose names are
still with us today: Milton Bradley and Parker Brothers.

Selchow & Righter, the company that brought out
SCRABBLE and TRIVIAL PURSUIT, was another early,
influential firm, though the firm sold other companies'
games and did not begin manufacturing its own until the
1920s. Many games produced during this period were still
educational, but fewer involved moral teachings, and
games became accepted as a form of leisure recreation for
the family.

By the late nineteenth century, American society had
begun to change rapidly. Industrialization led to a migra-
tion from the farms to the cities. Immigration rates rose
significantly as an infusion of different cultures moved
into the mainstream. Major advances were made in transportation and communication. Companies expanded
their regional sales areas and began to compete for the
same dollars.

By the early 1900s companies had turned to cutting
costs to increase profits. Games no longer had the same
sparkle—the coloring was less vibrant, the artwork
showed less attention to detail, the boxes were of less
substantial construction. The industry was now being run
by a new generation as the "old guard" died off or retired.

The Roaring Twenties, a time of gaiety (and gangster-
ism), was good for the game industry. The end of war
meant industry could turn from the war effort to the
home front. Americans had earned the right to enjoy their
leisure. Mah-Jongg became a craze, and Parker Brothers
and Milton Bradley, as well as a host of smaller companies, cashed in. Chinese checkers, introduced by a fledg-
ling J. Pressman Company, also became a fad. The Toy
Manufacturers of America, headquartered in New York,
became a strong, cohesive force for the industry. Many
events—the discovery of Tut's tomb, Charles Lindbergh's
flight, Admiral Richard Byrd's development of a "Little
America" base in Antarctica, and America's fixation with
the automobile—all became the subject of games as
games continued to reflect what was happening in society.

Then came the Great Depression of 1929. The game
industry didn't feel the Depression until around 1932,
because like movies, games provided inexpensive entertainment during troubled times. Backgammon was revived and jigsaw puzzles became popular. Most firms
weathered the difficult period, and 1936 and 1937 began

A magnificent game from the height of the Depression was
BUCK ROGERS 25TH CENTURY AD (John F. Dille
Co.,1934), which featured three exceptional folding
gameboards: "Siege of Gigantica," "Secrets of Atlantis,"
and "Cosmic Rocket Wars." (Krim collection)

another boom, with companies filling sturdier game boxes with more parts and pieces than ever before. New companies emerged, and a new game allowing players to make millions, MONOPOLY, became the rage.

The turbulence in Europe in the 1930s led to war, and once again we had to turn our manufacturing efforts toward defense. War games and games promoting patriotism and the United States naturally became popular. In 1941, Milton Bradley cut its game line from 410 to 150. As always, war took its toll, and some companies were forced out of the game business. But with recovery came new companies—and the popularization of a device that changed the course of culture. It wasn't a game box that changed the American game industry, it was a "box" called television. Television had two direct effects: it offered a form of leisure activity that took time away from other pastimes, such as playing games, and it allowed advertisers to reach a mass market. But perhaps more important, television affected the family, hastened our loss of innocence, and changed the way we lived.

Only the larger game companies could afford to advertise on television. Obtaining television show licenses for games became a major concern. More attention was given to the name and character on the game box than to the product inside. And the distribution of games changed as well, with large retail outlets in shopping centers replacing the small, independent toy stores.

The economic restrictions of World War II coupled with the dramatic changes in the game industry as a result of television less than a decade later forced many smaller companies out of business. In time, Parker Brothers was bought out, then Milton Bradley, then Selchow & Righter. Coleco, which had bought the 119-year-old family-owned firm of Selchow & Righter, went bankrupt. By the early 1990s, Hasbro, the small Rhode Island company that had made games in the 1950s under the name "Hassenfeld Bros.," owned the lot: Bradley, Parker, Selchow, Ideal, and a few others were all under the same roof, with the games operation centered at the Milton Bradley plant in Springfield, Massachusetts. This consolidation marked the end of an era that had flourished for more than a century and a half.

American Games: The Newest Collectible

Game collecting, as a hobby, was almost unheard of in 1980. The category of "toys and games" meant toys almost exclusively in the collecting arena. Few magazine articles or books ever mentioned American games, and little

GAME OF THE CHRISTMAS JEWEL, a McLoughlin gem, is a treasure inside and out and could be bought for pocket money in the 1970s and early 1980s.

KATE SMITH'S OWN GAME AMERICA, by Toy Creations, was war time patriotism in a package.

This collectible work of art is a section of the gameboard from Milton Bradley's FAST MAIL.

information was known about the companies that manufactured them.

Between 1978 and 1986, several things contributed to the phenomenal growth in the interest in games: the publication of Lee Dennis's article in Time-Life Books' *The Encyclopedia of Collectibles;* oversize, lavish books by British authors R. C. Bell and Brian Love; the formation of The American Game Collectors Association in 1985; my monthly "The Game Piece" feature in *Antique Toy World* magazine; numerous game exhibits; and the publication of Lee Dennis's *Antique American Games* in 1986.

As more games were brought out, as more articles were written, and as more collectors met, games began to come into their own as collectibles. Now games are advertised separately from toys. The garage sale bargains of under $25 have given way to auction prices into the thousands; rapidly escalating prices have commanded attention— and respect—for a burgeoning field. At the 1988 auction of the Dennis collection, McLoughlin's "Man in the Moon" was sold for $4,600; a short time later an unbelievable $31,000 was paid for an original hand-colored Darrow "Monopoly"! In 1992 at an auction of the Siegel collection, a Bliss "Game of Shopping" sold for $1500, while a rare

McLoughlin "Bulls and Bears" fetched an unexpected $28,000!

How to Use This Book

This book is devoted to the study of board games, card games, and skill-and-action games commercially manufactured in the United States. The book has three primary functions: (1) to provide a history of games, focusing on some of the major companies and the games they produced, (2) to advise both the beginning and experienced collector how to develop and maintain a game collection, and (3) to help collectors determine the relative value of a game.

Part I provides a brief history of games, beginning with ancient games and games from Africa, the Orient, and Europe and the game industry in the United States up to the present.

All the information the reader needs to start and maintain a game collection can be found in Part Two. It includes advice on buying, selling, cataloging, cleaning, repairing, displaying, and storing games. Also included are two special chapters, one on cross-collectible games— games that depict a theme of interest to collectors in other fields—and one on how to determine the date of a game.

Part Three is a guide to the game companies and the games they produced. Major and noteworthy American game companies are included, along with detailed histories of some of those companies. Game titles are listed, with current values for those games traded in the marketplace. There is also an exclusive section on how to determine the relative value of a game not listed in the book.

Two unique appendixes of cultural events and patents are aimed at the collector and the researcher. Another appendix is a listing of over 550 game companies not covered in the text.

Finally, in addition to a bibliography and index, there is a complete index of game titles, which also shows at a glance the manufacturing company and date of each of the games covered in this book.

PART ONE

A Brief History of American Games

Games Around the World

Ancient Games

Games have been a tool of education and moral teaching as well as a form of recreation for thousands of years. There are some claims that the first board games, games of MANCALA or WARI, may date back 7,000 years. The game of SENAT found in 1922 in the tomb of King Tut is known to be from about 3000 B.C., and another game board found in Egypt has been dated at somewhere between 4000 to 3500 B.C.

Identifying the earliest dates and even the country of origin of ancient games is difficult because these games have evolved over the centuries; sometimes the modern successor bears little resemblance to its early ancestor. Historians need to examine implements and play patterns to determine if the movement of playing pieces in two similar games suggests that one is the antecedent of the other.

The origin of games can be traced back to many countries and continents. Classic games are ones that have been played around the world for generations, in one form or other: MANCALA games were played in Egypt and the area around the Red Sea, and are still popular around the world, especially in Africa. CHECKERS, called DRAUGHTS in England, dates back to the twelfth century; CHESS was said to have originated either in India in A.D. 600 or China before A.D. 200; and BACKGAMMON, a variation of a game called TABULA (known as CHASING THE GIRLS in Iceland), goes back to the first century. Many of these early strategy games employed tactical maneuvers closely associated with warfare, the goal being to outmaneuver or outrace an opponent, or to trap an opponent's pieces or remove them from play.

DOMINOES, another world favorite, has a more clouded beginning: it is probably Chinese, its origin being between the first and twelfth centuries; DOMINOES are actually "flattened dice," the early sets and Oriental versions having one to six "pips" per half block and not having any blank halves. JACKS, now with star-shaped metal pieces, was played more than 2,000 years ago in Greece as KNUCKLEBONES, the name given it because it was played with the knucklebones of sheep.

How Games Survived

Most of the first American-made games were based on games from Europe, especially Britain, though the games may have originated in Africa and the Orient hundreds or thousands of years before.

REVERSI began as the game of ANNEXATION in England in the 1880s, and was brought to the United States a few years later (then eighty years later won an award as "best new game" under the name OTHELLO).

MAH-JONGG (spelled various ways and known by different names), had been the favorite game in China for centuries before it was introduced into this country around 1922. The game proved so popular and was so heavily imported under different names that in 1924 Congress declared that all imported sets had to be stamped with the name "Mah-Jongg." The early sets cannot be used with modern MAH-JONGG rules, especially since the number of tiles has changed, but collectors look for the early wood, bamboo, and especially ivoroid or ivory tiles that came packaged in unique wooden boxes with levels or drawers. The name "Mah-Jongg" means "sparrow of a hundred intelligences," and the game, like DOMINOES, was meant to be played with noisy abandon, players creating a clamor by slapping the hard tiles against one another and against the table top.

Another game we know today, PARCHEESI, one of the most popular games in the world with its different titles and variations, was the national game of India, where it originated more than 1,200 years ago.

NINE MEN'S MORRIS, known also as MORELLES or MILL, was popular among ancient civilizations, with the oldest boards having been found in Egypt. Versions of the game were played by Indians in America's Southwest. A NINE MEN'S MORRIS board drawn over a map of the United States received a design patent (a new, visual application of an old idea) in 1918, though the game was manufactured here long before then.

GO, an ancient game still popular in Japan, was introduced to Europe and the United States around the 1880s. GO-BANG, known in Britain also as SPOILS FIVE, was taken from GO-MOKU, which also originated in Japan. The game may have been played in the United States long before it received U.S. patent number 255,892 in 1882.

FOX AND GEESE dates back to twelfth-century Europe, probably originating in Iceland. The fox must capture enough geese so they cannot surround him, while the sixteen geese try to trap the fox so he cannot move. A good example of how games tell us something about the society from which they emerged is borne out by North American Indians playing this game with pieces representing a coyote and chickens.

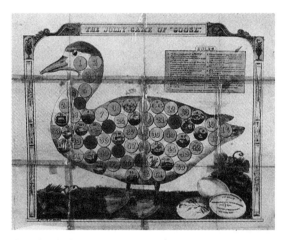

THE JOLLY GAME OF "GOOSE," from 1851, (J.P. Beach, N.Y.) the earliest known American version of the European classic, is an almost exact reverse copy of Laurie's NEW AND ENTERTAINING GAME OF THE GOLDEN GOOSE from England.

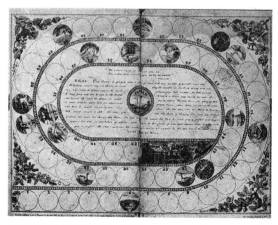

THE GAME OF GOOSE, 1855; vice versus virtue on a path spiralling toward the center.

FOX AND GEESE, 1945, by Stafford Products.

The GAME OF GOOSE, sent by Francesco de Medici in Italy to King Phillip II of Spain in the sixteenth century, became one of the most popular games in Europe. The earliest known American revision of GOOSE is from 1851, and its principle of virtue rewarded and vice punished in terms of movement along the gameboard path fit in well with the moral attitudes of the period. Rewarding good deeds or good luck and punishing bad deeds or bad luck was also the theme of the popular SNAKES AND LADDERS, and influenced many early American games, including Milton Bradley's first game, the CHECKERED GAME OF LIFE.

2

Beginnings of the American Game Industry, 1823–1900

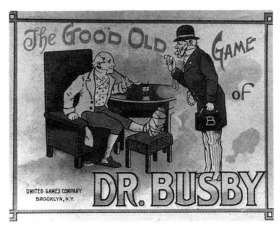

THE GOOD OLD GAME OF DR. BUSBY, United Games Co. (connected with Parker Brothers), Brooklyn, N.Y. (Fink collection)

Native Americans patterned game boards into the dirt and carved implements out of wood or bone. Early settlers in the United States played games that were copied from or brought from other countries. Although American-made playing cards were used in colonial America, games that used special cards were not manufactured in the United States until the late 1700s or early 1800s, and American-made board games did not appear until much later. Historian Katharine Morrison McClinton, in her book *Antiques of American Childhood,* mentions games of travel, history, and geography, which were "advertised by Nicholas Brooks in the *Pennsylvania Packet* as early as July 31, 1775," but it is not clear whether these games were of British or American manufacture.

Games with Cards

Few American-made card games have been found prior to 1840, and not until 1843 did any of them become widespread. In that year, W. & S. B. Ives of Salem, Massachusetts, published DR. BUSBY, probably the country's first popular card game. DR. BUSBY was a "game of families," with cards illustrating five members from each of four families; it was similar to games from France and elsewhere in Europe that had different numbers of families and family members. Ives was the most prominent name in American games prior to the emergence of McLoughlin in the 1850s. John McLoughlin began producing card games in 1850, and games using cards began to proliferate; other small printing and lithography companies, probably able to produce card games inexpensively through their printing operations, added games to their line of prints and paper goods. The box covers of many nineteenth-century games read "Published by . . . ," rather than "Manufactured by . . ."

Card games often employed small question-and-answer cards on history, geography, or literature; some were illustrated and, up until around 1860, hand-colored. These were the early games that helped educate America's youth. One of the popular forms of card game was called "conundrums," in which blank sections in a story were filled in with words or phrases written on small card strips. (A variation of this became popular in the 1950s, called MAD-LIBS.) The most popular of the conundrum games was PETER CODDLES, copyrighted in 1858 by Gould & Lincoln of Boston and based on its book, *Jessie, or Trying to be Somebody,* one of the series of "Aimwell" stories. Peter Coddles became a very well-traveled character, with many different companies putting out such titles as PETER CODDLES' TRIP TO NEW YORK and PETER CODDLES' TRIP TO BOSTON. The PETER CODDLES games put out by companies such as McLoughlin and Parker Brothers late in the 1800s usually depicted an older, sometimes bearded man on the cover; the Peter Coddles of 1858, however, was described as a boy of eighteen.

In 1861, August Smith produced what was to become another widespread game, AUTHORS, similar to the European game of QUARTET, which probably originated in Germany; two years earlier D.O. Goodrich of Boston had published PRESIDENTIAL QUARTETS (a game that probably succeeded an earlier game of "generic" QUARTETS). The Whipple & Smith AUTHORS game was either not protected by copyright or trademark laws, or, more likely, the laws were ignored, as was often the case (at least up until the new International Copyright law was passed in 1891); through the years, probably every major company published its own version of AUTHORS.

The First Board Games

The earliest gameboards were printed on paper and later on linen-backed paper, and by the 1840s board games were made by pasting a lithographed sheet on a piece of

Four AUTHORS games by different companies. (Fink collection)

Detail from Milton Bradley's BAMBOOZLE, OR THE ENCHANTED ISLE, 1876.

cardboard. The 18″ × 18″ board size used in the 1870s or even earlier (Milton Bradley's 1876 game of BAMBOO-ZLE, for example) is the same size used for most of the gameboards today, a result of standardization in printing and manufacturing.

Because games were expected to be instructive and educational, a large proportion of the nineteenth-century board games used maps and were based on history and geography.

The first American-manufactured board game that has been found is TRAVELLER'S TOUR THROUGH THE UNITED STATES, made in 1822 by F. & R. Lockwood, a family of New York booksellers. TRAVELLER'S TOUR THROUGH EUROPE is another Lockwood game sold later the same year. The lack of English imports after trade restrictions with Great Britain were imposed in 1809 may

have paved the way for companies such as Lockwood to manufacture their own games.

No record has surfaced showing any American company manufacturing board games for twenty years after 1822, though one would expect to find other games made during this period. The manufacture of board games in the United States resumed again in 1843 with the publication of the MANSION OF HAPPINESS by W. & S.B. Ives.

For over a century it was commonly thought that the Ives game was America's first board game. This myth was propagated even as early as 1894; the box cover of the Parker Brothers' MANSION OF HAPPINESS of that year read, "The first board game ever published in America." It is understandable, then, why the story persisted (and continued to be published) right through the 1980s, until some researchers discovered and examined the Lockwood game found in a New England museum. Another interesting point is that TRAVELLER'S TOUR THROUGH THE UNITED STATES appears to be purely American, whereas the MANSION OF HAPPINESS is a direct copy of its English namesake invented around 1800.

Games with a Moral

The MANSION OF HAPPINESS was based on the same moral concept as the GAME OF GOOSE, a popular game from Europe. The GAME OF GOOSE was the standard vice-versus-virtue game of the period, with players traveling a spiral path from a corner of the board into the center, and where virtue was rewarded by allowing the player to move ahead, while vice acted as a stumbling block, even forcing the player back to start. The first known American rendition, the JOLLY GAME OF GOOSE, was published as a folded paper board by J.P Beach of New York City in 1851. The game is nearly the exact copy of Laurie's NEW AND ENTERTAINING GAME OF THE GOLDEN GOOSE, copyrighted in 1848 in London, except that the design is reversed.

In the MANSION OF HAPPINESS, when a player landed on a space denoting a virtue, the player was directed to move ahead toward the Mansion of Happiness; when landing on a space illustrating one of the vices, the player was instructed to move back toward start. For example, a player who landed on space number fourteen, marked "Passion," had to return to space number six, "The Water"; the rule read: "Whoever gets in a Passion must be taken to the Water and have a ducking [sic] to cool him." Landing on Idleness sent the player to Poverty; players on the Road to Folly had to return to Prudence; the Perjurer was put in Pillory (a wooden framework with holes for the head and hands); the Sabbath Breaker was "taken to the Whipping Post and whipt"; any player who reached the Summit of Dissipation (a state of wastefulness) went to Ruin.

On the gameboard, printed under the title, was "an instructive moral and entertaining amusement." This was followed by a poem:

> At this amusement each will find
> A moral fit t' improve the mind;
> It gives to those their proper due,

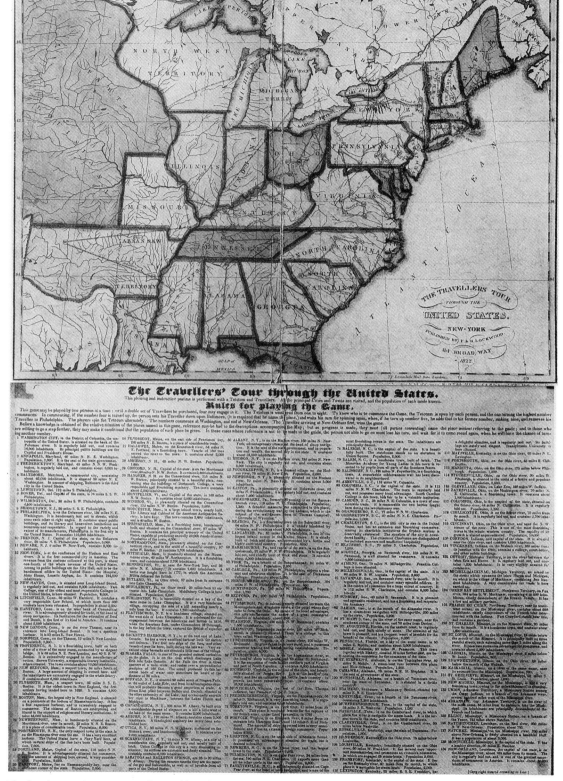

The first known American-manufactured board game, TRAVELLERS TOUR THROUGH THE UNITED STATES, 1822, F. & R. Lockwood. (Courtesy American Antiquarian Society)

Who various paths of vice pursue,
And shows (while vice destruction brings)
That good from every virtue springs.
Be virtuous then and forward press,
To gain the seat of happiness.

The tone of the game can be summed up best by two of the rules: "Whoever possesses Piety, Honesty, Temperance, Gratitude, Prudence, Truth, Chastity, Sincerity, Humility, Industry, Charity, Humanity, or Generosity is entitled to advance . . . toward the Mansion of Happiness.

"Whoever possesses Audacity, Cruelty, Immodesty, or Ingratitude, must return to his former situation . . . and not even *think* of Happiness, much less partake of it."

Milton Bradley's first game, the CHECKERED GAME OF LIFE, made in 1860, was similar: movement was on a checkerboard, with a player's move being one or two spaces left, right, or diagonally. The path took the player from Infancy to Happy Old Age. Landing on Bravery sent the player to Honor, Perseverance to Success, and Ambition to Fame. Gambling led to Ruin, and Idleness to Disgrace.

From Ives's MANSION OF HAPPINESS and Bradley's CHECKERED GAME OF LIFE alone one can gain some understanding about the concept of leisure time in that period. In the Ives's game Dissipation led to Ruin, and in the Bradley game, Idleness to Disgrace. Amusements were allowed, of course, but even the youngest children had much more responsibility than today's youth in the home and in the workplace.

No Dice

Movement of the playing pieces in the MANSION OF HAPPINESS and the CHECKERED GAME OF LIFE was governed by a teetotum, a top with numbers on the side, or one made by inserting a wooden shaft into a piece of cardboard (usually hexagonal or octagonal). Because of the religious and moral fervor during the mid-1800s, gambling was frowned upon and the dice so often associated with gambling games were considered "tools of the devil." Teetotums and spinners replaced dice in many

Teetotum from Ives's THE NATIONAL GAME OF THE AMERICAN EAGLE.

games. When the teetotum stopped spinning, the uppermost number dictated the number of spaces or the direction a player was allowed to move. The family taboo against dice was so strong that soldiers during the Civil War who carried them to gamble with would leave them behind when going into battle, so in case they were killed in combat, no dice would be sent back to the family as part of the soldier's personal effects. Because of this, Civil War battlefields are said to be an excellent place to unearth early bone dice.

The Major Game Manufacturers

W. & S.B. Ives published at least two dozen games between 1843 and 1853 and is credited with being the first major manufacturer of games in this country. After the dissolution of the partnership in 1853, the Ives family continued to make games into the 1880s.

Advances in commercial chromolithography around 1860 contributed greatly to the proliferation of game companies and the production of games. The artistry of the gameboards, boxes, and illustrated cards was made even more outstanding by the vibrant colors produced with the new technology.

McLoughlin Brothers, formed in 1858, is considered

Box from post-1860 version of the CHECKERED GAME OF LIFE.

THE GAME OF CITY LIFE OR THE BOYS OF NEW YORK
(McLoughlin Bros., 1889) contained cards illustrated with
"the scenes, characters, and incidents common to life in a
large city"; these characters include: wife beater, cruel
woman, strong-minded woman, street gamin, rum seller,
defaulting bank cashier, capitalist, dude, and the corner
loafer. (Mautner collection)

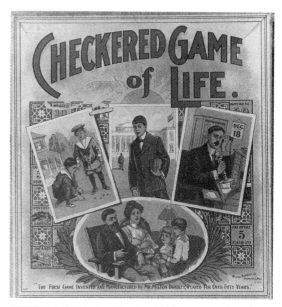

CHECKERED GAME OF LIFE, >1910. This repackaged
edition of Milton Bradley's 1860 game reads, "the first
game invented by Mr. Milton Bradley, played for over 50
years." (Mautner collection)

CHIVALRY, Geo. S. Parker's favorite game.

the granddaddy of American game companies. Beginning
with the rare, hand-colored card games produced by John
McLoughlin between 1850 and 1858, McLoughlin turned
out wonderfully illustrated board and card games that
some consider the most beautiful games ever published
in the United States. The company reached its peak in the
1880s and 1890s with superb games that reflected popular culture; many were quite large, using wood for the box
frame and incorporating bone dice, metal tokens and
figural wooden playing pieces turned on a lathe.
McLoughlin Brothers continued to produce exceptional
pieces right up until the company was bought out by
Milton Bradley in 1920.

Milton Bradley, like many game makers of the period,
was a draftsman and lithographer. Bradley turned to
games in 1860, when he produced the CHECKERED
GAME OF LIFE, another vice-versus-virtue game. His
success came when he issued a pocket-sized version in a
game pack (which could be the country's first commercial
"travel" game) designed for soldiers during the Civil War.
Bradley's games did not compare in quality with
McLoughlin games, but Milton Bradley was prolific; because he was one of the first to use the new lithographic
processes, he was able to mass-produce his games. Also,
Bradley was interested in education and was very active

in the new kindergarten movement. He produced school
supplies and optical toys in addition to educational games
for youngsters and their families.

George S. Parker, on the other hand, was a game player
interested in strategy games and games of amusement that
could be enjoyed by adults as well as children. With a
passion for inventing games, he started his own company
in 1883. Two years later he was selling Ives's games, and
by 1887 had apparently obtained the rights to the entire
Ives line. In 1888 one of his brothers joined the firm and
Parker Brothers was created. The company's 1894 catalog
stated, "Our new factory [in Salem, Massachusetts] is the
only large building in America devoted exclusively to
parlor games." Whereas Milton Bradley's games seemed
to be aimed predominantly at children and the family,
Parker geared a number of items to the adult market.

PILLOW DEX, from 1896. One of the most widely advertised games of the 1800s.

PARCHEESI, first manufactured in 1867.

Parker Brothers produced high-quality products throughout its early history and is one of the most popular names for collectors after McLoughlin.

Another early force in game distribution in the United States was E.G. Selchow, founder of the well-known Selchow & Righter Company. Selchow & Righter was initially a "jobber," selling games for other companies. Starting as E.G. Selchow & Co. in 1867, the company name was changed in 1880, ten years after John Righter joined the firm. Selchow's greatest contribution to game-playing in the United States was PARCHEESI, taken from the national game of India called PACHISI, and introduced around 1867; PARCHEESI has one of the earliest U.S. trademarks for a game—1874.

McLoughlin Brothers, Milton Bradley, Parker Brothers, and Selchow & Righter were the four major companies that were the driving force for the development of a new game industry in the United States. Other companies may have produced better games (or, at least, better-looking ones), but they didn't have the output or the staying power of the big four.

Many of the games produced during the 1800s by some of the smaller companies nonetheless have great value to collectors. E.I. Horsman, from New York, was noted mostly for introducing HALMA (though Bradley claims to have procured the game from the inventor in 1885). Many of Horsman's gameboards, some of them quite rare, rival McLoughlin's for beauty. Horsman, along with Parker Brothers and W.S. Reed, was among the first American game companies to advertise games in magazines. Early ads can be found dating back to 1887; by 1890, Milton Bradley, Selchow & Righter, and a host of smaller companies were also advertising their wares.

Two other leading companies before the turn of the century were R. Bliss Manufacturing Company and J.H. Singer. Bliss, a Rhode Island company, produced games after 1870 with almost the same attention to artistic detail as McLoughlin. Most Bliss games were skill-and-action games made of lithographed wood, such as target games and games with marbles, but the company's few board games were exquisite. Singer produced games primarily during the 1880s and 1890s. Many Singer games are tiny boardgames, but the highly intricate designs on the boxes make them very desirable.

H.B. Chaffee and Chaffee & Selchow, Clark & Sowdon, and W.S. Reed all produced exceptional board games

Detail of the board of Bliss's GAME OF WILD WEST, 1889. (McFarland/Boyea collection)

Singer's tiny board game, GAME OF YACHTING, 1890s.

during the late 1800s. Less prolific companies, such as Hamilton-Meyers, also produced games worth looking for.

The Embossing Company, noted for its small wooden games with embossed letters or numbers, was another early manufacturer. C.I. Hood & Co. and Woolson Spice Co., two firms that advertised heavily around the turn of the century, produced some of the earliest game "premiums"—games that could be obtained through the companies' products, Hood's Sarsaparilla and Lion Coffee, respectively.

Many other, smaller companies began printing card games in the nineteenth century, such as Adams, Noyes & Snow, J. Ottmann, Theodore Presser, Peter G. Thompson, West & Lee, and Whipple & Smith; the prolific Fireside Game Company produced a series of illustrated card decks just before 1900. Games by these companies are sought after as much for their historical importance as for their designs and illustrations. Except for Fireside and Peter Thompson, which were both located in Ohio, and for Bliss in Rhode Island, nearly all the major game companies in the 1800s were located in Massachusetts, New York, and Pennsylvania.

By 1900 there were dozens of U.S. companies supplying the American family with boxed games made mostly of paper and wood, all designed to educate and amuse. Games were becoming so popular they were even printed in Sunday newspapers as full-page supplements. The morality of earlier decades was changing—playing and leisure were accepted, and the strong family unit led adults and children to play games together (the box covers of many games of the period show three generations, male and female, playing the game). European immigration was high, and American culture was changing, turning from an agricultural society to one of industry. We had seen a war with Mexico, one among ourselves, and another with Spain in the Philippines. Evenings at home brightened as we went from gas to electric lights and listened to a new invention called the phonograph. We experienced a gold rush that moved the population westward, and the country was made smaller with the completion of the transcontinental railroad and the advent of the telephone and the wireless telegraph.

Nineteen more states had been added to the union than when Ives began production in 1843. Milton Bradley began opening offices around the country as companies aimed at a national market. Competition was fierce. As a result, the companies began to cut costs, and the era of beautifully lithographed, well-constructed games began to come to an end.

3

The Game Industry During the 1900s

Parker Brothers' THE UNITED STATES AIR MAIL game exemplified America's interest in air transportation. (Fink Collection)

Early Years of the Century

After 1900, fewer large games were produced, and the well-constructed wood-frame boxes gave way to cardboard ones. The large turned-wood playing pieces were replaced by small wooden markers. Less attention was paid to the ornamentation of the lithographic design. Game production or game buying may have slowed somewhat because of the financial panic in 1907. McLoughlin Brothers continued to produce excellent games, but they were not as outstanding as the ones from a decade before. Milton Bradley, still a prolific manufacturer, expanded his business, opening a branch office in Boston and building a new structure in Springfield. J.H. Singer went out of business. In 1904, an unknown, independent economist and inventor, Elizabeth Magie, obtained a patent for her LANDLORD'S GAME, the precursor for what was to become the largest-selling game in the world, MONOPOLY.

Parker Brothers incorporated in 1901 and then cut back on the development of new board games and began focusing more on card games. In 1902 the company started a fad when it introduced PING-PONG. This success was followed up with two classic card games in 1904 and 1906: PIT and ROOK. ROOK, invented by George Parker himself, allegedly became the largest-selling card game in the world. The company also began manufacturing a line of superb-quality wooden jig saw puzzles, and in 1909 the company's attention was turned solely to their manufacture.

Games continued to reflect social history. Aviation, America's fascination with the automobile, and polar expeditions and world expositions all proved excellent themes. Game manufacturers capitalized on the "animal dance" crazes like the "Turkey Trot" by illustrating game boxes with pictures of frolicking animals in various forms of dress; the Ouija board, invented decades earlier, began to stir some interest among the living, and Roosevelt's bear hunting prompted a nation's love for the "Teddy" bear,

Milton Bradley's GAME OF TRAFFIC expressed the nation's enchantment with the automobile. (Fink Collection)

which has persisted to this day—and which was the subject of many a game in the early 1900s.

World War I and Beyond

As America anticipated and then entered the first world war, the game industry went through its most significant changes since the 1890s. By 1915, four key figures, John McLoughlin, Milton Bradley, E.G. Selchow, and John Righter, had died. Bliss was no longer making games; E.I. Horsman turned from games to dolls. In 1920, one of the McLoughlin brothers died and McLoughlin sold out to Milton Bradley; The game industry was being run by—and catering to—a new generation.

In spite of the demise of smaller businesses that could not survive the restrictions, responsibilities, and economic hardships of war, the toy industry was growing and needed an umbrella organization. In 1916, the Toy Manufacturers of the USA set up permanent offices in New York, at 200 Fifth Avenue, an address still used today by many companies in the business. That was the same year the UNCLE WIGGILY game was born—a game that soon

A Dandy New Game for American Boys

All our soldier boys are marching home—but you can have a camp of your very own. A tent—a jolly state flag—and twenty brave men, ready to fight or play, just as you wish. Ask your dad to get you this new McLoughlin game—the American Boys State Camp. It's lots of fun!

Bing! down they go. Tenshun! Up again in strict order, guns shouldered, eyes right. You'll think you're a real general when you have these dandy soldiers to command! Tell your daddy he can get this new game for you at any store—just mention McLoughlin and you have it!

McLoughlin Bros. 890 BROADWAY
At 19th Street
New York City
·INCORPORATED·
ESTABLISHED 1828

This 1919 advertisement in *St. Nicholas* magazine promotes one of McLoughlin's last games, AMERICAN BOYS STATE CAMP.

Deluxe Parker Brothers' MAH-JONGG set. (Mautner collection)

A 1921 ad for THE UNCLE WIGGILY GAME, a favorite of children for generations.

J. Pressman's DELUXE TABLE TENNIS, ±1930.

proved as popular as the children's bedtime story books on which it was based.

Jigsaw puzzles continued to be popular through the war years and into the Twenties. MAH-JONGG became fashionable. Crossword puzzles turned into the latest craze, and were most likely instrumental in prompting the profusion of word games played with cards. The advent of radio, the discovery of Tut's tomb, and the airborne adventures of America's newest hero, Charles Lindbergh, were translated into board and card games and sold to a public anxious to play. The puritanism of the past became a memory as Americans created the "Roaring Twenties."

The year 1922 saw the emergence of a new company, J. Pressman Co., a small firm that sixty-four years later would become the oldest family-owned game company in America. Other companies appeared. Alderman-Fairchild of upstate New York began producing beautiful board and target games, while two other new companies, Wilder of St. Louis, Missouri, and Stoll & Edwards of New York City, started manufacturing boxed board games with wonderful lithography. Rosebud Art and Russell Mfg. Co. issued card games and small board games. Wolverine Supply & Mfg. began manufacturing games on lithographed metal boards.

Saalfield, a long-time publisher, started to increase its small line of games begun in the 1910s. And in 1927,

This 1924 ad from *St. Nicholas* magazine describes the virtues of Wolverine's all-metal board game, MOTOR RACE.

Whitman got off to a strong start by licensing such popular titles as Chester Gould's DICK TRACY (1937).

Parker Brothers' CALLING ALL CARS, ±1938, is collectible in the areas of police and radio (it was the title of a successful radio "crime reenactment" program), and is remembered by younger collectors who played the later version in the 1950s.

All-Fair's CARGO FOR VICTORY, 1943, was one of many wartime games with patriotic themes.

Selchow & Righter Co. stopped selling other companies' games and started making its own.

The Great Depression didn't appear to hit the game industry until around 1933. Parker Brothers' big break came only a few of years later, when the company bought MONOPOLY in 1935. No proprietary game (a game owned by one particular company) had ever gained such popularity around the world. The story is that the Depression paved the way for a game that allowed people to buy property and make millions, but one wonders why a similar game of the same period, Milton Bradley's EASY MONEY, didn't meet with equal success.

By 1936 Parker Brothers was producing its best games. Milton Bradley, noted for putting games into classrooms, made a classroom into a game and issued GO TO THE HEAD OF THE CLASS. In 1939 Bradley produced some of its best post-1900 games, including five substantial games based on films.

New companies emerged, among them Cadaco-Ellis, Einson-Freeman, Gabriel, National, Stoll & Einson, and Whitman. Transogram managed a transition from playsets to games.

Recovery programs inspired different products, and financial games besides MONOPOLY became popular. Mini-golf became the rage, sparking a spate of mini-boxed skill-and-action games. G-Men covered lots of territory, from movie screens to game boxes, and at least twelve mystery games were manufactured between 1936 and 1939.

As World War II began, companies got involved in the war effort. Milton Bradley cut its game line by 67 percent. Firms such as Wolverine could not use metal for their gameboards, and metal tokens were changed to composition pieces. CHINESE CHECKERS received a U.S. patent in 1941. Milton Bradley introduced the GAME OF STATES, and CHUTES AND LADDERS came out before the war's end.

During the slow recovery after the war, Bradley introduced CANDYLAND, and Parker Brothers bought the rights to the English CLUEDO and came out with CLUE. A small firm called the Production & Marketing Company began manufacturing a crossword game called SCRAB-BLE, which was soon to become the most popular word game in history (and eventually changed the course of the Selchow & Righter Company, which later manufactured and eventually bought the rights to the game.

The Television Era

The war and its aftermath did not have as great an effect on the game industry as did the invention of television. Suddenly there was a visual, live-action medium that could reach people instantaneously in every part of the country. This meant that companies could access a huge audience through advertising and could link their products with the favorite personalities watched by millions.

Only the larger companies could afford to advertise on television, thus widening the gap between the giants in the industry and the small manufacturers. Also, because of an initial lack of regulations in broadcasting, the advertisers could pander to children; youngsters were being told about the great products they should urge their parents to buy, and the "bandwagon" approach ("All kids have one, so should you") was prevalent. What went *in* the game box became much less important than the name or licensed character that went *on* it.

If a company could obtain the rights to manufacture a game based on a successful TV show or character, it could almost be guaranteed the same success as the program on which it was based or the popularity of its star. During the 1950s, many game companies, especially Milton Bradley, Lowell, and Transogram, began to produce more and more games linked to television shows. This meant that a business that once hoped to sell an item that would be a staple in the company's line for decades was now making a product that would be obsolete as soon as the program on which it was based went off the air.

The distribution of games changed as well during the 1950s, as a result of a growth in affluence. Shopping malls provided convenient one-stop shopping, and toy chains offered discounted products. The small game store owner

The cover photos of Marvin Milner and George Maharis make ROUTE 66 as popular to TV game collectors of today as the show was to fans in the early 1960s.

Lowell was one of the key companies to produce games based on television programs during the 1950s and early 1960s.

found it more difficult to compete, and by the 1990s many had gone out of business. Independent inventors and small manufacturers couldn't get their games into the large chains unless they backed the product with TV advertising.

The shopping mall helped hasten the demise of the small, independent distributor. It's ironic that the word "mall" derives from a game: the seventeenth-century European game of PALL-MALL, in which a wooden ball was driven down an alley, similar to the ways in which stores are lined up in a complex on either side of a pedestrian walkway.

Ideal, Lowell, and Transogram, along with Milton Bradley, Parker Brothers, Pressman, and Selchow & Righter, were the key companies from the 1950s on. Ideal (and Gabriel) was bought by CBS, which later sold its game division to Hasbro. Lowell and Transogram went out of business. After 124 years as a family-owned company, Milton Bradley (which bought E.S. Lowe in 1973) was bought by Hasbro in 1984; the company continues to produce games at its Springfield plant. After 119 years of family ownership, Selchow & Righter was sold to Coleco in 1986; Coleco filed for bankruptcy soon after and was then bought by Hasbro. In 1968, Parker Brothers was bought by General Mills; the company changed hands a couple of times, then was purchased by Hasbro in 1991. The Parker Brothers' factory in Salem was closed, ending a Parker legacy that had begun there 108 years before.

Hasbro, of Pawtucket, Rhode Island, now owns the games of Milton Bradley, Parker Brothers, and Selchow & Righter, plus some or all of the games from Coleco, Lakeside, Gabriel, and Ideal.

GROUCHO'S YOU BET YOUR LIFE was based on the highly popular show that began in 1951 and ran through the decade; this Lowell game advertises the show's sponsor, De Soto Plymouth, on the cover.

4

Games from the 1960s to the Present

Games after Prime Time

The prime time for twentieth-century American games, according to some historians, ended around World War II; others say the end came with the introduction of television, or when the turmoil of the 1960s created vast cultural changes in the United States. The prime time of television was its "Golden Age," which covered the early, live broadcasts through much of the innovative 1950s. Most of the collectible games after prime time are based on television shows, others on the events and famous personalities of the 1960s and 1970s.

The values of games from the 1960s and 1970s can be surprising. Many mid-1960s character items sell for as much as the striking board games from the turn of the century. From AS THE WORLD TURNS, based on the number-one daytime soap opera for nearly ten years, to THE LOVE BOAT, a comedy soap for nighttime viewers, games reflected the public's interest in everything from quiz programs to westerns to police, action, and adventure dramas. HOLLYWOOD SQUARES, CONCENTRATION, JEOPARDY, and a host of other quiz show games allowed viewers to play at home. LARAMIE, THE REBEL, and THE VIRGINIAN took us out west when we were housebound and our favorite shows weren't on. I SPY and PETER GUNN let us in for adventure, even if we couldn't hear the wonderful theme music.

The games from the 1960s are generally worth more than those from the 1950s, supposedly because the youthful age of the majority of the collectors doesn't allow for much nostalgic memory of the 1950s. But television-based games from the 1950s, such as ANNIE OAKLEY, CALLING SUPERMAN, DRAGNET, GROUCHO'S YOU BET YOUR LIFE, GUNSMOKE (which might be early 1960s), HAVE GUN WILL TRAVEL, HOPALONG CASSIDY, JACKIE GLEASON'S "AND AWA-A-A-A-Y WE GO!", THE LUCY SHOW GAME, MASQUERADE PARTY, PHIL SILVERS' YOU'LL NEVER GET RICH, RAMAR OF THE JUNGLE, THE RIFLEMAN, WANTED DEAD OR ALIVE,

and WHAT'S MY LINE, are definitely equal in value to the later games.

From the common COLOMBO, SIX-MILLION-DOLLAR MAN, and nostalgic VIDEO VILLAGE, to the more elusive HONEY WEST, LAND OF THE GIANTS, and ELIOT NESS AND THE UNTOUCHABLES, to the desirable THE RAT PATROL DESERT COMBAT GAME, ROUTE 66, and THE VIRGINIAN, games based on television programs form perhaps the bulk of the collectible games after 1960. A game such as MARY HARTMAN MARY HARTMAN is a treat because it includes photos of eight characters, one of whom was an almost unknown, Dabney Coleman. The choice games of the period include THE ADDAMS FAMILY, GILLIGAN'S ISLAND, GREEN HORNET, LAND OF THE GIANTS, THE MUNSTERS DRAG RACE GAME, THE MUNSTERS MASQUERADE PARTY GAME, and THE MUNSTERS PICNIC GAME.

Cartoon-character games are among the most valuable. All the Hanna-Barbera cartoon games are desirable: ADAM ANT, THE JETSONS (the 1960s, not the 1986 game), PEBBLES AND BAM BAM, PETER POTAMUS, RICOCHET RABBIT, and especially ROCKY AND HIS FRIENDS and ROSIE THE ROBOT.

The games based on television's silly situation comedies were once nearly worthless as collectibles, but they started to attract a large following in the 1990s. There is now moderate interest in I DREAM OF JEANNIE and PATTY DUKE and considerable interest in THE BEVERLY HILLBILLIES and MR. ED. One of the most desired games

THE MUNSTERS DRAG RACE GAME is as hot a collectible as Herman Munster's hot rod. It was put out by Hasbro in 1964. (Oglesby/Stock Collection)

MARY HARTMAN MARY HARTMAN, Reiss Games, 1977. Though Mary Hartman was the star of the TV show, a lesser-known Dabney Coleman might be the star of this game, since he is one of the actor/characters featured within. (McFarland/Boyea collection)

is the rare GREEN ACRES. These games are affectionately known as "the Nickelodeon series" because the shows on which they were based are in reruns on the Nickelodeon cable channel.

Non-TV character games of interest from the 1960s and 1970s include THE EXCITING NEW GAME OF THE KENNEDYS, THE TINY TIM GAME OF BEAUTIFUL THINGS, and THE TWIGGY GAME.

Subject matter also can make a 1960s or 1970s game valuable. The theme of THE WORLD'S FAIR GAME from 1964 makes it a choice item. Games connected with dolls are of interest to many collectors; for example, HEIDI, BARBI, and especially SKIPPER (Barbi's friend) and G.I. JOE, are all sought after.

Science-fiction is one of the most collectible themes. LOST IN SPACE, OUTER LIMITS, THE TIME TUNNEL, and THE TWILIGHT ZONE are all hot properties. Sci-fi games, along with monster games, such as Hasbro's WOLFMAN mystery game, are commanding the highest prices of the post–World War II games.

Rock-and-roll games are moneymakers. From HULLABALLOO, KISS, and THE MONKEES, to the common but high-priced BEATLE'S FLIP YOUR WIG game, up to the highly desirable CHUBBY CHECKER game and the CHUBBY CHECKER LIMBO ROCK game, rock 'n roll is here to stay. The range runs from a possible collectible of the future, DURAN DURAN, to the highly prized 1957 ELVIS PRESLEY, for which there have been fewer sightings in the past decade than of Elvis himself. The rare ELVIS PRESLEY, A PARTY GAME FOR THE YOUNG AT HEART, by Teenage Games Inc. of W. Springfield, Mass., may be the most valuable post-war game known.

Incidentally, not everything is escalating in price. During the early 1980s the Beatles game was valued at four times more than comparable items from the same period; by the 1990s the game was worth about the same as its 1960s counterparts.

Sports games, especially baseball, are collectible from any era. Milton Bradley's MAJOR LEAGUE BASEBALL included 150 player's cards in 1969 and 1971, with a short run in 1970; the games are in demand, especially because of the Pete Rose card that's included. The generic ACTION BASEBALL game from Pressman Toy may not have much value, but the same game with a player's name on it commands four to six times the basic price; the three licensed games, listed in order from valuable to more valuable, are CARL YASTRZEMSKI ACTION BASEBALL, ROGER MARIS ACTION BASEBALL, and TOM SEAVER ACTION BASEBALL.

Within each theme or category, scarcity and the look of the cover are the two primary things that affect the value of these games.

Contemporary and Future Collectibles

Contemporary collectibles are those games that people begin to collect when they are first sold by the manufacturer because the games represent a theme or character already popular in the collector's market. For example, because "Ninja Turtles" and "The Simpsons" are "hot" and have spawned a spate of licensed products, a collector will glom onto the first Turtles or Simpson games with the expectation that they will become valuable in the future. Similarly, collectors of McDonald's premiums will buy every item, including the games that are on the boxes of the packaged meals, as soon as they are available. Collectors of contemporary items are primarily interested in character-related premiums. The rule here is simple: If the public is buying up all the tee-shirts, stickers, key chains, mugs, and bric-a-brac of a particular character, chances are any games featuring that character will become desired items as well.

SPY VS SPY and THE JETSONS GAME, both Milton Bradley games from 1986, are being hoarded by some collectors who feel their value will increase because of their respective collectible themes: "Mad Magazine" and a cartoon character. THE SIMPSONS MYSTERY OF LIFE, a 1990 entry from Cardinal Industries, contains the die-cut cardboard illustrations of the four Simpson characters, including the incorrigible, but highly collectible, Bart. And watch for the CALIFORNIA RAISINS GAME, issued by Decipher in 1988 and based on a character-collectible.

Watch for "Cityopoly" games, based on the MONOPOLY style and theme but adapted to various locales and using the street names from the area (which, incidentally, was what happened to the LANDLORD'S GAME during its thirty-year evolution into MONOPOLY). In 1989, Elusive Dream Marketing Services, a California firm, took

GOOD OL' CHARLIE BROWN GAME, Milton Bradley, 1971. Though Charlie Brown is not a high-value item, this particular game may increase substantially in value because of the elaborate three-dimensional setup on the gameboard. (McFarland/Boyea collection)

THE TWILIGHT ZONE GAME (Ideal, 1964) is much harder to find than any of the television episodes in reruns.

SPY VS SPY, Milton Bradley, 1986. The popular feature in Mad Magazine, "Spy vs Spy," finally became a game in 1986. The many cards and the 13 plastic bombs, plus the spy theme and "Mad Magazine" connection might make this a hot item in the next decade.

THE SIMPSONS MYSTERY OF LIFE (Cardinal Industries, 1990). The collectibility of this recent game depends a lot on how good it is—the worse the game plays, the fewer sets that will be sold and the more purchases that will be trashed. As hot as The Simpsons are, this could be a major item in a decade. (McFarland/Boyea collection)

over a company that the year before had produced three "Cityopoly" games. In early 1991, after the company had added twenty-two cities to its line, Parker Brothers, owners of MONOPOLY brought a trademark infringement suit against the company, now selling as H.G.I. Marketing Services Inc. In an out-of-court settlement later that year, no money exchanged hands, but Tom Magee, head of H.G.I., agreed to change "Cityopoly" to "Metropoly." The original twenty-five-city Cityopoly games, which sold anywhere from 500 copies for Bakersfield, California, to 15,000 copies for Denver, Colorado, are expected to climb in value.

Avalon Hill Game Company is probably the only company that sells its earlier games at collectors' prices. What follows is an example of games advertised in its 1991 catalog. Keep in mind that the dollar amount shown is Avalon Hill's selling price, not necessarily the value we would place on the game. Most new Avalon Hill games sell for $16 to $25, with some as high as $40. BATTLE OF THE BULGE (1965, $50), BATTLE OF THE BULGE (1981, $100), BOWLBOUND (*Sports Illustrated;* last copy; $75), C&O/B&O ($200), CAESAR LEGIONS ($100), COLLEGE FOOTBALL (*Sports Illustrated;* last copy; $100), CONQUISTADOR ($35), EVENTS GAME (3M; last copy; $100), HANDICAP GOLF (*Sports Illustrated;* $75), KRIEGSPIEL (last copy; $100), OCTRIX

(3M; $50), PLOY (3M; last copy; $100), PUSHOVER (Aladdin; last copy; $100), SHENANDOAH (Battleline; $100), TRACK MEET (DECATHLON) (*Sports Illustrated;* $50), TRIREME (Battleline; last copy; $100), VENTURE (3M; $50)

Since 1952, Avalon Hill has produced mostly complex strategy games aimed at the "gamer" and aficionados interested in war and simulation games. In 1991 Avalon Hill introduced the BATTLE OF THE BULGE as the first in a series of faster playing, simpler strategy games aimed at the whole family. This historic-recreation two-player game (it has the Smithsonian imprimatur) is likely to become a collectible, as many first-of-their-kind Avalon Hill games are.

Mayfair Games, a company producing adventure and role-playing games, has a number of products that may become future collectibles. LONE WOLF AND CUB, based on the novels, will be a limited-run series because the U.S. licensor is no longer in business and the games will be discontinued. The role-playing DC HEROES is almost certain to become a collector's item because of the seventy-five character cards, featuring Batman, Superman, Wonder Woman, and other DC heroes. Another item, CHILL, billed as "the first horror role-playing game," is also likely to become collectible, considering the current interest in monster themes.

The Chicago-based Quaker Oats Co. has just come out with one of the best premiums to hit the breakfast table—a three-dimensional game on the back of boxes of "Cap'n Crunch" cereals (three different games in the series), with a plastic spinner and set of red and green/blue glasses inside the box.

At the International Toy Fair in New York every year, hundreds of new games are introduced by independent inventors or companies, most of which stay in business for only a few years. A small company may produce anywhere from 500 to 2,000 sets, and one of its "limited edition" games may jump in value. However, if the *name* doesn't become known, chances are the game will not be of much interest to collectors. But do keep an eye out for limited-release games that have interesting themes, good-looking graphics, or quality components. For example, ELDORADO, by Game Leaders, should become a collectible of the future simply because of the game's outstanding quality and the superb graphics on the gameboard. The board was drawn by Kunio Hagio, who did the illustrations for the *Indiana Jones* movie ads; the stark black game box houses beautifully illustrated cards and tokens, pads of small-sized $100, $500, and $1,000 bills, and a cloth bag containing colorful fake gemstones for playing pieces; the theme is a modern-day quest for the wealth of the treasure-laden Spanish statue of El Dorado.

The Future of the American Game Industry

The 1980s began a time of buy-outs and corporate takeovers. However, although Hasbro now controls the bulk of nonelectronic game manufacturing in the United States, many other companies still play a vital role in the industry. Pressman Toy Company, in business since 1921, is now the oldest family-owned game company in the United States. Cadaco, Cardinal, and Western Publishing are still active after many years in business. Newer companies such as International Games and Talicor have been making increasing contributions to the market.

Television still plays a prominent role in terms of what games get made, but with so much change in the game industry since 1980, it is difficult to predict what will happen by the end of the century. As computer and video games take over a larger share of the game market, companies are having a more difficult time placing board and card games. Traditional games no doubt will always be around, but fewer of them may come from the major companies.

5

Ten Classic American Board Games

Many of the classic American games still sold today were developed in the United States a long time ago or were played in different parts of the world for hundreds of years. In some cases, only the packaging has changed over time; in other instances, the names have been changed as well, and the games have been reinvented.

The histories of ten of America's most notable games are featured here, showing the true origins of some popular games, debunking the myths of MONOPOLY and COOTIE, and providing the first detailed account of SCRABBLE, as told by the inventor, Alfred Butts.

BATTLESHIP

A classic in Bradley's line since 1967, BATTLESHIP was formerly a pencil-and-paper parlor game that dates back more than sixty years. In 1933, ten years before Bradley produced its own pad-and-pencil BATTLESHIP-style game called BROADSIDES, THE GAME OF NAVAL STRATEGY, The Strathmore Co. published COMBAT, THE BATTLESHIP GAME. Two years before that, the Starex Novelty Co. of New York published SALVO, which, according to an article in a 1932 booklet by the Church Recreation Service, "was originated by soldiers in Russia, ten or fifteen years ago." Two other names for BATTLE-SHIP listed in the article were SWISS NAVY and SUNK, a version later published by Parker Brothers.

Other BATTLESHIP games include SALVO (Ideal, 1961), WARFARE NAVAL COMBAT (Maurice L. Freedman Co. of Providence, Rhode Island, 1940s), and CONVOY (Transogram). Nonaquatic variations of BATTLESHIP include WINGS (Strategy Games Co. of Venice, California, ±1932), using planes instead of ships. Subtitled "The New Olympic Game," it pictures planes flying over the Los Angeles Coliseum.

The collectible value of games of BATTLESHIP is determined primarily by the age of the game, the graphics, and the extent to which the game illustrates a military or wartime theme.

CHUTES AND LADDERS

Introduced by Milton Bradley in 1943, CHUTES AND LADDERS is based on SNAKES AND LADDERS, a moral-ity game from India, which the Bradley catalog called "England's most famous indoor sport." In the original game, if the player landed on the tail of a snake, a space indicating one of various vices, the player was forced to slide along the snake to a space closer to start; if the player landed on the bottom of a ladder, which specified a particular virtue, the player moved ahead by climbing the ladder. Vice and virtue were not included in any of the Bradley versions.

The phrase "back to square one" (according to author Eric Partridge), used by BBC commentators to help radio listeners follow football games using grid maps, was taken from SNAKES AND LADDERS, "where an unlucky fall of the dice took one from the top to the bottom line."

CHUTES AND LADDERS has only limited collectors' value and is of more interest to noncollectors who played the game as children.

CLUE

Imported from England in 1948 as CLUEDO, and licensed to Parker Brothers as CLUE, THE SHERLOCK HOLMES GAME, the game CLUE has the distinction of being the first to be made into a movie. Parker bought the game in 1949 and dropped the Sherlock Holmes name. CLUE has gone through several major graphic revisions.

The early games in which the board and parts box were separate and in which the rope was real rope (not plastic) are the only CLUE games that have much collectible value.

COOTIE

Herb Schaper is credited with inventing COOTIE, a game first put out in 1949 by Milton Bradley and now sold by that company. The success story, well documented in Filis Frederick's book, *Design and Sell Toys, Games, & Crafts,* has the fishing enthusiast-turned-game designer visualizing the plaything while working on a new kind of lure. But back in 1927, a pencil-and-paper version of the same game, called TU-TEE, was copyrighted by a "J.H.W." The name "COOTIE" was used as early as 1934 describing the game in *Leisure* magazine. Early COOTIE games are collected primarily for nostalgia and are relatively inexpensive.

MONOPOLY

Contrary to popular myth, MONOPOLY was actually taken from THE LANDLORD'S GAME, patented by Elizabeth Magie in 1904. Magie, who ascribed to the principles of economist Henry George, was interested in instilling the advantages of a Single Tax concept. She devised a game in which she hoped to point out the folly of a property ownership system where players attempted to become "monarch of the world." The game was even adapted for teaching economics at various schools, including Columbia University, where the board had New York City street names.

The popularity of THE LANDLORD'S GAME, which earned the title MONOPOLY sometime after 1910, spread throughout the country, becoming a favorite on college campuses. But in its thirty years of evolution, the game lost its original intent—the second half of the game (that part teaching the Single Tax system) was discarded, leav-

There is no longer any doubt that MONOPOLY developed from THE LANDLORD'S GAME, patented in 1904 by Elizabeth J. Magie (Phillips). Photo shows the parts box and all the implements, without the gameboard. (McFarland/Boyea collection; photo by Stan Blanchard)

The 1936 MONOPOLY "add on" called STOCK EXCHANGE apparently didn't fare very well, since it is so difficult to find. Stock certificate cards and "Advance to Stock Exchange" cards are mixed with Community Chest and Chance decks, as a paper overlay changes the "Free Parking" space on the MONOPOLY gameboard to "Stock Exchange." (McFarland/Boyea collection)

ing the game the race for financial dominance we know it as today.

Properties on the board were assigned regional street names of the areas in which the game was played. In Atlantic City, a group of Quakers and their friends made gameboards using names of local streets. Charles Darrow, thought by many to be the inventor of MONOPOLY, actually learned about the game from a friend. That friend, or possibly Darrow himself, misspelled the street name "Marven Gardens" when copying the board from the Atlantic City version; the error, "Marvin Gardens," remained on the board that Darrow later revised, copyrighted in 1933, and offered to Parker Brothers a year later. Parker rejected the game, so Darrow printed up and sold MONOPOLY on his own; his version did not come with any playing pieces but instructed the players to use common household objects such as buttons or keys. Eventually, either after learning about Darrow's success in selling his game or because a friend of the Parker family strongly recommended it, the head of Parker Brothers bought the rights and began manufacturing the game in 1935. Rich Uncle Pennybags, the mustached character who adorned the Parker Brothers' MONOPOLY board, box, and cards, was born a year later.

The company sold other games "by the famous inventor Elizabeth Magie Phillips," but it began minimizing her role and accentuating Darrow's in the story of MONOPOLY's development. By the early 1970s, Parker Brothers' press releases and countless articles written about the game's phenomenal long-term success all stated that MONOPOLY was invented by Darrow, and it became a rare feat to find Elizabeth Magie Phillips acknowledged anywhere.

An article about the true origin of MONOPOLY written in 1975 in *Game & Puzzles,* a magazine published in London, and a 1980s lawsuit between Parker Brothers and Ralph Anspach, the inventor of "ANTI-MONOPOLY," began to set the records straight. By 1991, in a press release issued by the Toy Manufacturers of America, Parker Brothers said that Darrow "developed" the game. More recent and more accurate releases have stated that Darrow "brought the game to Parker Brothers."

FINANCE, FINANCE AND FORTUNE, EASY MONEY, and possibly BIG BUSINESS all derived from THE LANDLORD'S GAME. In fact, some shared the same patent number—a second patent number given to Phillips for the revised 1924 version of her game put out by Parker Brothers in 1939.

So many MONOPOLY sets were sold (and the game has changed so little) that even those from 1936 may be worth little more than the cost of a new set, the value being in the wooden houses and hotels. (Collectors also look for different editions that have variations in the Chance or Community Chest cards.) The "Darrow MONOPOLY" and only some of the Parker sets from 1935 showing "pat. pending" or one patent number are of interest (see page 116); the MONOPOLY board showed two patent numbers (the Phillips's and the Darrow/Parker patent) from 1936 until Phillips's patent expired in 1943. Other collectible MONOPOLY editions are the special issue sets by companies such as Neiman-Marcus (all chocolate), the Franklin Mint (pewter tokens embellished with 24-karat gold), and Dunhill (solid gold playing pieces).

OTHELLO

The game of OTHELLO, allegedly named for Shakespeare's play because of the game's black and white pieces, supposedly was brought to the United States from Japan, introduced by Gabriel in 1976. Though it won awards for the "best new game," it is nearly exactly the same as REVERSI, a game popular during the 1950s and sold by McLoughlin Brothers in 1888. According to Saxon's *Everybody's Book of Indoor Games,* REVERSI was introduced in England around 1870 under the name THE GAME OF ANNEXATION and became ANNEX, A GAME OF REVERSES.

PARCHEESI

The GAME OF INDIA, known also as PACHISI, is one of the most widely played games in the world and the forerunner of Selchow & Righter's PARCHEESI (≤1867) and of the English game LUDO (1896). The rights to PARCHEESI were bought by E.G. Selchow from Albert Swift in 1867, and the game was trademarked in 1874, one of the earliest trademarks for an American game. PARCHEESI is now sold by Milton Bradley.

PARCHEESI versions and variations have been popular for a century, and have been produced by almost every major company under such titles as PACHISI, INDIA, HOME, POLLYANNA, LUDO, and SORRY. Because they are so common, most PARCHEESI variants after 1900 have very little value.

PENTE

Popularized in the United States by Parker Brothers after the company's purchase of the game in 1984, PENTE is a variant of a number of board games that were played in the Orient centuries ago, including GO, NINUKI-RENJU, and GO-MOKU. GO-MOKU, known in England also as SPOILS FIVE, was introduced in Europe around 1885 and is also known by the name GO-BANG. GO-BANG was listed as a "new" game in the McLoughlin Brothers' 1887 catalog. PENTE was revived in the United States in 1977 by Gary Gabrel of Pente Games of Stillwater, Oklahoma. Only the game's early ancestors, such as GO-BANG, have collectible value.

SCRABBLE

In 1931, as a result of the Depression, Alfred Butts (born in 1899 in Poughkeepsie, New York) was laid off from his position as an architect. Coming from a family background where games were a major form of amusement, he decided to invent a new game that would, according to his notes, "combine elements of luck and skill in the formation of words."

In 1932 Butts devised a game called LEXICO, which involved the random selection of tiles with letters on them, and gave a score for words formed. The game, which had wooden racks made from pieces of molding, used 100 tiles (the same as SCRABBLE), and the letter distribution was based on Butts's study of cryptography and on a letter-frequency count of words appearing on the first page of the *New York Times.*

There was no playing board. Words were not connected in a crossword pattern and were not assigned point values. The score for any word played was based on the

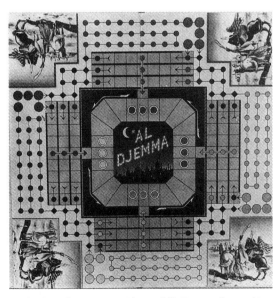

A PARCHEESI variation with a Middle Eastern theme, AL DJEMMA, was produced by Corey Games in 1944.

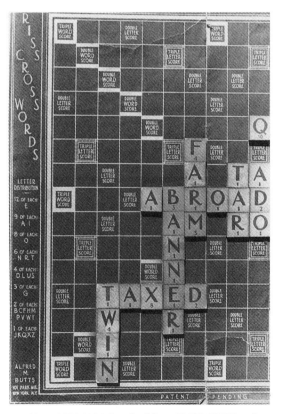

CRISS-CROSS WORDS evolved from CRISS-CROSS and began to approximate the look of the modern SCRABBLE board. (Courtesy of Alfred Butts and Robert Butts)

length of the word, with bonuses possible depending on the particular letters used.

Noticing the popularity of crossword puzzles in newspapers, in 1937 or early 1938 Butts decided to add a playing board to his game of letter tiles and to make the words intersect. He experimented with placing premium values on certain spaces on the board and to assigning each letter a numerical value. He called his new game CRISS-CROSS and applied for a patent. The application was rejected, Butts believed, because there was no novelty in giving numerical values to letters.

Butts continued to experiment. He changed the name of his game to CRISS-CROSS WORDS, changed the letter distribution and the values of some letters, and tried using different starting squares and different locations for the premium squares. Between 1938 and 1941 or 1942 he gave away or sold 100 sets of the game to friends and family; another 25 sets were made and distributed by a Connecticut bookstore owner.

In 1947 Butts was approached by James Brunot, a man with venture capital who had come across CRISS-CROSS WORDS and was looking to start a business. During the course of negotiations Brunot received legal advice indicating that CRISS-CROSS WORDS was not patentable and could not be protected by copyright because of the way in which the game had been marketed previously, but that "protection could be secured if substantial changes were made to the design of the game . . . and if it were renamed." In exchange for royalties, Butts agreed to allow Brunot to manufacture and market CRISS-CROSS WORDS. Brunot altered the design of the board, including making the center starting square a double-word premium space. He revised the rules, adding the fifty-point bonus for any word that used all seven of a player's tiles. And he changed the name to SCRABBLE.

James Brunot started the Production and Marketing Company in 1948, obtained a copyright for SCRABBLE,

and took over the production of the crossword game from the living room of his home in Newtown, Connecticut. From this point on, Butts no longer had any direct involvement in the game but continued to have a financial interest and was frequently consulted by Brunot. In a 1991 interview at his residence in New York State, Alfred Butts mentioned the good friendship and long association that had developed out of his business affiliation with Brunot, who died years earlier.

According to different reports, Brunot made twelve to sixteen SCRABBLE sets a day; by the time he had com-

A 1922 ad for UNCLE WIGGILY.

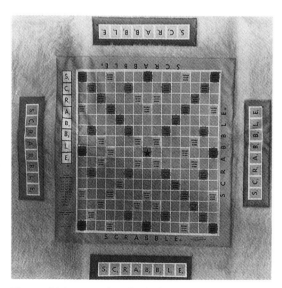

The vinyl SCRABBLE board is built in to the cloth table covering; its rarity makes it more valuable than other SCRABBLE versions.

Bradley's hard-to-find UNCLE WIGGILY'S NEW AIRPLANE GAME is worth much more to most collectors than the ubiquitous UNCLE WIGGILY game; shown here is the parts box from ±1930.

pleted around 2,400 sets in 1949, he was $450 in the red. But by 1950, word-of-mouth advertising had boosted the popularity of SCRABBLE so tremendously that Brunot's company could no longer keep up with the demand; by the end of 1952, the company was selling more than 400 sets a day. The sudden interest in SCRABBLE was uncanny, and one could only speculate what would make sales take off so unexpectedly. One theory is that the game was played at fashionable resorts around the country, and when vacationers returned home they looked to their local stores to carry the game. Another theory attributes some of the game's success to the owner of Macy's department store, who enjoyed the game himself and made certain that it was well stocked in his store.

Unable to keep up with the demand, Brunot contracted with the eighty-seven-year-old Selchow & Righter Company to have the gameboards manufactured. Selchow & Righter licensed SCRABBLE in 1953 and took over the manufacturing and marketing of the game. The Production and Marketing Company, which had moved to larger quarters, continued to produce sets to supplement those manufactured by S&R.

Selchow & Righter bought the rights to SCRABBLE in 1971. The SCRABBLE® BRAND CROSSWORD GAME is now owned by Hasbro-Bradley, the company that acquired Coleco after Coleco's bankruptcy following its purchase of Selchow & Righter.

J. Pressman's 1939 game WORDY was almost identical to SCRABBLE, except that the letter tiles were color-coded, each color corresponding to a particular point value. Lynn Pressman said that WORDY was a "knock-off" of SCRABBLE, indicating it must have been copied from the original CRISS-CROSS WORDS (unless the 1939 date is wrong). SCRABBLE was licensed to Cadaco in 1953 and published as SKIP-A-CROSS.

SCRABBLE has remained almost exactly the same in style and construction for more than forty years—thereby severely lowering the collector value of the early games. Only the deluxe or limited editions (such as the white ivoroid or the cloth-and-vinyl edition) have much value.

UNCLE WIGGILY

Based on the Uncle Wiggily Bedtime Stories of Howard R. Garis (1872–1961), a staff member of *The Newark Evening News* and writer of children's books. Uncle Wiggily Longears, an elderly rabbit gentleman, was created in 1910. The UNCLE WIGGILY game was initially introduced by Milton Bradley in 1916, although the first catalog listing wasn't until 1921. The game stayed in the Bradley line until 1966. In 1967 Parker Brothers obtained the rights to UNCLE WIGGILY and published the game for a number of years. And in 1989, both Milton Bradley and Parker Brothers reintroduced different versions of the same UNCLE WIGGILY game. Bradley had obtained the rights from Howard Garis's daughter-in-law, M. R. (Mabel) Garis; Parker claimed it was "exclusive licensee under the rights of the late Howard R. Garis." The Parker game more closely resembles the original UNCLE WIGGILY, the object being to reach Dr. Possum's office, number 151, which was both his address and the last space on the board. The Bradley version, noticeably different and abbreviated, doesn't mention Dr. Possum, and it has only 100 spaces.

Because of the large number of UNCLE WIGGILY games sold throughout its long history, the standard version has only limited value to collectors. The gameboard changed in 1923, 1949, and 1955; the games with the highest value are the very first ones and the ones with the composition rabbits or the metal rabbits (1947–53).

ORIGIN OF 25 CLASSIC GAMES

GAME NAME	DATE	ORIGINAL CO.	COMMENTS
BATTLESHIP	1967	Milton Bradley	Originally pencil & paper game; Published 1931 as SALVO, 1933 as COMBAT, ±1940 as WARFARE NAVAL COMBAT.
BLOCKHEAD	1954	Saalfield	Sold to Parker Brothers; now owned by Pressman; still uses original all-wood pieces.
CANDY LAND	1949	Milton Bradley	Still sold by Hasbro/Bradley.
CHUTES & LADDERS	1943	Milton Bradley	Still sold by Hasbro/Bradley.
CLUE	1948	Parker Bros.	Orig. English CLUEDO; Parker licensed it in 1948, later removed subtitle "The Sherlock Holmes Game"; early sets have real rope.
CONCENTRATION	1959	Milton Bradley	One of two TV games to outlive the television show; now sold by Pressman.
COOTIE	1948	Schaper	Originally pencil & paper game; sold 1927 as TU-TEE; reviewed as COOTIE, 1934 *Leisure* magazine; now sold by Hasbro/Bradley.
FLINCH	1902	Flinch Card Co.	Licensed by Parker Bros. 1904, then bought outright by 1936.
GAME OF INDIA	1901	Milton Bradley	Early PARCHEESI/PACHISI variant published by many companies; from Korean game of NYOUT; introduced to England 1896 as LUDO.
GAME OF THE STATES	1940	Milton Bradley	Still sold by Hasbro/Bradley.
GO TO THE HEAD OF THE CLASS	1938	Milton Bradley	Still sold by Hasbro/Bradley.
LIE DETECTOR	1960	Mattel	Revised by Mattel 1988, sold to Pressman 1989; revision eliminates smokers, replaces "teacher" with "psychic reader."
MONOPOLY	1904	Eliz. Maggie Phillips	Adapted by Charles Darrow 1933; bought by Parker Bros., 1935.

GAME NAME	DATE	ORIGINAL CO.	COMMENTS
OTHELLO	1976	Gabriel	Originally THE GAME OF ANNEXATION, then REVERSI by McLoughlin in 1888; sold by Hasbro/Bradley, now Pressman.
PARCHEESI	1867	E. G. Selchow	Earliest game trademark (1874); © 1867 by John Hamilton, assigned to Albert Swift 1868; now sold by Hasbro/Bradley.
PASSWORD	1961	Milton Bradley	Silver anniversary edition has been sold by Hasbro/Bradley every year since the 25th anniversary in 1986; out of production.
PIT	1904	Parker Bros.	Still sold by Hasbro/Parker.
RACKO	1956	Milton Bradley	Still sold by Hasbro/Bradley.
RISK	1959	Parker Bros.	Still sold by Hasbro/Parker as RISK/CASTLE RISK: 2 games, 2-sided board; CASTLE RISK = conquering Europe, not the world.
ROOK	1906	Parker Bros.	Still sold by Hasbro/Parker.
SCRABBLE	1948	Prod. & Mktg. Co.	Licensed 1953, bought 1971 by Selchow & Righter; still sold by Hasbro/Bradley.
SORRY	1934	Parker Bros.	Originally from England; still sold by Hasbro/Parker.
STRATEGO	1961	Milton Bradley	Early variations include Milton Bradley's Le CHOC, ca. WWI, and All-Fair's INTERNATIONAL SPY, 1943.
UNCLE WIGGILY	1916	Milton Bradley	First catalog listing, 1921; original style sold by Parker Bros., 1989; abbreviated version still sold by Hasbro/Bradley.
YAHTZEE	1956	E.S. Lowe	Originally game of YACHT, adapted by Lowe; Bradley bought Lowe Co. in 1973.

PART TWO

Collecting Games

6

Starting a Game Collection

If you want to build a collection for other than investment purposes, look for games that *you* like. Unless you're buying games for resale, don't buy something that you wouldn't want to keep.

Many collectors of early games collect games primarily for their graphics—that is, for the illustrations, color, and design on the game box, the gameboard, and even the cards. Collectors of later games, especially games made after 1960, are more interested in the theme or licensed character. Some collectors focus on the implements—all the odd-shaped pieces of wood, metal, pewter, Bakelite, bone, celluloid, and even ivory that were used as markers or figurines in games. Other collectors buy games according to theme or historical and cultural significance. Some collectors are interested only in the nostalgia value of a game—they are looking for the games of their childhood. And still other collectors look for games that play well (after all, play *was* the main purpose).

Area and Range of a Collection

As a starting collector, you might want to consider what kinds of games to collect and what the range of the collection will be. Will the collection be limited to American games or include European (and other) games as well? Will it include folk-art games and games with no identifiable manufacturer? Will it have board games, card games, and skill-and-action games or specialize in just one area? Will the collection focus on one theme, such as sports, cartoon and character games, war games, mystery games, television games, or strategy/simulation games? Will it consist of games noted for their graphics, their play value, their components, or their social and cultural significance?

What period will the collection deal with? There are a number of major "collecting periods," including:

1. The early pre-mass-market games, before the beginning of the Milton Bradley Company in 1860

2. Late nineteenth century, from 1860 to either 1900, 1910, or 1920 (collectors feel the "Golden Age" of games ended somewhere between the cessation of the large,

The incredible lithography exemplified by McLoughlin's THE KNOCKERS GAME (±1900) is one of the reasons many collectors favor games by that company.

BOOM OR BUST is a game many people remember from their youth. The game plays well and has an interesting design and components.

What to Look for in a Game

What to look for in a game depends on whether you're looking primarily at the box cover as art, at the theme or components as a symbol of social history, or at the entire game as a form of education or recreation.

Collectors concerned primarily with the possible appreciation in value of a game should look for games that are graphically striking or thematically significant and in very good or excellent condition. However, many collectors buy some games in poor condition because the games may be affordable and repairable. And once a collector becomes familiar with the games that are available in the marketplace, he or she may be willing to purchase a game in poor condition, or one that is missing components, if it might be difficult to locate again.

Unless purchasing a rare item, avoid games that have mildew or are faded or badly stained. Soot or water stains may be permanent, but dirt can be cleaned off; many a dingy-looking game has been bought for little money and then turned into a beautiful (and valuable) piece just with a little soap and water (see "Cleaning Games," in Chapter 9).

If you're collecting pre–World War II games as an

THE WONDERFUL GAME OF OZ (Parker Brothers, 1921), because of its beautiful lithography, its Wizard of Oz theme, its nostalgic connection to literature and film, and its impressive pewter implements (in deluxe sets) is certain to appreciate in value more rapidly than most other games of the same period.

beautifully lithographed games around 1900 and the purchase of McLoughlin by Milton Bradley in 1920)

3. Between the world wars, 1914–44 (including the post-depression, prewar boom)

4. From the mid-1800s up to World War II

5. Post WWII to the present

6. Before television, or before the first TV-based game in 1950, or up to the years of the influence of early television, around 1955

7. The television era, from 1950 to the present

8. The period either before or after the social change of the mid-1960s (an easy identification point is the introduction of the ZIP code in 1963)

9. The latest generation, from about twenty-five years ago to the present.

You might want to collect games from just one year, say, the year of your birth, or the year of a major historic event, such as the stock market crash of 1929.

Some collectors collect one type of game, such as games with spinning tops (clockwise from top left): HI POP (Advance, 1946), ZIP-TOP (Deluxe, ±1935), BULL IN THE CHINA SHOP (MB, 1937), and FLASH (J. Pressman, ±1935).

Parker Brothers' THE PIED PIPER OF HAMELIN is a cartoon game, a Disney item, and a game based on a film—three elements guaranteed to ensure its position as a highly collectible game.

investment, look for games by McLoughlin Brothers, Bliss, Parker Brothers, All-Fair, Wilder, Selchow & Righter, Singer, and the very early companies such as Ives; select games that are graphically striking or that represent special themes (see Chapter 7, "Cross-Collectible Themes"). Many early Milton Bradley games and specific games by smaller companies also might make a good investment. If your interest is in primarily post–World War II games, you can pay less attention to the company but should look more to the theme; check resource and price guides to find out what character collectibles are popular. Look for premiums and limited editions as well as games based on events or on material from other media (television, film).

Find out what games are sought after by other game collectors, and what games are good supplements to other collecting specialties (for example, the BARBIE game is a desired item for Barbie doll collectors). In all cases, choose games that are complete (including instructions) and in very good to excellent condition.

A word of caution, however: games are subject to fads and to supply and demand like anything else. Some themes may fall out of favor over time. Or most "theme" collectors may have already acquired a particular game, and the game collectors might be unwilling to pay the high premium the theme collectors once accepted. And occasionally someone uncovers a warehouse of a particular title and suddenly the market is flooded with that game. Also, make sure you get the whole story about what's currently popular. Some speculators, for example, knowing that baseball games can fetch some of the best prices for games, have paid dearly for those from the early 1900s only to find out that the collectors want very early games or games with the names of players or teams, and are not necessarily interested in generic baseball games.

In general (and with all else being equal), board games have greater value than card games, and larger games are worth more than smaller ones. With the exception of war or military, cartoon character, and other special theme games, games from the nineteenth century and character games from the 1960s and 1970s are more valuable than most general games from 1920 to 1960.

The Most Common Games

Some game titles, such as BINGO, AUTHORS, or PIT, show up at almost every flea market or antique show. These are often the least expensive games a collector can find. Common games, such as AUTHORS, can vary greatly in value depending on the illustrations on the box and cards; the earliest games of PIT, on the other hand, are nearly all the same and are omnipresent, making it the most common and least valuable game made. In addition to the four most common "generic" classics—backgammon, checkers, chess, and dominoes—the list of common early games includes:

ANAGRAMS	AUTHORS	BEANO
BINGO	CHINESE CHECKERS	DOCTOR BUSBY
FISH POND	FLINCH	JACK STRAWS
KENO	LOST HEIR	LOTTO
MONOPOLY	OLD MAID	PARCHEESI
PETER CODDLES	PICK UP STICKS	PIT
ROOK	SNAP	TIC-TAC-TOE
TIDDLEY WINKS	TOURING	

Most of these titles were in the public domain and were published by many different companies. FLINCH, MONOPOLY, PARCHEESI, PIT, ROOK, and TOURING were "proprietary" games, published by a specific company: FLINCH was put out by the Flinch Card Co. and then Parker Brothers; MONOPOLY was sold by Darrow and then Parker Brothers; PARCHEESI was published by E.G. Selchow and Selchow & Righter, though there are also sets

This 1906 ad covers two of Parker Brothers' four most popular and long-lasting card games (the other two are FLINCH and TOURING).

THE LOST HEIR is a common title, but each cover seems to offer a completely different interpretation. The two shown here are by Milton Bradley (left), ±1900, and McLoughlin, 1893; the McLoughlin cover illustration is almost the same as on other McLoughlin games, such as ERRAND BOY.

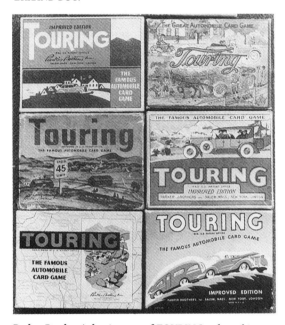

Parker Brothers' classic game of TOURING, released in 1926, was sold for decades and eventually was succeeded by MILLE BORNES; though the game is common (and usually inexpensive), it is interesting to trace the changes in the automobiles, mileage cards, and delay cards of the many different versions. It is difficult to pinpoint the exact date of any edition, since each was out for a long period, and often two editions carried the same date (clockwise from upper left): 1937, 1926, 1926, 1937, 1947, 1954, and 1937.

by H.B. Chaffee; and PIT, ROOK, and TOURING were made by Parker Brothers.

Though common, some of these games may be valuable. Some have attractive or unusual covers or contents. Also, some collectors *specialize* in these games and try to find all the titles in the series. For example, some collectors try to amass the complete assortment of AUTHORS games; since various versions of AUTHORS were published by a multitude of companies, the authors depicted in the many decks available represent an interesting sampling of American and European literature. Also, many of the authors were pictured on the cards, allowing one to collect a photo history as well.

CHINESE CHECKERS games, popular in the late 1920s, all seem to be about the same—usually illustrated with a dragon or Chinese motif. What makes some of the games highly collectible are the marbles.

DR. BUSBY can be valuable if it was made by Ives, or has an exceptional cover, or contains cards depicting black characters.

Every major company published at least one AUTHORS game, and they're all different. Though common, some sets are valued for their illustrations or selection of authors.

OLD MAID games (clockwise from top left): Milton Bradley #4263; Milton Bradley #4114; McLoughlin; Milton Bradley #4116, 1937; Milton Bradley #4113; Whitman #3029, 1927); the two cards (one a black collectible) are from Parker Brothers. Note that the McLoughlin cover has the same illustration used on McLoughlin's THE MERRY GAME OF OLD MAID board game.

FISH POND games take on all shapes and sizes, and some, such as a few of the large McLoughlin ones, command a high price because they have such extraordinary illustrations.

JACK STRAWS is an early version of PICK-UP-STICKS. Some valuable sets have intricately carved "tools," usually in wood and sometimes in bone or ivory.

MONOPOLY can be found everywhere. But the early Darrow sets (and even earlier prototypes) are very valuable, as are some of the 1935 Parker Brothers' sets and the deluxe versions.

OLD MAID is another ubiquitous title that some collectors specialize in. The different versions offer a unique assortment of characters and caricatures. (During the late 1800s the counterpart to OLD MAID, called OLD BACHELOR, never caught on. The early versions of OLD MAID depicted the character as an unattractive spinster, but recent editions, in light of social changes, have made the bachelorette much prettier. Some OLD MAID sets have cards with black characters.

PARCHEESI hasn't changed for more than 125 years. And neither has the value, unless you find a very early one or an interesting variation by a company other than Selchow & Righter. The eight tiny bone dice in the earlier sets make up over half the game's value.

PETER CODDLES was quite a traveler, his trips taking him mostly to New York and Boston. However, if you've been on one trip, you've been on most. Only the box cover illustration determines the value for games in this series.

PIT is one of the most common and least valuable games; the notable exception, however, is the version with the cover by famous cartoonist John Held, Jr.

SNAP, like OLD MAID, is of interest to some collectors because of its caricatures and cartoon illustrations. Many early SNAP games had one or two pairs of black characters, making these sets more desirable.

TIDDLEY WINKS games may be fun to play, and some have cute covers, but they're extremely common. Some sets, however, such as some produced by J. Pressman, are valuable because they contain glass cups made by the Akro Agate Company, the same company that made the marbles that now command a high price.

Many of the newer character collectible games, based primarily on television and film characters, are common because of the huge numbers of them that were manufactured. Popular titles such as COLUMBO, KOJAK, MAN FROM U.N.C.L.E., and some of the JAMES BOND versions are found at most shows and do not command much value.

The Most Sought-after Games

Many collectors would love a McLoughlin MAN IN THE MOON or RIVAL POLICEMEN, a Bliss DETECTIVE game, or a Darrow MONOPOLY. But at prices in the thousands of dollars, these games may no longer be on our active wish list. However, there are a number of other more recent titles that, for whatever reason, collectors seem to be looking for—for example, THE BARBIE GAME, BOOM OR BUST, CABBY, THE MUNSTERS, MYSTERY DATE, RED BARBER'S BASEBALL, and STAR REPORTER. Games taken from Hanna-Barbera cartoon shows (especially the more obscure WALLY GATOR and excepting, perhaps, THE FLINTSTONES) command very high prices. The monster games made by Hasbro, including FRANKENSTEIN, THE CREATURE, PHANTOM OF THE OPERA, and WOLFMAN, are becoming among the hottest theme games.

Games from "old rock 'n roll television," including THE BEATLES' FLIP YOUR WIG GAME, CHUBBY CHECKER, ELVIS PRESLEY, HULLABALLOO, THE MONKEES, THE PARTRIDGE FAMILY, and SHINDIG, have made a hit with collectors. Games from television's silly situation comedies (referred to affectionately as "The Nickelodeon lineup" because of that cable channel's programming), such as THE BEVERLY HILLBILLIES, BE-WITCHED, GREEN ACRES, and PETTICOAT JUNC-TION, are escalating in value. In fact, many of the most collectible titles come from games based on television

Selchow & Righter's CABBY (1938) is a game often asked for by collectors and players alike. The collectors like the theme and the metal cars and celluloid rings, and players enjoy it because it is "the game with rules made to be broken."

OUTER LIMITS (Milton Bradley, 1964) is a game with great graphics, a TV base, and science-fiction theme—all of which make it one of the most desired games of the postwar period. (Oglesby/Stock Collection)

shows, from OUTER LIMITS in the science-fiction genre to GUNSMOKE, one of a host of popular TV western games. The key here is games that are "cross-collectible" (see Chapter 7).

Buying Games: Where to Look

The best place to find games is at a game convention, be it a gathering of "gamers" at a convention such as Origins, or a collection of collectors at the regional get-togethers and annual convention of the American Game Collectors Association (see list of clubs for information).

The next best place to find good games, especially television games, is at a collectibles show. Games are starting to show up at more and more toy shows, but only "general" toy shows, not those that specialize in trains or dolls or such. Ephemera or "paper" shows are also good for finding games. The type of show will determine the type of games: toy and collectible shows with lots of merchandise from the 1950s and 1960s are likely to have television and character collectible games; paper and ephemera shows with early prints and books may have an assortment of nineteenth-century games.

Many people buy games without ever leaving home—and often without ever seeing the game. Publications such as *Toy Shop* now include classified listings specifically for games and contain information about good auctions. Collectors, dealers, and shops are doing more and more mail-order business in games. To date, there have been only isolated incidents of game collectors being "ripped off" through buying by mail, and the collectors' network is tight enough that unscrupulous dealers will not last long. If you are making a purchase sight unseen, be sure to get a detailed description of the game, especially concerning condition. Keep in mind that many sellers (especially if they're neither dealers nor collectors) refer to a game as "mint" when it is, in fact, only "very good." Also, ask the seller to give you a five-day-return privilege. The accepted custom is that the buyer sends a check for the game before the game is mailed out.

Antique shops often have games, though they are liable to be more expensive than those found at a show. Sometimes, however, a shop owner who normally doesn't deal in games will come across a few (such as in a box lot with some toys) and will price them inexpensively. Flea markets, if they deal in antiques, are great places to get games at great prices—*if* you can find any.

As games become more popular, auction houses are starting to carry more of them. Auction prices for games can be lower than shop prices (if it's a small or local auction that most people in the game community don't know about), but more likely prices will be higher. It only takes two people to escalate the price in a bidding war for a game.

Game collectors will tell you anything you want to know about their hobby—except their sources for buying games. A collector will share information about games, game companies, organizations, and conventions, but the best shops, shows, flea markets, and auctions are the best-kept secrets.

One final word about where to find early games, or, in

this case, where *not* to find them: with rare exceptions, the days of locating old treasures at garage sales are over; the earlier games now seem to be out of the attics and in the hands of knowledgeable collectors and dealers. However, the more recent games are emerging with every spring house cleaning. With luck, you might be able to pick up a $50 television theme game for $2 at a garage sale or church bazaar.

Cataloging Your Collection

Every collector should develop a detailed system of record keeping. For example, certain information, such as the address or theme, may help date a game if no date is shown; recording box dimensions helps differentiate between two different versions of the same title and reminds you of the game's format, whether a vertical or horizontal; notes about the components or game play may help link that game to a similar one.

The easiest system of record keeping is probably to begin with 3″ × 5″ index cards (you can maintain a computer file also, but it is best to keep the raw data on cards). Try not to abbreviate key words, since companies may have used different forms of the same word at different times, and these differences can be used as an indication of the date of the game. Following is the information you will want to include on each card:

Full title of game, including second-line copy
Company of manufacture
Company logo, if any (include a rough drawing)
Company address (take note of words such as "published by" or "manufactured by," and include the street address if given)
Date shown or approximate date (including clues to dating the game)
Size of container (box, envelope, parts box, etc.)
Size of open gameboard
Copyright information, if given
Patent number, if given
Inventor's name, if given
Full description of box cover illustration
Description of box style (i.e., "box bottom board")
Contents of game (including inserts, such as advertising inserts)
Cross-references in the instructions (references to other games by the same company)
Condition of box and contents
Notes about the game's theme, style of play, or relation to other games
Month and year of purchase
Price paid
Additional notes, such as unusual wording on the instructions or cards, calligraphic styles, or design of the box wrap, can be written on the back of the card

7

Cross-Collectible Themes

Cover of All-Fair's JAV-LIN, a prized black collectible.

The theme of a game is one of the primary factors contributing to a game's value. Many themes make a game cross-collectible; that is, the game is sought after by nongame collectors who collect any items relating to the theme.

Cross-collectible themes include: advertising, airships (especially zeppelins, hot-air balloons, and biplanes), animals (especially cats and various breeds of dogs), architecture, bears (especially Teddy), black characters, bridges, broadcasting (short wave, radio, television), catastrophes, children, circus, cities, comic and cartoon characters, education, finance, fire-fighting, fortune-telling, historic events, holidays (especially Christmas/Santa Claus), military, monsters, music, mystery, occupations, personalities, politics, post office, radio sets and speakers, shopping, skyscrapers, space, sports (especially baseball), the Statue of Liberty, transportation (including airship or airplane, automobile, bicycle, boat, horse and buggy, motorcycle, train, and trolley), travel, war, western (cowboy) themes, and World's Fair, plus games based on books, films, plays, radio and television programs, and games illustrated by famous artists.

Often a cross-collectible game will be of more value to the theme collector than to a game collector; for example, a baseball memorabilia collector is likely to offer more for a game picturing early baseball players than the piece

Among highly collectible radio games are (clockwise from upper left) games by Bradley, Parker, Wilder, and Bradley.

An 1889 ad for WILLIAMS' INDOOR BASE BALL GAME, priced at $1 then and valued at over $1,000 now.

Train cover from Milton Bradley's FAST MAIL.

would be worth to a game collector. Some games are cross-collectible in more than one area, such as a game based on a television show with a war theme (for example, COMBAT).

A 1904 ad for STAGE (C.M. Clark Publishing Co., Boston), a game with illustrations of the most famous theater actors and actresses of the time.

Bowling is one sport that translates better into a skill-and-action game than a board or card game. These two board games by Parker Brothers were published around the turn of the century. Since the bowlers are women and elves, the games are even more collectible. (Krim Collection)

This 1922 version of Parker Brothers' ACROSS THE CONTINENT has one of the best transportation theme covers of the first half of the twentieth century. (Krim Collection)

The historic and complimentary rendering of Indians makes this WILD WEST game by Ullman Mfg. Co. of New York a desired collectible.

Though games featuring stage actors, movie stars, and radio and television personalities are all valuable cross-collectibles in the areas of theater, film, and broadcasting, the highest values are for games featuring the *characters* made famous by many of these actors. For instance, though William Boyd's name is as well known as that of the character he portrayed for years on radio, in films, and on television, Hopalong Cassidy, a collector is much more interested in Hopalong Cassidy memorabilia than William Boyd items; a Milton Bradley HOPALONG CASSIDY game from the television era is more sought after than an earlier Bradley game, MOVIE LAND LOTTO, which includes pictures of Hoppy star William Boyd during the early, pre-cowboy part of his film career.

It would be impossible to list all the games published in the many cross-collectible categories. The few themes discussed here represent some of the most widely collected areas of interest, and the games listed exemplifying each theme are meant to serve only as a representative sample.

Advertising Games and Premiums

Since the 1890s, companies have used games to promote their products; games were among the many items offered as premiums to consumers for using the company's product. Often the game was found inside a box, such as a box of cereal. Or the game may have been the box itself (a path game on the back of the box with playing pieces to be cut out). Sometimes you had to send away for the game, enclosing box tops or labels, and maybe a little cash to cover postage and handling. Some games that were also available in shops were given as prizes for collecting product wrappers (such as Bee Soap) or for selling subscriptions to magazines (such as *Youth's Companion*).

Sectional checkerboard puzzles were the most common premiums, followed by checkerboards. Small card games and thin, one-piece board games were also popular give-aways.

Some games advertised a number of products. LITTLE SHOPPERS by the Gibson Game Co. is perhaps the best example, and possibly the most valued game of its type. It had one of the most beautiful box covers of any game of that time; the brightly colored illustration showed a huge department store packed with women and girls in period dress. The gameboard pictured and named twenty-four products, and included a cardboard cutout of each product container, made to be set into a wooden stand. Some of the products shown are Cat's Paw Heels, Diamond Crystal salt, Domino sugar, Dutch Boy paints, Edison Mazda lamps, Fleishman's yeast, Ivory soap, Mennen's powder, Necco wafers, Pillsbury's Best flour, and Sunshine biscuits.

Once in a while, a sponsor such as the Coca-Cola Company joined forces with a major manufacturer, such as Milton Bradley. The result was a regular game with an ad for the product on the box, such as Milton Bradley's BROADSIDES, "Compliments of the Coca-Cola Company." Since the value of a premium game depends primarily on the value behind the name of the sponsoring company, most Coca-Cola games would be very desirable premiums.

Among the first companies to use games heavily to promote their products were the Woolson Spice Company and C.I. Hood. Around 1903, Woolson Spice Company of Toledo, Ohio, and Kansas City, Missouri, published at least sixty card games, all of which advertised Lion Coffee, usually on every card. Lion Coffee was "sold only in one-pound packages with a beautiful card (or game) in each package"; the back of each card carried the message, "Drink Lion Coffee."

Another company, C.I. Hood, like Woolson Spice, also advertised heavily during the late 1890s. "Hood's Sarsaparilla purifies the Blood, strengthens the Nerves, sharpens the Appetite, and cures That Tired Feeling" was written on every domino in the HOOD'S DOMINOS set (±1899). HOOD'S SPELLING SCHOOL (1897), which was "sent to any address for eight one-cent stamps," consisted of a box of small cardboard letters, with instructions listing ten letter-transposition word games, such as ANAGRAMS. Hood claimed that in addition to teaching spelling and word building, SPELLING SCHOOL provided "peculiar and helpful mind training." The words "Take Hood's Sarsaparilla" were written on the back of every cardboard letter. HOOD'S WAR GAME, U.S. Vs SPAIN (1899) could be had for 25cents; this card game, similar to AUTHORS, taught you about the key locations, battles, and heroes of the Spanish American War while reminding you that "Hood's Sarsaparilla Is The Best Money Can Buy."

In the early 1900s the Domino (sugar) company made its own advertising game, which was, naturally, a game of dominoes. On the back of each of the twenty-six small paper dominoes was an advertisement in verse, such as: *When lovely woman goes a shopping / For table needs, you may rely. / Into the grocer's she'll be dropping / To CRYSTAL DOMINO SUGAR buy."*

The Boston Herald issued a card game around 1905 called GAME OF SUCCESS, which contained a series of "Want Ad" cards, and then the corresponding success ("ad answered") card. A copy of the *Boston Herald* or the *Sunday Herald* was clearly visible in each drawing, or was depicted more subtly.

In 1915 the Household Words Game Company of Washington, D.C., tried a novel idea consisting of a card game with a different manufacturer's product advertised on each card. Each manufacturer then marketed the game in a slipcase printed with its own company name. In each case, the game title was GOING TO MARKET. Products advertised included Kelly-Springfield, Knox Gelatine, Libby's, Post Toasties, Sherwin-Williams, Welch's, and Willys-Overland Co. Four cards in the deck were devoted to each company, so that firms such as Beech-Nut could advertise a different product on each card: chewing gum, mints, peanut butter, and bacon. In playing the game (similar to GO FISH), the player would have to ask for a particular card by name and description, such as "Give me Ingersoll, the Watch that Made the Dollar Famous"; the entire game became a series of commercial messages. GOING TO MARKET is of great interest to advertising collectors; some sets have a Coca-Cola card in them, making them even more valuable.

The use of premiums reached its heyday during the golden age of radio in the late 1930s and 1940s. Announcers reminded listeners throughout the show that they would be told by the end of the program how to get their special character premium. In 1940 you could take your Captain Midnight Flight Patrol Membership card to any Skelly gas station and you would be given a free RINGO JUMPO game, which, the announcer assured us excitedly, contained genuine Mexican jumping beans "gathered by daring Mexican Indians from reptile-infested underbrush."

PREMIUM No. 137.

Delivered free by mail to your address ———
For 200 BIG BLACK BEES cut from the Wrappers of BEE SOAP, Or for 45 BIG BLACK BEES and 62c. in POSTAGE STAMPS.

THE ROYAL GAME OF INDIA.

PARCHEESI *THE BEST HOME GAME*

No Parlor Table Game has ever been published which has given so **universal** satisfaction to **young** and old; can be played by two, three or four persons; children and adults are fascinated with it. It is bright—exciting—attractive. For twenty years the best families have had it in their homes, and so enjoyed it that now it is always called for when the question arises, "What shall we play?"

FULL PARTICULARS ON EACH BEE SOAP WRAPPER.

COLGATE & CO., - 6 Dutch Street, New York.
YOUR GROCER KEEPS BEE SOAP.

Colgate customers could get a PARCHEESI game from Colgate quickly by sending in 200 bees cut from the wrappers of Bee Soap. (Do you know how many bees there were per wrapper?)

Plate 1 (overleaf)

Clockwise from noon: STEEPLE CHASE, McLoughlin Bros.; NAPOLEON, THE LITTLE CORPORAL, Parker Bros.; DIAMONDS AND HEARTS, THE GAME OF CITY LIFE, OR BOYS OF NEW YORK, THE IMPROVED GAME OF WHAT D'YE BUY, THE PLEASING AND INSTRUCTING GAME OF COUNTRY STOREKEEPER, THE JOLLY GAME OF OLD MAID AND OLD BACHELOR, CINDERELLA, OR HUNT THE SLIPPER, all McLoughlin Bros.; GAME OF BOY SCOUTS, Milton Bradley; GAME OF DRUMMER BOY, J.H. Singer. *Courtesy of the Debby and Marty Krim Collection*

Plate 2

Clockwise from 11 o'clock: BILLY BUMPS' VISIT TO BOSTON, Geo. S. Parker; MAGNETIC JACK STRAWS, E.I. Horsman; GAME OF POLITICS, OR THE RACE FOR THE PRESIDENCY, W.S. Reed; GAME OF TIDDLEDY WINKS, Chaffee & Selchow; GAME OF WANG, Clark & Sowdon; CORNER GROCERY, Parker Bros.; FIVE LITTLE PIGS, J.H. Singer; HOUSE THAT JACK BUILT, McLoughlin Bros.; JUMBLES, Clark & Sowdon; DAISY JACK STRAWS, J.H. Singer; SOCIETY, West & Lee; CUCKOO, A SOCIETY GAME, J. H. Singer; THE GAME OF AUCTION, Milton Bradley; THE ORIGINAL GAME OF LETTERS, Noyes, Snow & Co.; PAWS & CLAWS, Clark & Sowdon; INDIA, Milton Bradley; VIGNETTE AUTHORS, E.G. Selchow.

Plate 3

Clockwise from 10 o'clock: RAMBLES THROUGH OUR COUNTRY, American Publishing; THE GAME OF RADIO FLASH, Rosenwald-Milius Co.; FISH POND, Edgar O. Clark; HEL-LO TELEPHONE GAME, J.C. Singer; OLD MAID, Chaffee & Selchow; DR. QUACK, Russell; ABC, Parker Bros.; GAME OF TELEGRAPH MESSENGER BOY, McLoughlin; BLACK CAT FORTUNE TELLING, Parker Bros.; KOMIKAL KONVERSATION KARDS, Selchow & Righter; THE PIGGERIES, OR WALKING THE PLANK, McLoughlin/Spear; RIP VAN WINKLE, Parker Bros.; A SHEAF OF WHEAT, Milton Bradley; CATCHING MICE, McLoughlin Bros.; COMIC CONVERSATION CARDS, J. Ottmann; WYHOO, Milton Bradley.

Plate 4
Clockwise from 1 o'clock: HOOK, Milton Bradley; GAME OF INTERNATIONAL SPY, E.E. Fairchild; GES-IT, Knapp Electric; HORNET, Samuel Lowe; ELOPING!, Game Creations; ED WYNN, THE FIRE CHIEF, Selchow & Righter; PEEZA, The Toy Tinkers; CABBY, Selchow & Righter; DEFENDERS OF THE FLAG, Noble & Noble; INDIAN AR-ROW HEADS, Sam'l Gabriel Sons; STOP THIEF, Einson-Freeman; CONSTRUCTION GAME, Wilder; GANG BUST-ERS GAME, Whitman; THREE MEN IN A TUB, Milton Bradley; GOOD THINGS TO EAT LOTTO, Sam'l Gabriel Sons; HUNGRY WILLIE, Transogram.

Plate 5

Clockwise from center: GAME OF WEMET GOLF, McLoughlin Bros; FOOTBALL, Parker Bros.; TEN PIN DICE; NECK & NECK, Embossing Co.; AYDELOTT'S BASEBALL, Aydelott; TEN PIN CARDS, McLoughlin Bros.; CHECKERSPORTS; PITCH 'EM, Wolverine.

Plate 6

Clockwise from 1 o'clock: POP-UP STORE GAME, Milton Bradley; BUNKER POKER, Milton Bradley; GROUCHO'S YOU BET YOUR LIFE, Lowell; THE PERILS OF PAULINE, Louis Marx & Co.; BLUFF, Saalfield Publishing; D-DAY, Avalon Hill; FEARLESS FIREMAN, Hassenfeld Bros.; FIVE STAR FINAL, Parker Bros.

Plate 7
From left to right: MAGGIE AND JIGGS, Milton Bradley; THE KATZENJAMMER KIDS HOCKEY, Jaymar; REG'LAR FELLERS, Milton Bradley; ADVENTURES OF POPEYE GAME, Transogram; THE GAME OF ABBIE AN' SLATS, Milton Bradley; LOTTO, Milton Bradley; TIDDLEDY WINKS, Milton Bradley; QUICK WIT, Parker Bros.; SKIPPY, Milton Bradley; BUSTER BROWN AT THE CIRCUS, Selchow & Righter; WHO'S THE GENIUS?, Frederick A. Stokes; FOOLISH QUESTIONS, Wallie Dorr; TOM AND JERRY, Milton Bradley; PIT, Parker Bros.

Plate 8
Clockwise from noon: LINERS AND TRANSPORTS, PLANET PATROL, TWO GAME COMBINATION, U.S. MAIL AND CHECKERS, all Milton Bradley; STREAMLINED TRAIN GAME, Rexall; GRANDE AUTO RACE, Atkins; AIR MAIL, Milton Bradley; THE AIR MAIL, The Archer Toy Co.

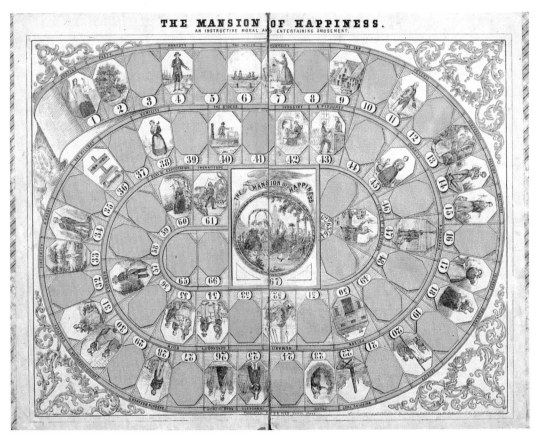

Plate 9
MANSION OF HAPPINESS, W. &
S.B. Ives.

Plate 10
Clockwise from 1 o'clock: PLANTERS
PEANUT PARTY, Planters; BUST-
ER BROWN GAME AND PLAY
BOX; BRING 'EM BACK ALIVE;
TYE ROBINSON RACE RECORD;
PARCHEESI (wartime YMCA sol-
dier's packet), Selchow & Righter;
SPIN-A-WORD GAME; GAME-
LANDS, Marx; GAME OF SOCKO
THE MONK, Einson-Freeman.

Milton Bradley's FLAGSHIP AIRFREIGHT from 1946 unobtrusively shows an American Airlines van and the AA insignia on the cargo plane. (Fink Collection)

There are lots of advertising games and game premiums, most of them in the hands of those who collect the products being advertised. Appliances, foodstuff, gasoline, health products, and other household items were all sponsors long before television. Many games either advertised a product or were available only by sending away to the sponsoring company: see the Appendix, "American Companies That Made Games," for listings and values of games made by companies not necessarily in the game business.

Cartoon and Comic Characters

Many popular characters from the cartoons and comics, from The Yellow Kid of the late 1800s to the superheroes of the 1960s, were featured in games. Milton Bradley Company was the major producer of cartoon character board games, and Whitman offered a large assortment of comic card games. There is some overlap between cartoon characters and radio and television characters: Red Ryder began as a comic strip and then was adapted for radio; Charlie McCarthy and Howdy Doody were marionettes who started in radio and television, respectively, and later became cartoon characters in comic books; Superman and Blondie (and Dagwood) covered all the media from comics to radio to television to movies.

The FELIX, MOUSE AND TRAP GAME (manufacturer unknown) is a very early, very rare Felix the Cat item. (Krim collection)

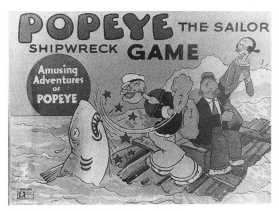

POPEYE THE SAILOR SHIPWRECK GAME (Einson-Freeman, 1933). (Courtesy Just Kids)

Many cartoon series became games, with the gameboard and box cover drawn by the original artist. The art-into-games gained momentum in the 1920s with BRINGING UP FATHER (1920), from the cartoon strip by George McManus, KEEPING UP WITH THE JONESES (1921), illustrated by Pop Momand, and REG'LAR FELLERS (1926), picturing the workmanship of Gene Byrnes.

Among the major cartoon and comic characters who decorate games, most of which are still available but are becoming increasingly more difficult to find, are: Abbie and Slats, Alice in Wonderland, Alvin and the Three Chipmunks, Andy Gump, Barnie Google and Spark Plug, Batman, Beany & Cecil, Blondie, Bugs Bunny, Buster Brown, Casper, Charlie McCarthy, Chester Gump, Deputy Dawg, Dick Tracy, Donald Duck, Ella Cinders, Felix the Cat (early version is very rare), Flintstones (common), Foxy Grandpa, Happy Hooligan, Howdy Doody, Huckleberry Hound, Jetsons, Katzenjammer Kids, L'il Abner, Little Lulu, Little Orphan Annie, Mickey Mouse, Moon Mullins, The Munsters, Nancy & Sluggo, The Nebbs, Peanuts, Pinnochio, Popeye, Red Ryder, Road Runner, Rocky & Bullwinkle, Rootie Kazootie, Ruff & Reddy, Skeezix, Skippy, Smitty, Snoopy, Snow White, Superman, Terrytoons (including Heckle & Jeckle, Dinky Duck, Tom Terrific, and Little Roquefort), Tom & Jerry, Toonerville Trolley, Wally Gator, Walt & Skeezix ("Gasoline Alley"), and Winnie Winkle.

Games Illustrated by Famous Artists

Many games can be considered works of art. And in some cases, the box cover, the gameboard, the cards, and even the instruction sheet for a game was drawn by a famous artist, illustrator, or cartoonist.

Not only were a number of games illustrated by famous artists, but some games were actually based on the drawings of these popular illustrators.

Peter Arno (1904–68): illustrated the box cover of BONANZA (Parker Brothers ± 1940). Arno, perhaps the premier artist for *The New Yorker* in the 1930s through the 1950s, sold his first cartoon to the magazine in 1925.

Wonderful animal illustrations by Harrison Cady are the highlight of Saalfield's Thornton Burgess game HOOT.

Harrison Cady (1877–1970): illustrator of "Peter Rabbit," he drew the characters of the Thornton Burgess stories, including the Burgess board game ANIMAL GAME and card game HOOT (1940s), both made by Saalfield.

J. N. Ding (Jay Norwood Darling, 1876–1962): illustrated the box cover and cards of one edition of QUIZ OF THE WIZ (H.J. Phillips Co., 1921). Ding was an editorial cartoonist who won the Pulitzer Prize for his illustrations in 1924 and again in 1943; he drew regularly for the *New York Herald Tribune* and the *Des Moines Register and Tribune*.

H. Boylston Dummer (1878–1945): drew the cover illustration for a series of Milton Bradley games and puzzles, including BINGO and LOTTO. Some of the games appear

H. Boylston Dummer, another artist who drew animated animals, possibly made one large illustration for Milton Bradley, which was then cut up to use on at least three different games. Dummer's signature appeared on one.

to have an incomplete image, and it is possible that different sections of the same picture were used for different games. An illustrator of children's books, he was known for his nature drawings. Dummer's playful style depicting clothed animals playing sports and games is unmistakable.

Rube Goldberg (1883–1970): illustrated and signed the cover and card backs of FOOLISH QUESTIONS (Wallie Dorr Co., ≥ 1931), plus the 52 cards that featured the "foolish answers" to his foolish questions. Goldberg is known for his whimsical "chain-of-events" cartoons, popular from the early 1900s through the 1940s. The name of the game comes from the name of his cartoon series from around 1931.

Johnny Gruelle (1880–1938): drew the box covers for games (mostly by Milton Bradley Co.) and puzzles (mostly by Madmar Quality Co.) featuring the characters from his series, Raggedy Ann and Andy.

John Held, Jr. (1889–1958): provided one signed illustration for the cover, card backs, and instructions of the 1919 edition of PIT (Parker Brothers, originally 1904). Held, whose cartoons appeared in *Liberty* and *The New Yorker,* became popular satirizing the fads and styles of the Roaring Twenties pre-depression era.

Charles Lederer (1856–1925): invented and designed KUTI-KUTS in 1922 for the Regensteiner Corporation, Chicago, two years after publication of his book, *The Lederer Art Course.* The cartoonist for *Harper's Weekly, The New York Herald,* and *The New York World* used characters divided into four sections (hat, head, chest, and legs), allowing the player to make interchangeable characters (similar to the POPEYE card game). The head section was drawn so it could be used either side up; each section also had a letter, and points were scored by making four-letter words.

Peter Max (1939–): modern "pop" designer devised and illustrated a cardboard chess set sold by Kontrell Industries of New York in 1971; two pieces of intricately illustrated heavy diecut cardboard would fit together to form a stand-up playing piece.

John McCutcheon (1870–1949): illustrated and signed the cover and cards of BIRD CENTER ETIQUETTE (Home Game Co., 1904), touted as "the artistic and social hit of

RAGGEDY ANN'S MAGIC PEBBLE GAME (Milton Bradley, 1941), with illustrations by Johnny Gruelle.

a decade" containing "original drawings by the world's greatest cartoonist." The game was based on McCutcheon's 1904 book, *Bird Center Cartoons*, which in turn came from his series of *Bird Center* drawings that satirized pretentious Americans. McCutcheon first published cartoons in the 1890s, in the *Chicago Record-Herald*, gained fame, and won a Pulitzer Prize in 1932 for a cartoon in the *Chicago Tribune*.

A. A. (Alan Alexander) Milne (1882–1956): English poet and illustrator responsible for the box covers and gameboards of the WINNIE THE POOH games, one produced by Kirk Guild in 1931 and another by Parker Brothers in 1933; *Winnie the Pooh* was written in 1926 as one in a series of four books scripted for Milne's son Christopher Robin, whose name appears on the Parker board.

Maxfield Parrish (1870–1966): designed at least two target games for Parker Brothers, one with many small soldiers and the other, a 1913 game entitled MAXFIELD PARRISH SOLDIER, with one soldier two feet high; the soldier held an air gun that could be taken from him and used to make the soldier's head nod when hit; a Parker catalog describes the game as "probably the first toy elaborately designed by an artist of international fame." Possibly one other Parker soldier game is purported to have used Parrish's illustrations. The Parrish soldier became the model for many additional Parker soldier games that do not bear his name and probably were not drawn by him.

Tony Sarg (1882–1942): noted for illustrating children's books, blocks, and a set of musical cubes, he also drew the covers for a number of games.

Hendrik Willem Van Loon (1882–1944): illustrated the pictorial map gameboard of Parker Brothers' WIDE WORLD GAME from 1933. Van Loon's THE STORY OF MANKIND game, published by Kerk Guild in 1931, was based on his 1921 book by the same name. In spite of Van Loon signing his full name at the end of the game's instructions inside the box cover, Kerk Guild incorrectly spelled his first name "Hendrick" in the title.

Gluyas Williams (1888–1982): illustrated and signed the cover of QUICK WIT (Parker Brothers, 1938). Williams was one of the foremost cartoonists for *Life* magazine during the 1920s and for the *The New Yorker* in the 1930s and 1940s.

THE GAME OF ROBIN HOOD (Parker Brothers, 1893).

LITTLE GOLDENLOCKS & THE THREE BEARS, 1890, is McLoughlin Brothers at its best. (Krim Collection)

Games Based on Books

Stories for children and classic fairy tales have always been great sources for games. ALICE IN WONDERLAND, CINDERELLA, JACK THE GIANT KILLER (from "Jack and the Beanstalk"), PETER PAN, PETER RABBIT, PETER COTTONTAIL, and RIP VAN WINKLE are all games based on children's literature. Many games have been created from the characters of Robin Hood and Robinson Crusoe, and have been taken from the stories of Beauty and the Beast and Goldilocks and the Three Bears. Since the late 1800s, children's books and stories have been given a three-dimensional life through games.

BLACK BEAUTY, by Stoll & Edwards, 1921; based on the 1877 book by Anna Sewell (her only work); a copy of the book was included with the game.

ELMER WHEELER'S FAT BOY GAME, by Parker Brothers, 1951; Based on *The Fat Boy's Book: How Elmer lost 40 lbs. in 80 days* by Elmer Wheeler, published around 1948; this is probably the only game ever based on a diet book! The game came with four wooden pawns, which were the same height as regular pawns but twice as wide.

IVANHOE, by Geo. S. Parker, 1886; the game was, according to its ad sheets, "founded on the famous story of Sir Walter Scott."

THE GAME OF THE LITTLE COLONEL, by Selchow & Righter, ±1936; based on *The Little Colonel* by Annie Fellows Johnston, 1895; the instructions for this board game state that the game was based on the book, even though the 1935 Shirley Temple movie was also mentioned.)

THE LITTLE COLONEL, by McLoughlin Brothers, ±1900; this beautifully illustrated card game was manufactured "under license of L.C. Page & Co., owners of the © and ™ of The Little Colonel."

THE VAN LOON STORY OF MANKIND GAME, by Kerk Guild, ≥1921; based on Van Loon's award-winning 1921 book, *The Story of Mankind,* with illustrations by the author. (The book was made into a 1957 movie starring Ronald Coleman and a stellar cast, including the Marx Brothers, who didn't even appear together.)

TREASURE ISLAND, by Gem Publishing, 1922; Stoll & Edwards, 1923; Stoll & Einson, 1934 (the same as the 1923 Stoll & Edwards version except for different color-

ing); Harett-Gilmar, 1950s; all based on the Robert Louis Stevenson classic from 1883.

WIDE WORLD GAME, by Parker Brothers, 1933; based on the works of historian, artist, and traveler Hendrik Willem Van Loon.

THE WONDERFUL GAME OF OZ, by Parker Brothers, 1921 (long before the 1938 film); based on *The Wonderful Wizard of Oz* by Frank L. Baum, published in 1900; this great game, especially the version with the large pewter pieces, is highly prized by collectors. Oz games were also made by Whitman (THE GAME OF THE WIZARD OF OZ, 1939) and Milton Bradley (OFF TO SEE THE WIZARD, 1960s), two by Cadaco (1950s and THE WIZARD OF OZ GAME, 1974), and THE WOGGLEBUG GAME OF CONUNDRUMS from Parker Brothers, 1905.

Games Based on Characters from a Book Series

In an 1856 PETER CODDLES game by Gould & Lincoln, the origin of that popular character was identified as being "based on the Aimwell stories." The Bobsey Twins (beginning in the 1920s), Dave Dawson (from the 1940s), Cherry Ames (since the 1940s), and Tom Swift (starting in 1910, with the Tom Swift Jr. series beginning in the 1950s) all were characters who jumped from the pages of

The Selchow & Righter version of THE LITTLE COLONEL, ≥1935.

Cadaco's 1974 THE WIZARD OF OZ. (Oglesby/Stock Collection)

The original NANCY DREW MYSTERY GAME by Parker Brothers (top), was marked 1959, but the instructions indicated 1957; a more recent edition is shown on the bottom.

books into boxed games. Three of the most popular games based on a book series are:

HARDY BOYS TREASURE GAME, by Parker Brothers, 1957 and 1960s; based on The Hardy Boys series by Franklin W. Dixon (Edward Stratemeyer) which began 1927–28.

NANCY DREW MYSTERY GAME, by Parker Brothers, 1957; based on the Nancy Drew series by Carolyn Keene (Edward Stratemeyer); Stratemeyer also took over the Horatio Alger series, and penned Tom Swift, the Rover Boys, and the Bobsey Twins.

THE UNCLE WIGGILY game by Milton Bradley, 1916; based on the Uncle Wiggily series of bedtime stories, introduced by Howard A. Garis in 1910; all Uncle Wiggily collectibles are popular, including UNCLE WIGGILY'S NEW AIRPLANE GAME from 1931 and the many Uncle Wiggily picture puzzles that appeared in the mid-1940s (all Milton Bradley); many noncollectors look for the version of this game that they grew up with. Because of the game's popularity, many copies of UNCLE WIGGILY are still on the market, and therefore the high price tag sometimes attached to the game is unjustified.

Mystery Games

Mystery and detective games have been around since at least 1889 and have been popular since 1933; they reached their peak in 1936 and 1937, the time when the gangster movie was in its prime, and began a resurgence in 1954, when companies began basing more games on

THE DETECTIVES game from 1961 (based on the TV show starring Robert Taylor) replaced the 1960 PHILIP MARLOWE game when that six-month-old Philip Carey vehicle went off the air the same year the game was released. The games were identical. (Oglesby/Stock Collection)

National Games brought SHERLOCK HOLMES back to the drawing board around 1940 for perhaps the first time since the Parker Brothers' games of 1904. (Krim collection)

television shows as the mystery was establishing itself as a staple of that medium.

The games listed here, adapted from mystery, crime, police, and detective literature, radio, and television, span the period from an early Bliss detective game in 1889, through the first mystery character game (Sherlock Holmes) in 1904, to some of the games encompassing the first three decades of television.

ARREST AND TRAIL	Trans	1963
BARETTA	MB	1976
BURKE'S LAW	Trans	1963
THE CASE OF THE ELUSIVE ASSASSIN	Ideal	1967
CHARLIE CHAN (board game)	MB	1937
CHARLIE CHAN (card game)	Whit	1939
CHARLIE'S ANGELS	MB	1977
COLOMBO	MB	1973
CLUE	PB	1948
THE GAME OF DETECTIVE	Bliss	1889
THE DETECTIVES	Trans	1961
DETECTIVE CHASE from EIGHT GAMES IN ONE	Whit	1936
DICK TRACY CARD GAME	Whit	1941
DICK TRACY CRIME STOPPER	Ideal	1963
DICK TRACY DETECTIVE GAME	Eins-Free	1933
DICK TRACY DETECTIVE GAME	Whit	1937
DICK TRACY PLAYING CARD GAME	Whit	1937
DICK TRACY SUPER MYSTERY CARD GAME	Whit	1941
DICK TRACY THE MASTER DETECTIVE GAME	S&R	1961
DRAGNET	Trans	1955
G-MAN (Carolyn Wells; card game)	MB	1936
THE GODFATHER GAME	Family Games	1971
THE HARDY BOYS MYSTERY GAME	PB	1978
HAWAII FIVE-O	Remco	1968
HAWAIIAN EYE	Lowell	1963

HONEY WEST	Ideal	1965
INTRIGUE	MB	1959±
IRONSIDES	Ideal	1967
JUSTICE	Lowell	1954
JURY BOX (six editions in the series)	PB	1936 & 1937
KOJAK	MB	1975
MANHUNT	PB	1937
MELVIN PURVIS' G-MEN (board game)	PB	1936
MR. REE	S&R	1937
MOD SQUAD	Remco	1968
MURDER ON THE ORIENT EXPRESS	Ideal	1967
PERRY MASON	Trans	1959
PETER GUNN	Lowell	1960
PHILIP MARLOWE, DETECTIVE	Trans	1960
PHILO VANCE	PB	1937
PHOTO CRIMES	PB	1937
PUBLIC ENEMY #1 (target game)	Marx	1960±
77 SUNSET STRIP	Lowell	1960
SHERLOCK HOLMES	PB	1904
SHERLOCK HOLMES	National	±1940
SLEUTH	3M	1971
STARSKY AND HUTCH	MB	1977
SURFSIDE SIX	Lowell	1961
SUSPICION	TSR	1977
TRAPPED	Bettye-B	1955
THE UNTOUCHABLES	Trans	1961
WHO DUN IT	Cadaco	1959
WHY (Alfred Hitchcock)	MB	1958

THE CASE OF THE ELUSIVE ASSASSIN was an Ellery Queen mystery board game. The same game, with the gameboard removed, became the excellent card game SLEUTH. The original version of THE GODFATHER GAME is an unusual collectible because it was packaged in a thin plastic violin case. MURDER ON THE ORIENT EXPRESS carried the Agatha Christie name. SUSPICION was a notable departure for TSR, a company known primarily for role-playing games.

Incidentally, COLOMBO was the exact same game as Alfred Hitchcock's WHY; PERRY MASON has the exact same board and similar cover as DRAGNET; and PHILIP MARLOWE, DETECTIVE was identical to THE DETECTIVES.

Sometimes included in the mystery genre category are the games based on spy shows and films, including GET SMART ELECTRONIC QUIZ GAME (Lisbeth Whiting, 1960s), ILYA KURYAKIN CARD GAME (MB 1966), I SPY (Ideal, 1965), I SPY CARD GAME (Ideal, 1966), JOHN DRAKE SECRET AGENT (MB,1966), THE MAN FROM U.N.C.L.E. (Ideal, 1965), and THE MAN FROM U.N.C.L.E. CARD GAME (MB, 1965).

Games Based on Films

It is surprising that so few games were based on movies prior to the 1950s. (Perhaps once television games became the rage, companies were more motivated to base games on movies as well.) Selchow & Righter's THE LITTLE COLONEL (±1936) and Parker Brothers' 1921 THE

WONDERFUL GAME OF OZ were both based on the books, not the movies. Not only are movie games more valuable because of their movie tie-in, but most of them were more substantial in construction, components, and design than other games of the same period. Milton Bradley made at least five movie-based games in 1939 alone, all of which had exceptional graphics, thick gameboards, and large playing pieces. Some of the games taken from films before the era of television include:

THE BIG TRAIL: Parker Brothers, ≥1930; based on John Wayne's first film, directed in 1930 by Raoul Walsh for Movietone; contains four lead pioneer figures.

THE BLACK FALCON OF THE FLYING G-MEN: Ruckelshaus, 1939; the intensely colored, beautifully illustrated cover, along with the G-Men theme and the game's rarity, makes this a high-value item.

THE EGG AND I: Capex Co., 1947; the film (which was based on a book about starting a chicken ranch) starred Fred MacMurray and Claudette Colbert; the game offers enough wooden pieces to build a small chicken ranch.

THE GRACIE ALLEN MURDER CASE, Milton Bradley, 1939; based on the 1939 movie of the same name, and, of course, picturing its star.

THE GREAT LOCOMOTIVE CHASE GAME, Walt Disney, 1956; this small cardboard premium game is valued because it features the film's star, Fess Parker.

GULLIVER'S TRAVELS, Milton Bradley, 1939; Max Fleischer's 1939 film is a feature-length cartoon of the Jonathan Swift tale.

PECK'S BAD BOY WITH THE CIRCUS, Milton Bradley, 1939; based on the RKO film of the same name starring Tommy Kelly and Spanky MacFarland.

OUR GANG TIPPLE TOPPLE GAME, All-Fair, 1930; based on the "Our Gang" series, the game cover shows Jackie Cooper and all the gang members.

THE PIED PIPER OF HAMELIN, Parker Brothers, 1934; based on Walt Disney's "Silly Symphony."

PINOCCHIO, Milton Bradley, 1939; the date of the game predates the 1940 Disney film on which it was based (game companies sometimes license a game during a film's production and ship it to retail outlets to coincide with the film's release).

THE PRISONER OF ZENDA, Parker Brothers, ≥1937; films were made from Anthony Hope's classic in 1927, 1937, and 1952.

SNOW WHITE, Milton Bradley, 1939; based on the first full-length Disney cartoon, which premiered in 1937.

THE THIEF OF BAGDAD, Selchow & Righter; based on Alexander Korda's 1940 film of the same name.

Detail of the board from THE PIED PIPER OF HAMELIN (Parker Brothers, 1934).

The control panel from CAPTAIN VIDEO (Milton Bradley, ±1952).

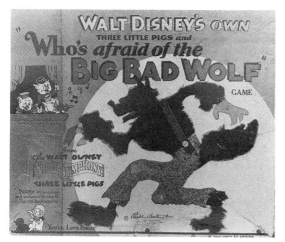

WHO'S AFRAID OF THE BIG BAD WOLF (Parker Brothers, 1933).

JACKIE GLEASON'S "AND AWA-A-A-A-Y WE GO!" TV FUN GAME is as valuable to TV collectors as the lost episodes are to *The Honeymooners* buffs. The game was put out by Transogram.

THREE MEN ON A HORSE, Milton Bradley, 1936; based on the 1936 Mervyn LeRoy film, which was adapted from the George Abbott and John Cecil Holm play.

WHO'S AFRAID OF THE BIG BAD WOLF, Parker Brothers, 1933; this game based on Walt Disney's "Silly Symphony" boasts a "patented color scheme" on its gameboard.

Many recent film heroes, real and animated, have become the subject of games, including James Bond, the Ghostbusters, Indiana Jones, and Teenage Mutant Ninja Turtles—these might be the collectible games of the future. Other games based on recent films and that are already beginning to escalate in value are THE LEGEND OF THE LONE RANGER, KRULL, DUNE, and STAR WARS.

Games Based on Television Programs

Take your pick. Almost any nationally telecast show that lasted (and many that didn't) had a game based on it. CAPTAIN VIDEO and HOPALONG CASSIDY were among the first games, followed by a spate of stunt and quiz-show games, with BEAT THE CLOCK and BREAK THE BANK being the earliest. One popular game, CONCENTRATION, was based on the TV show of the same name that began in 1958; what is interesting, however, is that the TV show was itself based on a game—a simple game using only a deck of cards. One version of this game, called PICK A PAIR, was written up in the November 1933 issue of *Childlife* magazine.

GENE AUTRY'S BANDIT TRAIL, CALL MY BLUFF, DRAGNET, JACKIE GLEASON'S AND AWAAAY WE GO!, GEORGE GOBEL, ARTHUR GODFREY'S PAR-TEE GOLF, GROUCHO'S TV QUIZ, ALFRED HITCHCOCK'S WHY, and SWAYZE are just a handful of games from the early days of television. The popular early westerns led to such games as BONANZA, RIFLEMAN, WAGON TRAIN, and WANTED DEAD OR ALIVE, and then gave way to the police and mystery programs on which CHARLIE'S ANGELS, DRAGNET, and PETER GUNN were based.

Even some daytime soap operas became games, such as AS THE WORLD TURNS, a 1966 entry based on the program rated the most popular daytime show for nearly ten years. Also, quiz programs have proved particularly durable, and FAMILY FEUD, HOLLYWOOD SQUARES, JEOPARDY, THE MATCH GAME, PASSWORD, and WHEEL OF FORTUNE have all been popular games as well as long-running shows.

Milton Bradley and Transogram, and possibly Ideal, were the major companies responsible for the spate of television games. Transogram sometimes duplicated the same game for different programs, changing only the character on the cover when one detective show, or actor, was replaced by another. In 1954, Lowell began producing a considerable number of television games. Lisbeth Whiting and Bettye-B were both small, high-quality companies that also specialized in TV-based games.

TV games are still very popular, and they still come and go as the shows on which they are based gain and lose favor. Only PASSWORD and JEOPARDY kept selling while the programs on which they were based were off the air (1968–70 for "Password" and 1975–77 for "Jeopardy"). If trends continue as they have been (a big *if*), then the television games of today will become the choice collectibles of tomorrow.

Games Based on Personalities

Many famous people lent their names to games, the name of the personality becoming a part of the title. The names of radio personalities, television stars, and, very often, sports heroes helped to sell games from the 1930s onward. Some notable examples include:

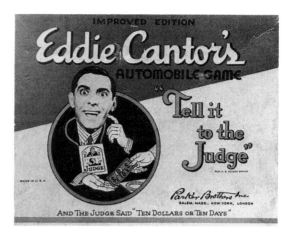

EDDIE CANTOR'S "TELL IT TO THE JUDGE" (Parker Brothers, ±1936); this "improved edition" features Cantor's face on the gameboard, as opposed to the faceless angular board from around 1933.

ALFRED HITCHCOCK'S WHY	MB	1958
ARNOLD PALMER'S INSIDE GOLF	David Bremson	1961
ARTHUR GODFREY'S PAR-TEE GOLF	Herald Toy	1954
THE BEATLES FLIP YOUR WIG GAME	MB	1964
BING CROSBY'S CALL ME LUCKY	PB	1954
BOAKE CARTER'S STAR REPORTER	PB	1937
BO McMILLAN'S INDOOR FOOTBALL Indiana	Indiana Game Co.	1939
DAVE GARROWAY'S GAME OF POSSESSION	Dexter Wayne	≥1952
DAVE GARROWAY'S TODAY GAME	Quality Games	1960
DREW PEARSON'S PREDICT-A-WORD	Dee Jay Products	1949
DURAN DURAN	MB	1985
EDDIE CANTOR'S "TELL IT TO THE JUDGE"	PB	1930s

ELVIS	Boxcar Enterprises	1978
ELVIS PRESLEY	Teenage Games	1957
GRACIE ALLEN'S GAB	Texall Corp.	1950
GROUCHO'S TV QUIZ	Pressman	±1954
I'M GEORGE GOBEL AND HERE'S THE GAME	Schaper	1955
JACKIE GLEASON'S "AND AWA-A-A-A-Y WE GO!"	Trans	1956
JIMMY DURANTE'S SCHNOZZLE GAME	NY Toy & Game Co	±1940
KATE SMITH'S AMERICA	Toy Creations	1940s
LESTER PATRICK'S OFFICIAL HOCKEY	Toy Creations	1940s
MAJOR BOWES AMATEUR HOUR	Warner Mfg.	≥1954
SCARNE'S CHALLENGE	John Scarne	1949
SWAYZE	MB	1954
THE TINY TIM GAME	PB	1970
TOM HAMILTON'S FOOTBALL	PB	1946
TRUMP, THE GAME	MB	1989

8

The Dating Game

A copyright date or date of publication can often be found on the box cover of a game, sometimes just on one apron, on the instructions (after the title of the game or at the very end of the instructions), or even on the gameboard (by the title or in one of the lower corners). In a card game, the date might be on the joker or title card if not on the box. Sometimes, however, game manufacturers did not print a date on a game. Most early Milton Bradley games, for example, don't show dates.

A number of things besides dated boxes or instructions, catalog listings, or dated advertisements can help you determine when a game was manufactured. The patent dates, company name, logo and address, the game number, the theme of a game, box and gameboard illustrations, the box construction, game implements, the box wrap, the written copy used in instructions and on game cards, inscriptions, even the title—all may provide clues as to the approximate date of a game.

Companies such as Transogram printed all their copyright dates in Roman Numerals. To help those unfamiliar with the system, here is how it works: M= 1000, D=500, C = 100, L = 50, X = 10, V = 5, I = 1.

When the *C* precedes an *M,* subtract the 100 from the 1,000 (which makes it 900); when the *X* precedes an *L,* subtract the 10 from the 50 (which makes it 40); when the *I* precedes the *X* or the *V,* subtract 1 from the 10 or the 5.

Most roman numerals on games will begin with "MCM," which is 1900. A game from the 1800s will begin with "MDCCC." (Easy to remember: on an American game, if there is a *D* in the roman numeral, the game is from the 1800s.) "MDCCCLXXXIX" = 1889; "MCMIV" = 1904; "MCMXXXVI" = 1936; "MCMXLI" = 1941.

Patent Numbers

What is the difference between a patent, a copyright, and a trademark? A patent grants an inventor the rights to an invention for seventeen years, protecting that inventor from anyone else claiming ownership of that invention or illegally earning money from it. A copyright refers to the form or manner of expression of an individual's work rather than to the content, and is a protection against fraud and piracy. The instructions for a game are often copyrighted. Copyrights under a 1909 law were good for

twenty-six years, with a renewal allowable for the same period. A new copyright law that took effect in 1978 extended renewals to forty-seven years; copyrights secured in or after 1978 expire fifty years after the author's death. The copyright symbol © is usually followed by the date, pinpointing at least the latest date of a game's invention. A trademark, on the other hand, is a registered identification of goods or services, preventing anyone else from using the mark in commerce. The symbol ™ next to a title carries no date and can be of little use in helping date a game.

Patent numbers can be helpful because the numbers correspond to specific years. But keep in mind that a patent date refers to the first time a game was legally documented. The game may have been in existence for a number of years prior to receipt of the patent. For example, Wolverine's THE MOTOR RACE was first sold in 1922, but it did not receive a patent number until 1925. On the other hand (and probably more likely), a game may have been made many years *after* the patent date shown on the game, as patent dates are valid for seventeen years. For instance, if you find a MONOPOLY game with the two patent numbers (the 1924 Phillips patent and the 1935 Darrow/Parker patent), remember that thousands of MONOPOLY games were made showing those patent numbers between 1935 and 1943. Also, different editions of the same game can have the same patent number.

See Appendix B for a list of dates for patent numbers issued between 1843 and 1972.

Company Name, Logo, and Address

The name of a company may have changed over the years, or the company may have incorporated, enabling you to determine if a particular game was made before or after a certain date. For example, J. Pressman & Co. became Pressman Toy Co. in 1947, so any "J. Pressman" game would be from 1922 (the founding of the company) to 1947. Parker Brothers incorporated in 1901, so "Parker Brothers Inc." on a box tells you that the game can be no earlier than 1901. A game with one name on the box, for example, "Parker Brothers," and another on the instructions, such as "Parker Brothers Inc.," suggests a version of a game that was manufactured some years earlier. The logo on the box may also help date a game, since many companies that were in business for decades kept updating their logos. Companies frequently changed addresses or opened offices in other cities. For instance, McLoughlin Brothers moved from 24 Beekman Street to 30 Beekman in 1861, so a game with the former address would indicate it was made between 1858 and 1861. Milton Bradley opened offices in New York in 1892, so a Bradley game with "Springfield and New York" could not have been made prior to 1892. Note, however, that the absence of "New York" does not necessarily mean the game predates 1892.

Item Numbers

The number of a game can *sometimes* be helpful. Wolverine's games were made using sequential numbers from item #29 in 1922 to item #44 in 1929 or 1930, but then the sequence jumped to game item #142 in 1930. (It seems improbable that item numbers 44 through 142 were all nongame products and all made during 1930.) Around 1901–2 Milton Bradley began using a four-digit numbering code beginning with "4″ to separate the game line from the company's educational products. The second digit referred to the production year, but *not* the decade. Therefore, item 4712, for example, may be from 1927 or 1937. Also, Bradley reused some of its numbers, especially if it reissued a game many years after the original production.

Themes and Events

One of the best ways to determine the period during which a game was made is by the theme. Many games were produced immediately after some particular historical event or popular fad. The discovery of King Tut's tomb in 1922, for example, or the Lindbergh flight in 1927 gave rise to numerous games. The BIG APPLE game by Rosebud Art was produced in 1938, just one year after the "Big Apple" dance started a new dance fad. Of course, games representing a particular theme may have been produced years after the event that inspired the game, but in most cases the connection was immediate.

Seemingly insignificant events in history can also help. For instance, the advent of ZIP codes is an event that can be helpful to a game collector. The "Zone Improvement Program" code started in 1963. A game made after 1963 might not show a ZIP code next to the company address, but a game *with* a ZIP code could *not* have been made *before* 1963.

For help in dating games by themes or milestones see Appendix A for a list of dates of major occurrences, fads, events, technical advances in printing and manufacturing, and inventions between 1843 and 1972.

Game Titles

Game titles can serve as clues to dates of games in the same way as themes. For example, "Little America," the second-line copy of Parker Brothers' ADMIRAL BYRD'S SOUTH POLE GAME, dates the game after 1928, when Byrd established his "Little America" base.

CHIN-CHOW, PE-LING, MAH-CHUCK, CHING-CHONG, and many other Chinese names or American-Chinese variations, such as SUM-FUN, all probably date to the Mah-Jongg craze between 1922 and 1924. In 1924 all imported Chinese sets were required by the government to have the name "mah-jongg" stamped on them because of the confusion of all the different titles.

Illustrations and Design

The gameboard and box illustrations of many of the earliest games, prior to 1860, were colored by hand. By 1860 the lithographic process was refined so that the illustrated paper sheets could be mass-produced and pasted onto the box or gameboard.

The type of illustration on the box cover or gameboard may be a clue to the period of game. Early automobiles pictured on the box, for example, could date the game between 1903 and around 1920. Clothing is always a good indication of the era of a game. Things such as skyscrapers in illustrations, or an Art Deco style can help date an item. The list of significant dates in the Appendix A will be helpful when trying to date a game by its illustrations as well as by its theme.

The visual style or graphic design, including type styles and use of colors, can also help in assigning a game to a particular period. The geometric designs and bold colors

The LITTLE AMERICA ANTARCTIC GAME by Whitman, ≥1928, gives recognition to explorers Perry, Scott, Amundsen, Schachelton, Cook, and Byrd; the establishment of the "Little America" base by Byrd in 1928 dates the game as being probably shortly after that date. (Krim collection)

The term so closely associated with World War II would suggest that, by title alone, BLACKOUT should be from around 1940; the Milton Bradley game was produced in 1939.

particular to the Art Deco style, for instance, can help date a game from around 1925 to the mid-1930s. Another example is the difference between Selchow & Righter Company's use of script on their boxes and gameboards from the 1920s and 1930s and its use of block lettering in the 1940s.

Box and Gameboard Construction

Some early gameboards taken from the European style of manufacture were folded paper or a linen-backed paper with no cardboard backing. But even the earliest Ives and McLoughlin lithographed paper gameboards were mounted on cardboard. Companies such as Selchow & Righter, however, sold paper "pin-the-tail" variants in envelopes right through 1927. It is interesting to note the 18½″ × 18½″ litho-on-cardboard folding board from the 1840s is the same standard-size board still used today (standardized by the mechanics of the printing process, no doubt).

Game "packets" consisting of small folded boards attached to the outer covering were produced by McLoughlin in the 1860s and 1870s. Oversize wooden boards made to look like books were popular in the 1870s and 1880s, sometimes packaged in a slipcase. In the mid-to late 1880s Parker Brothers produced large build-up boards (see the Glossary), the early ones containing a parts tray that slid into the hollow portion of the box bottom. Box bottoms with wooden sides were popular to about 1920.

Through the 1920s game boxes were made in numerous sizes, with most games being square rather than rectangular. This was true partially because games from the turn of the century through the 1920s often were sold as a gameboard and a separate parts box. In the 1930s, more and more games were packaged in the now-traditional rectangular format (approximately 19″ × 10″), the gameboard being packaged inside the box. Many games, such as EDDIE CANTOR'S "TELL IT TO THE JUDGE" or CLUE, can be found as a separate board and parts box and "all-encompassing" game box. When the dates on two versions of a game are the same, assume that the separate parts box is from an earlier edition.

Game Implements

It is difficult to date a game using only the implements as a guide, but considering them along with box construction, theme, and illustrations can be a valuable tool. Playing pieces for the earliest board games were made of ivory, bone, or paper, or were small, round wooden markers or cardboard disks with metal rims. By the 1880s large wooden pawns, turned on a lathe, and two-dimensional figural metal pieces (on a metal base) were in vogue. In the late 1930s large, die-cast (fully three-dimensional) metal pieces were in use. Composition pieces (pieces that look like plaster and have poor definition) often replaced metal pieces during World War II. Bakelite pieces were popular around the 1920s and

into the 1930s. By the late 1940s and 1950s plastic pieces had become standard.

Teetotums, devices shaped like tops with numbers on them, were used in early games to avoid the cultural stigma attached to dice. Early dice were often much smaller than those of today—some with sides less than one-quarter inch—and were commonly made of bone or wood; dice were also made of ivory or die-cut folded metal (so they were hollow). Spinners, consisting of metal arrows attached to small pieces of cardboard or affixed directly onto the gameboard, can be found in many games throughout the nineteenth and twentieth century.

The games that used the most implements—heavy boards, assorted cards and various shapes and sizes of wooden pieces, money, score pads, dice—were made between 1936 and 1940 as companies rebounded from the depression.

Box Wraps

The box wrap is the paper that covers the entire box and onto which the litho sheet is pasted. Box wraps were often a geometric design, while the litho sheet bore the illustrations and printed words. By comparing the box wrap on a dated game with the box wrap from a game with no date by the same company, you may be able to determine that the undated game is from the same period as the dated one.

By the 1910s, some companies had begun replacing the two-sheet box wrap and paste-on litho with a wrap-around litho—an illustrated sheet that covered the entire box lid, including the aprons; by the 1940s most games were packaged this way.

Written Copy and Other Clues

Sometimes, at least a range of years can be deduced through a game's written copy. For example, card games that make reference to "Indian Territory" must have been produced before Oklahoma statehood in 1907. THE GAME OF AMERICAN STORY AND GLORY, by William Langdon, contains cards representing eleven presidents; since the eleventh president, James Polk, was in office between 1845 and 1849, the game was most likely made during that period. A game that mentions a velocipede (a bicycle with a large front wheel) probably predates the mid-1890s, by which time velocipedes had been replaced by bicycles.

Games were often given as gifts, especially at Christmastime, and many of these were inscribed on the box bottom or even right on the box cover. Unless a game was a best-seller on the market year after year, there is a good chance that an inscribed game was manufactured within a year or two of the handwritten date.

Early game boxes were repaired by sewing the box. Though it is not known exactly when this process stopped, one can assume that sewn games are from the nineteenth century, and that sewing the box was phased out when tape became more readily available.

9

Caring for Your Games

Most collectors do their own cleaning and minor repair work on paper games. The best way to handle, clean, and repair paper is the way archivists and other professionals do. Special materials, including acid-free glue and paper, and advice on how to use them can be obtained from most large art supply stores. If you are working with particularly old and fragile cloth or paper gameboards from the nineteenth century, you should seek professional help.

Cleaning Games

One of the best bargains a collector can find is a soiled game. Dealers are often afraid to try to remove dirt and grime from a paper box or gameboard for fear of removing some of the paper or color with the dirt.

Not all soil and dirt comes off. Stains, including simple water stains (which turn white paper a light brown), may be impossible to remove, as are ink marks and coal dust. A good on-the-spot test is to wet your finger and rub it gently on an inconspicuous part of the box cover of a game you're considering buying: if you wind up with a clean spot on the box and a dirty finger, there's a good chance the game will clean up well.

Paper Games   Many collectors have their own miracle cure for removing dirt from a game box or board. Sometimes the simplest remedy is the best: mild soap and a little water. Most games after 1860 were made with coated stock—paper with a protective finish on it. This kind of paper can be cleaned. Coated stock is shiny and reflects light, whereas the paper used for the earliest games, such as those that were hand-colored, is dull and nonreflective.

Always test a small area first. Put a small amount of nonabrasive liquid soap (non-detergent hand soap or dishwashing liquid) on a damp sponge. Beginning near the edge using a circular motion, gently rub the sponge on the paper. If the edges are worn, keep the sponge away from the exposed cardboard. Keep rinsing and resoaping the sponge, and wipe the cleaned area with a well-rinsed and wrung-out damp sponge. You may have to clean the game more than once, so don't allow the surface to become too wet. Let the game dry completely between cleanings. As you rub, check to see if the paper is being rubbed off or is buckling, and if it is, stop cleaning.

To remove ink markings, rub them with a kneadable

soft art eraser. A pencil eraser may rub off some of the coloring. Just remember that an eraser acts as an abrasive and can remove paper as well, so work carefully.

Some collectors have used Murphy's oil soap and Meltonian clear shoe cream to clean paper games, but their long-term effects are unknown.

Wood or Metal Games   Bare wood can be cleaned a lot more vigorously than paper. Use soap and water or the same furniture cleaner and polish that you would use on regular wood furniture.

If the game is one with drawings on the wood, you need to be as careful as you would with paper. Using liquid soap and water, test a tiny area first to see if the color comes off or fades; use a white sponge or cloth to see if it is picking up any of the color from the wood. Clean with short strokes along the grain of the wood rather than across it. A light coat of Simonize wax put on gently and rubbed off quickly should remove dirt and dust.

Lithographed metal games pose a similar problem to painted wood: you want to clean the design, not rub it off. Do not use any abrasive cleaner or household cleaner you are unsure of; Mr. Clean™, for example, will take the paint right off. Blue Magic™ *may* work on lithographed metal if you buff it off immediately after putting it on. Once again, try a small test area first; watch out for flakes of metal, and remember that any powder or polish that gets caught in a groove or crease and is not buffed out is liable to turn white. The best metal cleaner is the right combination of wax, oil, and polish, without any grit, that will bring out the color. One toy restorer recommends Meguiar's Mirror Glaze # 7, which can be purchased in an automotive store.

Repairing Paper Games

Basic repairs to cardboard game boxes and gameboards can be made easily. Like dirty games, a "flat" game (one with all the aprons torn off) can be purchased for a fraction of its normal value and then rebuilt into a sturdy box cover. Tape and stickers can sometimes be removed without leaving a trace.

Removing Stickers, Tape, and Glue   One of the most annoying things a collector comes across is a price sticker on the box cover. Never try to pull off a sticker without using rubber cement thinner. (Look for Carter's Rubber Cement Thinner in 4 fl. oz. bottles in an office supply store.) Put the cement thinner in a tiny clean oil can or use an eye dropper. Saturate a corner of the sticker, then try gently peeling back the corner. Apply more cement thinner as you slowly peel off the sticker. Try not to lift up on the sticker but to fold it over so the non-sticky side is against the box; press down as you slide the sticker along on the box. If the paper begins to lift off with the sticker, try the same procedure at a different point on the sticker.

Use this technique also for removing tape used to keep the aprons attached to the box cover; you can then reattach the aprons using glue. If there is clear tape on the box cover, it may be better to leave the tape on than risk losing some of the paper underneath.

The box bottom can be reinforced with tape, since this

part of the game is not seen. But tape becomes brittle, turns yellow, and loses its sticking power, so we recommend using glue. *Never* use tape on the outside of the box cover or on the gameboard.

Coloring in and Replacing Lithography   In general, you should do no more to a game than clean it and take steps to keep the game from further deterioration. You should not adulterate a game by coloring it. However, many collectors feel appearance is more important than "historical originality." If a swath has left a white patch on a uniformly colored background, some collectors will color the swath the same hue as the background. Similarly, coloring in the edges of a game box also may make the game look less worn, and it will certainly make the game photograph better. A better alternative, however, is to touch up the photograph, not the game. Over time, any color applied to a game box or board will fade differently from the colors of the original lithography.

If a large piece of lithography is missing from a gameboard or box and the board and box have the same illustration, use the new color photocopying technology to restore the damaged area. Make a copy of the good illustration, cut out the piece or section that matches what is missing from the damaged litho, and glue it in place in the same way you would fit a puzzle piece into the middle of a nearly completed picture.

Do not alter the original state of a game by coloring in or replacing any missing litho if you intend to sell the game. If you sell a game that has been colored in, touched up, or repaired in any way, include these facts in your written or verbal description of the game. When you're buying a game, be sure to look for areas that may not be original.

Repairing Aprons   The most common problems with regard to the condition of games are torn and missing or split aprons and worn edges. To strengthen or replace an apron, set the cover on a flat surface with the aprons pointing up. Using either a household glue such as Elmer's or Weldbond, or a special archivists' glue (which will not become brittle), reinforce weak or thin aprons by running a thin line of glue along the inside edges. If the corner is split, put some glue on the end of each apron, then hold the two aprons together with a paper clip, keeping the longer end of the clip on the outside of the box (this may take some patience at first). Push the two aprons firmly together, then add a little more glue to both the inside and the outside of the corner. Don't worry too much about getting glue on the paper clip; when the clip is removed carefully, it will snap off, leaving the glue and litho paper (hopefully) still adhering to the box. Wait until the glue dries completely (24 hours is a safe bet) before removing the paper clip. Do only one corner at a time (or two corners diagonally opposite) and wait for the glue to dry completely before working on the other corners.

If you are replacing an apron, set the apron so it is perpendicular to the box top or bottom and place a block or book along the outside of the apron to keep the apron upright. The apron should stand without support on the inside, especially if the ends rest against the ends of the other aprons; otherwise use any small but heavy item as support on the inside but leave yourself room to glue along the edge. Run a thin line of glue along the inside of the edge. You can also glue the corners at this time, or, if there is some bending in the aprons, wait until they are firmly attached and the glue is dry before connecting the corners.

If you are repairing a flat game (all aprons are detached) or one in which the ends of the aprons are bent or warped, you would do best to purchase a corner vice. This enables you to secure two aprons in a steady, upright position after glueing them together at the ends. When the glue is dry, attach these two aprons to the box cover. Then glue the other two aprons together and attach them to the cover.

An apron that's torn in the middle can be held with a paper clip or, better yet, a "tweezer clamp"; this "reverse tweezers" is an oversized tweezer-like device whose arms are crossed over so that the tweezer is clamped shut when at rest and opens when the arms are squeezed. Try a hardware store.

A few hints: glue the inside edges and let dry before glueing the corners; use as little glue as possible (it will dry better); work directly on a flat counter or tabletop, or, if you don't want to get glue on it, place aluminum foil or wax paper rather than paper on the table or desk.

If you are missing an apron, you can make a copy of one of the aprons on a color photocopy machine, and rebuild the box by cutting a piece of cardboard the size of the apron, then glueing the copy paper to it. Any game offered for sale which has been repaired, especially if parts of the box are not original, should be so noted in the description.

After you have replaced an apron, or if the edges of the box are worn, turn the box over so that the aprons are facing down and place the box on a block or book. Place a thin line of glue along the the edges and corners. The glue may be white when wet but should dry colorless.

Flattening Warped Boxes   It is difficult to repair split or detached aprons when the box is warped. To solve a warping problem, you need something very flat and very heavy; for large boxes we recommend an unabridged dictionary or the equivalent. The trick is to wet the entire inside of the box (except if it is a box bottom board). Do this with a wet (not just damp) sponge or a plant mister, or you can even pour a little water—not too much—right into the box and move it around to cover the entire inside. Pour out any excess water, place the cover on a flat surface, and place any flat, heavy object inside—preferably one that is nearly the same size as the cover.

If you have a warped box bottom board, turn the bottom upside down and wet the uncoated cardboard. Then place the box on a block or book and place a flat, heavy weight on top of it as explained above.

If your gameboard is warped, using water may not help and in fact may harm the board by seeping under the lithographed paper. The best thing is to place the board (in an open position if it is a folded board) under as large and as heavy an object as you can for a few days.

Sewing (a Stitch in Time)   Before the 1870s and before household tape was readily available, games were repaired with "button" thread or embroidery thread (regular sewing thread is too thin, though sometimes material like old fishing line was employed); they were stitched or sewn. In keeping with this practice, some collectors prefer to sew an apron on an early game rather than glue it. Using a needle and a piece of yarn, commence sewing, moving from box to apron to box in an even, spiral fashion.

Controlling Insect Damage and Mildew

You will not see the tiny insects that eat your games, but you might see the effects: paper edges that look as though they have been chewed instead of cut, or little specks on the board or box where the lithography is missing. If there is any sign of insect damage, clean the game and air it thoroughly. You may want to spray the game or the area in which it is stored.

Mildew damage is much more common, and more devastating. Mildew is a fungus that eats away at paper and spreads easily. It grows on the outside of a box, or inside, especially along the edges or in the corners. The first sign of mildew is a slight bluish dust that feels almost velvety to the touch. Mildew will not wipe off easily with a dry cloth, and it does not smear when wiped with a sponge.

Be very careful if you buy a game that is mildewed; it may not clean well or you may lose some of the lithography in the cleaning process. Keep infected games away from other games until you are sure the mildew is gone, as it can travel from one game to another. Most important, keep all games away from dampness so you can prevent mildew in the first place.

If you suspect mildew, clean the game thoroughly, wipe it dry, and then air it out. If you discover too late that a game is covered with mildew, you will need to clean the game with a bathroom mildew remover. Wear gloves and work in a well-ventilated room; spray the box directly (whether it is coated stock on the outside or plain cardboard inside) and wipe clean with a damp sponge. Test a small area first. Let the game air dry.

Collectors have suggested putting a sheet of fabric softener in a game box to help prevent mildew. It has not yet been determined whether this does in fact work. However, a sheet of used fabric softener such as Bounce™ (just save them when they come out of the dryer) at least gives a fresh smell to a game when kept inside the game box.

Displaying Games

There are various ways to show off your collection and still keep your games safe from damage. You need to be careful about light, temperature, and humidity, and the methods you use to secure a game in a display.

The Effects of Sunlight, Temperature, and Humidity
Keep games out of direct sunlight and away from spotlights and other bright light, or the colors will fade. If you are selling games at an outdoor market, your games can lose color in just one day of bright sunlight.

Keep games away from areas of extreme heat or cold, and away from areas with great temperature fluctuations.

If the lithographed paper on the box or board expands or contracts at a different rate from the uncoated cardboard, the game will warp. Extreme temperature changes might also cause games to become more brittle.

The most important rule to follow is to keep games out of damp areas or they will get mildewed. If your games are displayed in a basement that might tend to become humid during the summer months, use a dehumidifier, keep a fan running to circulate the air, and check the games regularly, inside and out. Keep games away from damp basement walls (especially stone ones) so air can circulate behind the games. Games should also be kept out of very dry areas or they may become brittle.

Using Rubber Bands If you must use rubber bands to keep boxes closed, make sure the rubber bands are flexible and not too tight. If they stay on too long, are exposed to direct sunlight, or are kept in a room that gets too hot, they may disintegrate and fuse to the box cover. If you use rubber bands, replace them regularly. Never use cheap rubber bands; instead, look in an office supply store for rubber bands packed loose by size in large boxes. Buy the largest thin size available, and make certain it has a good stretch to it. One suggested choice is Plymouth rubber bands, size 33. The huge, brick red rubber bands can be used for most larger games.

Often the edges on a game box are worn because rubber bands have been removed and replaced carelessly. This book may be the first to explain how to put rubber bands on a box. First, on a flat surface such as a table top, place the game so that one end is protruding beyond the edge of the table. Stretch out the rubber band to its fullest, then slide it over the end of the box. Slide your hands up so that you release the bottom of the rubber band first, letting it grab the bottom of the box, then gently let the rubber band touch the sides of the box and let go. There is no need to place a rubber band in the center of a box; use *two* rubber bands, placing them right near the edge on opposite ends of the box. Do not slide the rubber band along the box edge; if you need to move the rubber band, lift it up.

Naturally, to remove a rubber band, reverse the procedure: lift the rubber band from the middle, slide both hands under the rubber band and to the opposite sides, and stretch and lift the rubber band so it is no longer touching the box top or aprons. If you have to slide a tight rubber band off a box, make sure the rubber band is sliding along the edge of the box bottom only. (If you are considering buying a rubber band-bound game in a shop or at a show, ask the dealer if you may take the rubber band off rather than letting him or her do it.)

An alternative way to secure a box with a rubber band is to use a very large rubber band, hook it over the top of one of the box corners, run it diagonally under the box, then pull it over the opposite corner.

Some collectors, rather than use rubber bands, prefer to use a large, soft yarn tied around a game to keep the box from opening.

Most collectors have more items than they have room for. To properly exhibit a game inside and out takes a lot of open shelf space, so most collections are relegated to a display of the game box only. How to display a

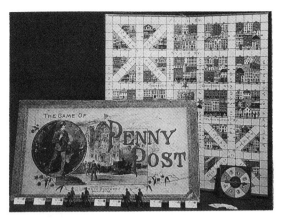

A simple display of the components of THE GAME OF
PENNY POST (Parker Brothers, 1892). (Photo courtesy of
P. Mautner)

collection is as individual a choice as what games you
like to buy.

Many collectors use wall displays with narrow shelves.
Boxes are set up vertically, sitting on one apron, either
leaning against or flush with the wall. Either the bottom
of the box has to be far enough away from the wall to keep
the game from tipping forward, or the game must be
secured near the top. One of the best ways to do this is
with clear fishing line; it is not necessary to secure each
game separately, merely to run the line along the entire
length of the shelf (provided the shelf is not too long).

Also, you can tie clear fishing line around each of your
games, then hang each game on a hook attached to the
wall.

At least one collector uses a gridwork of connecting
frames on his wall, with the left side of the frame from one
game acting also as the right side of the frame for part of
another game. Each opening is measured to fit a particular
game, so removing one from the display means replacing
it with another of equal size. Though none of the aprons
are visible this way, the wall of framed games is impressive.

Since you don't want to shine spotlights on your
games, the best lighting consists of spotlights, floor lamps,
or track lights along a wall, with all the bulbs directed at
the ceiling, all the light on the games being reflected light.

Glass cases or any setup with glass shelves make
effective displays, especially as you can set out some of the
implements next to the box. Games with bottom-box ads
should definitely sit on glass. Mirrors can also be employed with good effect.

Displays are as varied as the imagination. One collector
has games sitting in hollowed-out stumps and covered
with glass, making an interesting table. Another collector
has an "apron" display—100 thin games with illustrated
or patterned aprons are slid into a turn-of-the-century
sheet music cabinet so that only the aprons are visible. (It
may not show off the best of the games, but it keeps them
safe and secure and within easy reach.)

Handling and Storing Games

As with much of the information in this chapter, some of
the suggestions here will seem obvious. However, it is
surprising how many obvious "rules" are broken, and,
though no one "infraction" will destroy a game, continu-
ous abuses will certainly cause unnecessary wear or even
damage.

Criminals wear gloves to keep from leaving fingerprints—clean hands are not enough. Fingerprints come
from the oil in the body, and excessive handling will leave
games soiled. Always lift any game larger than about seven
inches square with two hands, not one. Using two hands
you can balance a game easily by holding it from the
bottom only without having to secure it by pressing your
thumbs on the box cover.

Store games vertically, with a sheet of acid-free paper
or cardboard between each game. When storing games for
long periods, do not use rubber bands, because they may
decay and adhere to the box.

Do not stack your games; the weight of the games
might crush the ones on the bottom. If you have to place
games one on top of the other, cross-stack them (that is,
alternate vertical and horizontal placement) or place each
game on top of a slightly *smaller* game; this way, each game
is being supported by the edges of the game below, and
nothing is pressing directly on the cover litho. Also, when
games are stacked with the smallest on top and are carried
or moved, they can slide around more easily, allowing the
bottom of one game to scrape across the litho cover of the
game below.

1 0

Selling Games

An 1897 *McClures* ad from GESCHÄFT, OR THE GAME
OF BUSINESS by Chaffee & Selchow.

Eventually you may want to sell some games as you upgrade your collection or as your interests change. Many collectors buy certain games strictly for resale, with the hope of making a nice profit. If you do this, the price you will get will be based on supply and demand or on the interest of the particular buyer. Remember, the value of a game you want to sell is only whatever someone is willing to pay for it.

The Buyer-Seller Relationship

When you buy a game in person, check the game thoroughly for any damage or missing implements. Most sellers or dealers usually will not accept returns if the buyer had the opportunity to examine the game before buying.

If you are buying or selling a game through the mail, there are certain formalities to follow. The seller is obliged to give as detailed a description of the game as possible, especially with regard to condition. The buyer is expected to send a check for the game and the seller will wait for the check to clear before shipping the game.

Bargaining is usually acceptable, especially if the purchase is for more than one item, but this depends on the dealer. Both the buyer and seller should establish who will pay the cost of shipping and handling, or whether a fee will be added on (usually between $3 and $10). Return privileges also should be agreed upon between the buyer and the seller. A seller should allow a return privilege and stipulate the period in which returns are allowed, usually within five days of receipt of the merchandise.

Of course, the best system of buying and selling is still the barter system, and an even trade makes everyone happy; in trading with a colleague you should be willing to give up an item that may be worth up to twice the value of the item you're getting. In trading with a dealer, the dealer needs to feel that the game being acquired is more salable, if not more valuable, than the game being relinquished.

Where to Sell Your Games

Games can be sold at auctions, flea markets, or antique shows, on consignment, or through an advertisement.

Auctions often bring the best prices for specialized merchandise and cross-collectible items. A baseball game, for example, will bring a better price from a collector of baseball memorabilia than from a game collector, and the baseball buyers follow the auctions. Using an auction house is not cheap: you will usually have to give the auctioneer between 15 and 33 percent of the money your game brings, up to a certain figure (the percentage drops if the item sells for over a certain amount, such as $1,000.) Popular auction houses might charge more, but they have the advantage of being able to reach substantially more people and they may get higher bids. Prospective bidders would be part of a small but select group, and the consigner's fee, if any, would be minimal.

A flea market or antique show may be a good place to sell a game that is difficult to describe and that will be appreciated more if seen. Standard games with good cover illustrations will do well. Know your market: some flea markets are geared for low-end bargains only, and some antique shows do not attract game buyers. Some toy shows attract only die-hard mechanical toy enthusiasts with no interest in games. Shows featuring collectibles may be your best bet; paper ephemera shows are becoming increasingly popular. Setting up at a major show may cost between $100 and $300—or even up to $500 at select shows; find out whether tables are included in the cost and, if not, whether they can be rented or if you have to bring your own. Remember that hotel and travel costs can drive up your expenses considerably. Also, setting up in some states requires that you get a vendor's number and collect sales tax.

And keep in mind that you never sell as much as you would like at a show, so when the show is over you'll still have games to sell. That might mean another investment in more games down the road to set up at another show, especially if what sold at the first show was the best of your merchandise. If you like buying for resale, or if you enjoy the "early bird" shopping privilege accorded to the dealers who set up, you might consider selling at a few local shows each year.

Selling on consignment means finding an antique dealer who is willing to sell your merchandise in exchange for a consignment fee, usually 10 to 50 percent. Since games are subject to damage easily, you don't want your games displayed where there is unrestricted customer access; games of higher value should be locked in display cases and shown to prospective customers by a salesperson. The advantage of consignment selling is that your item is on display at a set price until it is eventually sold.

Advertising games for sale is perhaps the easiest method of selling, but usually you must list a phone number and risk being inundated with phone calls long after an item has been sold. Your best bet is to have a list of items for sale, and provide descriptions *and* selling prices.

Game buying and selling is a year-round event, but some seasons may be better than others for selling. Early spring is a good time to sell games, since many buyers have not attended shows all winter and are anxious to make new purchases. Except for shops located on the summer tourist circuit, antique shops usually do their best business in spring and fall, and that's the time when there are the most antique and collectible shows. For the buyer, the first shows of spring may offer the best pickings, and the last shows of the autumn may offer the best bargains before some dealers pack up for the winter. Like new games, collectible games may sell well prior to Christmas, when they are bought as gifts; often the games bought by noncollectors at this time of year are those they remember from their youth.

11

Determining Values

Many factors contribute to the value of a game, including the type of game, age, company, graphics or illustrations, theme, and condition and completeness. Also important are size, rarity, implements, box and board style and materials used for construction, and even the title of the game and how well it plays. The value of a game is also influenced by the market conditions at the time in the area of the country in which the game is for sale.

Price fluctuations are the rule rather than the exception, and particular games have been seen at some antique shows for more than twice what they were priced at another nearby. "Auction fever" drives some of these prices even higher. Yet buyers who spend a lot of time in the field often stumble upon great bargains—in 1990 one collector paid twenty-five cents for a MANSION OF HAPPINESS found at a local flea market (it was valued at over $250 at the time)! Around 1984 another collector paid twenty-five dollars for an 1886 baseball card game (Egerton Williams's INDOOR BASE BALL) which he later sold to a baseball card collector for $1,150, because nine of the players illustrated on the cards were in the Baseball Hall of Fame.

Keep in mind that the value of a game is not necessarily what the selling price is, but rather the price someone is willing to pay for that game. At auctions, the value may be determined by only two bidders—the third highest bidder may have offered a bid nowhere near the others'. An antique game might sell at auction for twice the sale price marked at an antique show.

There is never any question about buying a game you want if the price is right, but what do you do if the game seems overpriced? Then the key question is, What are the chances of finding the game elsewhere? Only experience will tell you that—and hopefully this guide, which will help by pointing out some of those treasured games that are difficult to find. Putting suggested prices and values aside, after you have bargained for the best price, you must decide the value the game has to you." Too often many of us have passed up a desired game because of price, unfortunately never to come across the game again.

The Changing Market

Values for games are increasing rapidly. Between 1985 and 1990 many games increased in value by over 400 percent! The escalation has slowed somewhat since then. Games represent a new, hot addition to the collectibles market, and game prices are expected to increase substantially over the next few years. The best games should continue to gain in value rapidly; but more than one collector has suggested that in this more sophisticated collectors' market, mediocre material might actually start to decline in value. Common games, of course, and games with poor box-cover graphics will appreciate very little. The games that will be subject to the highest increase in value will be television games, games based on cartoon and comic characters, games with cross-collectible themes, such as military and transportation, games with Art Deco covers and high-quality illustrations, nineteenth-century litho-on-wood skill-and-action games, and large board games prior to 1920 with good lithography, especially by companies such as McLoughlin, Bliss, and Parker Brothers.

Criteria for Evaluation

The various factors that contribute to the value of a game are discussed here in general terms. Every game is different, and there is no formula for weighing the different factors. For instance, without carefully examining both games, it would be difficult to guess whether a small board game with superb graphics would be more or less valuable than a much older, larger wooden skill-and-action game with uninteresting graphics. Understanding some generalizations, however, makes it possible for the collector to assign relative values to games not listed anywhere. Just keep in mind that with every generalization there are many, many exceptions.

Type of Game   Board games are more valuable than card games. The value of a skill-and-action (S&A) game depends primarily on its complexity, construction material, size, and age; S&A games may be less valuable than comparable board games from the same period, though early S&A litho-on-wood games and target games with rifles may be worth more.

Combination games—compendiums that offer more than one game in a box—are not highly valued. Different patterns were drawn on one game board so that various games could be played on the same board, and often the resulting graphics were unappealing.

Age of the Game   All else being equal, the older the game, the more valuable it is—up until around 1900. After 1900, theme and "license" become more important, making war games from the 1940s or personality games from the 1950s more valuable than "ordinary" games from the early 1900s. Because of the illustrations, Art Deco games from the late 1920s and 1930s might be more valuable than games from the 1910s. Television games from the 1960s are generally more valuable than those from the 1950s (and we're not sure whether this is due to the quality of the games or the quality of the programs). Collecting is "generational"; collectors of older games generally prefer games depicting film stars they remember, for example, than earlier games showing equally famous stars from the silent era; a large group of 1990s people are collecting games from the 1960s on—a decade from now, the 1960s games may lose favor to those of the 1970s.

Publishing or Manufacturing Company McLoughlin is the number-one name in games. When Milton Bradley bought McLoughlin in 1920, Bradley reissued some of McLoughlin's games under the Bradley trademark; these games, exactly the same as their McLoughlin counterparts except for the name and the few years difference, are valued at one-half to one-quarter the price of the equivalent McLoughlin games.

Because of the quality of their graphics, both Bliss and Singer are key names to look for in nineteenth-century games. Games by E.G. Selchow and George S. Parker are valuable because of their place in history, with E.G. Selchow manufacturing from 1867 until the company became Selchow and Righter in 1880, and George Parker carrying his own from 1883 until his company became Parker Brothers in 1888. Parker games throughout the 1800s are highly sought after.

After Milton Bradley's first game, THE CHECKERED GAME OF LIFE, in 1860, the Milton Bradley Company through the years became the most prolific game company. But only a few of the early board games, such as BAMBOOZLE, could be considered truly outstanding. The Milton Bradley name is the most common on the market, and the discerning collector needs to pick through a lot of Bradley items to find the choice pieces.

If we were to try an arbitrary ranking of desirable major companies prior to 1920, we might come up with this order: McLoughlin, Bliss, Singer, George S. Parker, E.G. Selchow, Parker Brothers, Chaffee & Selchow, Clark & Sowdon, Milton Bradley, Horsman, Ottmann, and Selchow & Righter.

One of the best companies to look for after 1920 is All-Fair (Alderman Fairchild). Once again, an arbitrary ranking of primary companies from 1920 through the 1950s might be Parker Brothers, All-Fair, Wolverine, Wilder, and Milton Bradley. Stoll & Einson, Stoll & Edwards, Embossing Co., and Rosebud would come next, followed by Pressman, Transogram, and Whitman—three companies that produced some exceptional products but whose games in general were made of inferior material (thin cardboard) and displayed only ordinary graphics.

Some of the other noteworthy companies whose games you should be able to find dating from the mid-1800s to World War II include Ives, Theodore Presser, Peter Thompson, W.S. Reed, and West & Lee from the nineteenth century, and American Toy Works, Cadaco (Cadaco-Ellis), Cardinal, Corey, Einson-Freeman, Gabriel, Game Makers, Jaymar, E.S. Lowe, National Games, Jim Prentice (Electric Game Co.), Russell, and Toy Creations from this century.

In the 1950s and 1960s the key names were (in addition to Parker Brothers and Milton Bradley, of course) Transogram, Lowell, Ideal, and possibly Hasbro (Hassenfeld Bros.). Bettye-B, a lesser-known company that manufactured games for only a few years, made exceptional products, but the name is not highly valued. With the exception of these companies and a few specialty companies, such as Avalon Hill, 3M, and TSR, company name is not an important factor in game values after 1950.

Graphics, Lithography, and Illustrations The most important thing to many collectors of pre–World War II American games is the graphics—which means the quality of the lithography and the illustrations. Games having intricately detailed illustrations with vivid colors bring the best prices. Early games that are hand-colored are especially valuable. Special design styles, such as Art Deco, are also in favor. The graphics on the box cover are primary; those on the gameboard or cards are secondary. Box covers are seen (and valued) as art. Since the illustrations also reflect the theme of the game, graphics and theme are closely related.

Theme The theme is the most important thing to many collectors, especially those who collect post-1950 games, including the use of noted characters. The most valuable games are often those depicting personalities or cartoon characters. The theme of a game frequently makes the game cross-collectible (see Chapter 7). Illustrations of the theme on the box cover increase the value of the game even if the name or play of the game has nothing to do with the theme illustration. Some collectors focus on games of one theme only; for example, all games depicting early forms of transportation, or just music games, or games dealing with money and finance. The best personality and character collectibles include all the Disney characters, the Brownies, and Wizard of Oz material (there are at least six WIZARD OF OZ games), plus cartoon characters from television, monsters, and stars of film and television.

Sports games are the most valuable when they refer to actual sports figures. Baseball games are so numerous that generic baseball games from this century that do not name any teams or players have relatively little value; but baseball games featuring famous players may command the highest prices.

Condition, Completeness, and Size If an antique vase has a chip in the rim, clearly its value is greatly diminished. Naturally, if a game is in poor condition, it too will lose a lot of its value, but it is more difficult in dealing in this paper medium to determine just how much value is lost when the condition is less than excellent.

Some problems with condition are encountered frequently, such as split aprons, worn edges, dings, soiling, and slight warping. These problems should not affect the value too much as long as the game's cover lithography is bright and clean. Minor problems can be corrected, but problems such as swaths, punctures, missing aprons, and stray marks are more difficult to overlook. Since most games are prized primarily for their box cover illustrations, the key question is how much the imperfections affect the illustration. An unobtrusive swath in the upper corner may be of minor consequence, but one in the middle of the illustration could devalue the game as much as 40 percent.

Missing implements may not matter if the missing pieces are common wooden markers, but if intricately designed metal figural pieces are missing, the value of the game could drop 20 percent to 50 percent. Missing cards in a card game can also reduce the game's value by 50 percent if the card is necessary for play (such as an illustrated character card in an AUTHORS-style game, as opposed to "Chance" cards, which are plentiful, all Chance cards allowing for similar options of play). Missing instructions are less of a problem now that the American Game Collectors Association has set up an archives of game instructions. Also, attractive gameboards selling without boxes should fetch more than equally attractive empty game boxes. Regarding size, all things being equal, the larger the box, the greater the value.

Rarity   Rarity is important only with respect to games by major companies. A rare Bliss DETECTIVE has a considerable four-figure value. The same game by an unknown company, even if the game were a one-of-a-kind, would be worth much less. Ives's MANSION OF HAPPINESS, once thought to be the first board game made in the United States, or Milton Bradley's first game, THE CHECKERED GAME OF LIFE, are *relatively* inexpensive because they are not rare items.

Availability should not be confused with rarity. The large McLoughlin ROUND THE WORLD WITH NELLY BLY (1890) may not be seen that often anymore because most major collectors already have a copy. The game is definitely not rare, especially compared with the few known copies of McLoughlin's RIVAL POLICEMEN.

Implements   Though what is on the box cover is usually more important than what's inside it, the implements can add value to a game. Die-cast (heavy molded) metal pieces (such as the pewter pieces in Parker Brothers' WIZARD OF OZ) are the best, followed by metal figural pieces (such as automobiles or little people, like the messenger boys in McLoughlin's DISTRICT MESSENGER BOY), and then composition figural pieces (such as the plaster/composition pieces that replaced the metal ones during wartime in Parker Brothers' CONFLICT). Large, nicely shaped enameled wood pawns also add value, as do hard rubber, Bakelite, and of course ivory pieces.

Value is also affected if the game has multiple gameboards, interesting teetotums (spinners), wooden blocks, or an excess of cards. Between 1936 and 1940, bounding back from the Depression, many companies produced games with an unusually large and varied assortment of implements.

Box and Gameboard Style and Construction   The style of the game and the material used to construct it are important. Metal gameboards (such as those made by Wolverine) are generally worth more than their cardboard counterparts, though the lithography on the paper boards is usually better than on the metal ones. Wood boxes are preferred over cardboard, and, predictably, heavy card-

board is more desirable than thinner cardboard. Unusual boxes, such as Family Games' GODFATHER GAME originally packaged in a violin-shaped box, will obviously be worth more than their rectangular counterparts.

Games with removable gameboards are valued more highly than games with build-up boards, which, in turn, are better than box-bottom boards. Some early cloth boards may be worth more than traditional gameboards, but that is because they are usually more rare and much larger than standard boards, and they make excellent wall hangings. Combination games (multiple games in one set) and early bookshelf games (frequently three-game sets) have less value than standard boxed board games.

Geographic Location   As with all merchandise, games are priced differently in different areas of the country. They have the highest value in California and New York City, followed by other large, East coast metropolitan areas. New England, where most games were made and where now most games are found, probably sets the standard, with games getting more expensive as you approach New York, and then less and less expensive the further you move west from New York. The Midwest—Chicago and St. Louis, for example—might offer the most games for the best prices. Further west, prices are low but merchandise is scarce. Maine, once the best hunting ground for games, has been picked over pretty well, and prices have begun to rise. As the game collecting field grows in popularity, the collectors' market will become more national and the prices for games will be less influenced by geography.

Title   A title should not have much effect on a game's value in theory, but a *good* title *may* add just a little bit. Good titles are those that are funny or evoke instant recognition because of their social relevance. LOGOMACHY, for example, doesn't do as much for a game as HOW SILAS POPPED THE QUESTION. Without any information about a game, a collector is certain to be more interested in THE BLACK FALCON OF THE FLYING G-MEN than ONINO or CROSSWORD LETTER GAME. One wonderful 1858 title is TRAVELS AND SOJOURNS OF ICHABOD SOLO ESQUIRE AMONG THE PEE-WEE INDIANS.

Playability   There *are* collectors who buy old games because of the way they play. These collectors are in a completely different category than those who are concerned with the factors affecting value discussed previously. For them, the strategy of game play is the most important factor determining value, with historical significance being secondary. Avid strategy game player/collectors look primarily for Avalon Hill and 3M games, plus a myriad of other companies, such as TSR, dedicated to simulation and role-playing games.

PART THREE

American Game Companies, with Listings and Values

12

How to Use the Listings

Game Listings   The games listed in Part Three come from the author's collection, from other collections as indicated, and from auction catalogs, game company catalogs, and early advertisements and other printed material. We have tried to provide a representative sampling of games for each company, from common games to those that have never been seen for sale; listings from printed resource material are provided for historical/reference purposes.

Price vs. Value   "Price" (as indicated in some listings) refers to the original retail selling price of a item; value refers to an approximate worth assigned to an item at a particular time. (The term "retail" followed by a price indicates the advertised selling price of the game when produced.)

Values have been determined by using the guidelines explained in Chapter 11, and by looking at recent auction and sale prices for the listed items or comparable items. For many of the games listed, the author has arrived at the value assigned with the help of appraisal information obtained from as many as five other established collectors who have independently evaluated the games in these listings.

The values indicated for games listed here serve only as a rough guideline in suggesting an approximate retail *price one might expect to pay for the game, complete and in excellent condition, at an antique shop or show in a major antique area.*

A dealer may price a game much higher than the value shown (the selling price often depends on how long the dealer has had the item). On the other hand, if you own one of the games listed and hope to sell it to a dealer who is buying it for resale, bear in mind that you may get less than half of the listed value, whereas at a good auction, your game *may* bring nearly twice the value indicated. There is no established value for any game, and there is often a wide range of opinion as to what a particular game's value should be. Please keep in mind that the purpose of this section is not to *set* values, but to try to reflect them. Ultimately, the important point is what a certain game's value is to *you*.

The value assigned is shown as a dollar amount at the end of the listing. If no dollar amount is shown, one of two notations will appear:

nva: no value asssigned—there is no record of the game having been sold or traded or otherwise appraised in recent years, but the game is known to be in at least one museum or private collection.

ref: reference material—the name of the game has been found in a book or article, in a newspaper or magazine advertisement, or in a company catalog, or has been cross-referenced in another game by the same company; it is not known whether a copy of the game is in any collection.

The notation "Auc.," followed by a month/year date and a dollar amount (with condition remarks where applicable) indicates that the item sold at auction in the month shown for the amount shown—a price that may have been much higher than the value attributed to the game. Keep in mind that "auction fever" tends to increase prices, and that it takes only two people to "bid up" an item far beyond what most other collectors would pay.

Dates   The dates shown after the company name indicate the period the company was in existence. If the company produced games during only a portion of its history, the dates of game manufacture appear separately.

The date shown after a game listing indicates the earliest date the game was known to have been manufactured.

Where an exact date is not known, "±" is used to indicate "circa," a period on or around the date given; to be more precise in the approximate date attributed to a game, the symbols "≤" and "≥" have been used: "≤" indicates on or earlier than the year shown, and "≥" indicates on or later than the year shown. For example, if a listing of a game was taken from a 1932 catalog when the previous years' catalogs were not available, the date would show ≤ 1932 since the game may have been in the company's line prior to the 1932 catalog; similarly, if a game is not dated but was based on a 1927 event, the listing would be ≥ 1927.

Dimensions   When available, the dimensions of a game box are given to the nearest quarter inch; the first figure indicates width, the second, height; box depth is given if it exceeds two inches. Gameboard size is given only if it is a folding board whose width is different from the box width.

Dimensions are approximate and are given only to offer a perspective size for purposes of comparison. When different-sized editions of the same games were made, the sizes usually differed markedly; if you have a game that measures within an inch of one listed, the difference is not significant, especially in terms of value.

Where actual dimensions were not readily available, the following terms have been used to denote relative size of the box: "card pack" = size of deck of playing cards, "very small" means one of the dimensions is less than three inches, "small" refers to games up to about seven inches in either dimension, "medium" can mean any game with dimensions between seven and about fourteen inches, "standard" refers to the size of most games of today (approximately 19″ × 10″), and "large" is used to denote oversized games.

Comments   The address shown for a particular company may have been that company's address only for one period of its term in business; different addresses are shown where known and sometimes can be used to help determine the period in which a particular undated game was produced. When noting the address on games or printed material, be aware that "200 5th Ave., New York" is that of the Toy Building and was used by many companies from around 1920 on; the company may list the New York address (where it has offices or a showroom) but have its main office and factory in another state.

The companies listed here are known to have produced more than one game of collectible value, or to have made a significant (or unusual) contribution to the market. Also see Appendix C.

Where a company was known at different times by two names (for example, J. Pressman & Co. and Pressman Toy Co.), the company history is written as one history, but the game listings are divided into the appropriate periods.

Company names are alphabetized by the best-known version, with alternates (earlier or later) also listed. Game titles are also arranged by "best known" words: THE MERRY GAME OF OLD MAID will be alphabetized under OLD MAID; THE ORIGINAL GAME OF ZOOM under ZOOM; although full and complete titles are given.

Adams & Co.
21 and/or 25 Broomfield St. (1865)
14 Broomfield St. (1885)
Boston, MA
1860s–1877

An early publisher of card games, such as KONICAL KONVERSATION KARDS and THREE MERRY MEN, Adams & Co. sold its entire stock and copyrights to E.G. Selchow (see listing) in 1877, but may have resumed game production in the 1880s.

MIXED PICKLES, 1867
ref

SQUAILS
$65

The Adgame Co.
Washington, DC
1932

In 1932, Elizabeth Magie Phillips published THE LANDLORD'S GAME AND PROSPERITY, based on her 1924 patent, which was eventually bought by Parker Brothers. Her original 1904 patent for THE LANDLORD'S GAME became the forerunner of MONOPOLY.

Josiah Adams
Brick Church Chapel, NY (1845)
71 Nassau St., NY (1846)
1840s

Early manufacturer of card games, such as THE ERRAND BOY and NEW WORLD GAME OF AMERICAN HISTORY (both 1845).

THE GAME OF KINGS, 1844/45
$115

Advance games
126 Fifth Ave., New York 11, NY
1940s

BENGALEE, ±1940
#1166; PARCHEESI style game; cover illust shows Arabs playing the game under palm trees, with camels and walled village behind.
$35

HI POP, 1946
S&A; boxbot bd with wood center insert, wood dowel with spring, four beads.
$35

LOOPING THE LOOP, 1940s
$40

THREE POINT LANDING, 1942
#242; gameboard, four wood markers, destination cards, spinner; on the version examined, the box was larger than the intended wraparound litho, so the portion of the litho that should have been on the box apron is on the cover; similarly, the gameboard is folded off center so that the large half fits snugly in the larger box.
$55

Akro Agate Co.
Clarksburg, WV
1930s + 1940s

Akro produced glass marbles and other glass items and provided marbles for games such as CHINESE CHECKERS. It also made the glass cups for some of J. Pressman's TIDDLY WINKS games, quadrupling the value of those usually ordinary products. The company produced at least two of its own games, which sell for much higher prices to marble collectors than game collectors.

CLICK, 1930s
S&A; marble roll game.
$85

KINGS, 1931
#41; 11 × 7; die-cut folded board, 34 marbles; 2-person CHINESE CHECKERS style game.
$95

Alderman, Fairchild Co.
 AllFair
 E.E. Fairchild
1922–1929 Rochester, NY
1929–±1935 , Churchville, NY:
1935–≥1950s, (E.E. Fairchild: Rochester/Rochester 2, NY)

Harry O. Alderman and Elmer E. Fairchild had been producing paper boxes and novelties in Rochester since 1900 and began manufacturing games in 1922. They moved to nearby Churchville in 1929, when the Toy and Game Division of the company became a separate entity and the company incorporated. At that time, E.E. Fairchild was President and Herman G. Fisher (who later went on to start Fisher-Price) was Vice President. The company logo was "AllFair," but the word was hyphenated when used as text.

The firm showed rapid growth in its early years, and opened offices in the Toy Building in N.Y. in 1924. In 1926 the company had three factories (including one that made fancy boxes) and employed 250–300 people. Sometime before 1936 the "Alder-

man" name was dropped, though every item was still called an "All-Fair" game; E.E. Fairchild's name was put on the boxes, along with a Rochester address. Fairchild tried licensing and picked up some big bucks: Frank Buck and Buck Rogers.

E.E. Fairchild produced puzzles up until 1975, but further research is required to determine when during the late 1950s, '60s, or '70s the company ceased game production.

All-Fair made its best (most collectible) games during its first decade. The use of interesting, detailed illustrations, vivid color, and contemporary themes (radio, King Tut) gives good value to most All-Fair games. In the early period the company also made more games depicting black characters (usually in a comical, stereotyped fashion) than perhaps any other company of that time; these games, though racially insensitive, are highly collectible today.

All-Fair catalogs rarely surface and, though small, are valued at well over $100 each. The 1928 catalog (listed as "Catalog No. 22") is more collectible than most because its cover features an illustration by cartoonist Oscar Hitt, who illustrated game box covers for a few companies and drew All-Fair's HI-WAY HENRY game. Another nongame collectible is a game display consisting of a wooden base and a cardboad cap that secures four gameboards in an upright position. The display is rare, but lack of demand keeps its value low.

The listing below includes almost all the games (other than generic games such as checkers, LOTTO, etc.) produced by the company during its heyday, between 1922 and 1932.

ADD-TOO, 1940
$20

AIR DERBY: See CAPITAL CITIES AIR DERBY

ANIMAL AND BIRD LOTTO, 1926
$20

AUTHORS, ≥1945, E.E. Fairchild
#623-3; 5 × 4; card game; wraparound cover litho was sealed to the boxbot.
$20

(Fink collection)

AUTO RACE, 1922
Possibly All-Fair's first game, but not uncommon; (see also SPE-DEM AUTO RACE)
$110

AUTO RACE JR., 1925
$70

BATTLE OF BALLOTS, 1931/32
$60

BASEBALL, 1926
S&A; metal board in wood frame is baseball diamond with three-speed pitch mechanism and swinging bat; retail $7.50 (compare price with the $1.50 charged for the year's most deluxe board game, PIRATES GOLD.)
ref

BEAN-EM, 1931
#376, 19¼" × 10; bean bag toss game; illust of black characters "Mose," "Sambo," and "Rastus."
$175

BINGO, ≤1929
Target game.
$25

BOW-O-WINKS, 1931/32
#501; S&A; tiddledy winks game; bldup board sits on angle as players attempt to snap wink into dog's mouth; illust of three bulldogs.
$70

BUCK ROGERS IN THE 25TH CENTURY, 1936
Card game; 5 × 4; 35 cards incl 18 dif illust in exceptionally vivid colors (17 pairs plus odd "Killer Kane" card); instr card; yellow and red cover shows Rogers and blue space ship; © John F. Dille Co.; exceptional game because of quality and color of illustrations; highly cross-collectible because of Buck Rogers theme.
$310 Auc. 10/91 $311

BUNKER GOLF, 1931/32
#421
ref

BUSTO, 1931/32
#504; S&A; tiddly wink variant.
$15

THE CAPITAL CITIES AIR DERBY, 1929
#307; gameboard, four metal planes, four special wood dice with colors to match planes, cardboard dice cup, instr in cover; board with marbleized back shows U.S. map; cover is map, illust of single engine prop plane and N.Y. and San Francisco.
$150

CAPTAIN HOP ACROSS JUNIOR, 1928
#410; 11½" × 11½"; bldup bd with attached spinner shaped as propeller; four metal monoplanes on short pedestals.
$85

(Fink collection)

CARGO FOR VICTORY, 1943
#553; 13¾" × 9¾"; board, 16 cardboard cargo ships plus eight subs fit into cardboard ring stands.
$55

CHENO, 1932
#430; bookshelf strategy game with Backgammon inside, CHENO outside.
ref

CITIES, 1932
$40

CITIES, ≥1945,
Card game; 5 × 4; wraparound cover litho was sealed to the boxbot; dif card back from first edition.
$35

COMBINATION TENNIS AND BASEBALL, 1930
ref

DIM THOSE LIGHTS, 1932, All-Fair
#427; S&A; boxbot bd with attached metal rims forming the underside of headlights on motorcycles and cars; probably ten each of two colors of cardboard disks; disks tossed onto board and sliding into metal rims would block out headlights; one of the few games to show motorcycles.
$240

FLAP JACKS, 1931
#420; S&A; 15¾" × 12¾"; die-cut bldup bd has five holes for pancakes, ten pancakes (five each of two colors); cover illust shows cook serving flapjacks to three children.
$80

FORTUNE TELLING, 1920s
card game; 36 cards (four suits of 1–9).
$30

FORTUNE TELLING, ≥1945,
Card game; 5 × 4; wraparound cover litho was sealed to the boxbot.
$25

FRANK BUCK'S BRING 'EM BACK ALIVE GAME, 1937
#627–2; card game; 5 × 4; 36 cards, with three fitting together to make picture of one animal; card back has signed photo of Buck; instr sheet has ad for CITIES, SKIPPY, AUTHORS, BUCK ROGERS, FORTUNE TELLING, and "the modern interpretation of OLD MAID"; cover has drawing of leopard and inset photo of Buck, apron has red on yellow silhouettes of dif animals.
$95

GENERAL HEADQUARTERS, 1940s
$50

GLY-DOR, 1930/31
15¾" × 12½"; bldup bd with spinner, four wood pawns.
$70

HI-HO-ROLO, 1930
ref

HI-WAY HENRY, 1928
#309; one-piece bldup boxbot gameboard, four die-cut Hi-Way Henry cars, four special dice (one side showing "blowout"), dice cup; subtitled, "cross country 'Tin Lizzy' Race;" wonderful board and box cartoon illustrations are drawn by Oscar Hitt; based on his Hi-Way Henry comic strip syndicated in 80 newspapers. Rare.
$650

HOP ACROSS: See CAPTAIN HOP ACROSS (JR.)

HORSES, 1927
15 × 10; board unfolds to 28½" × 9½"; four litho on wood horses (numbered 7, 11, 13, and 23) 3" long on wood stands, between 75 and 80 chips in three colors with embossed horse and rider on both sides, six betting boards, deck of cards, instr in cover credit

Modern Makers, Inc., Utica, NY, and do not mention All-Fair; game was probably produced by Modern Makers in 1927 and taken over by All-Fair 1929/30; entire game is done with classy gold on black motif with red borders, the emblem being silhouette of trumpet-blowing angel on horseback.
$75

GAME OF INTERNATIONAL SPY, 1943
13½″ × 10; gameboard, 48 cardboard pieces in four colors, 48 cardboard ring stands; forerunner of STRATEGO, except object is to capture the spy, and there are no bombs and different rules of capture.
$85

JACE PEARSON'S TALES OF THE TEXAS RANGERS, ≥1955, E.E. Fairchild
#921–100; 16½″ × 8½″; gameboard, 12 wood pawns, six cardboard disks, 18 cards, die, instr sheet; based on the TV show 1955–59; © Screen Gems, Inc.; this is one of the last (if not *the* last) of the notable All-Fair games.
$45

JAUNTY BUTLER, 1931/32
#503; S&A; bowling game.
$75

JAV-LIN, 1931
#379; S&A; 15¾″ × 12¾″; die-cut bldup bd in vertical format shows big lipped native pointing to one of six holes; four wood javelins made with wood ball tip and feathers attached to wood shaft; cover illust shows black big-lipped native with leaf/grass shirt, earrings, necklace, leg and arm bands, and throwing spear while other looks on in island shore setting.
$175

JOLLY COP RING TOSS, 1928
#415; S&A; die-cut "Mulligan in a mellow mood" two-piece die-cut figure on wood base, 4 reed rings.
ref

JOURNEY TO JUPITER, 1950s
ref

JOURNEY TO THE TREASURES OF PHARAOH (See TUTOOM)

KO-KO THE CLOWN, ±1940
#731; 9¾ × 7¼; pin-the-tail variant with 15 × 25 paper board; instr in cover; part of series with MONKEY SHINES and TREASURE HUNT.
$20

MATCH 'EM, 1926
$20

MONKEY SHINES, ±1940
#731; 9¾ × 7¼; part of series with KO-KO THE CLOWN and TREASURE HUNT.
$20

NOAH'S ARK FISHING GAME, 1930
ref

OLD MAID, 1920s
Card game; 5 × 4; cards signed Vernon Grant; wraparound cover litho was sealed to the boxbot.
$30

OLD MAID, 1930s
Card game; cards showing elfin characters in various occupations, plus instr card and card back.
$25

OLD MAID, WITH CHARACTERS FROM FAMOUS NURSERY RHYMES AND FAIRY TALES, ±1940
Card game; 5 × 4; 35 cards incl pairs of Cinderella, Snow White, Little black Sambo, and an excellent illust of Alice in Wonderland (shown with Mad Hatter and Rabbit), plus 13 others and the Old Maid; instr card.
$40

OUR GANG TIPPLE TOPPLE GAME, 1930
#359; S&A; ball rolling target game; hitting the correct spots on the illustrated fence target on stand causes characters to pop up on top of fence; instr in cover; black Mammy character plus named stars Farina, Fatti, Wheezer, Pete and Mary Ann.
$260

PATCH WORD, 1938
#654-2; card game; 5 × 4; 54 cards with letter and value on each of 52, plus two wild cards; instr sheet has ad for SWEEPS, POTLUCK, and BINGO; cross word game has sample crossword on red, white, and blue cover.
$15

PIPERS 3, 1931/32
#509; retail 25¢.
ref

PIRATES GOLD, 1926 and ±1935
Catalog listings indicate the former included a gameboard, 16 metal pirates, eight dice, and four dice cups, and retailed at $1.50; the latter, #604 had a spinner and game pieces.
ref

PIRATES GOLD, 1940s
#609; 8½″ × 10½″; boxbot bd, four wood markers, spinner, instr on board; Fairchild name appears inside thin boxbot apron; simple path game with pirate illustrations does not have the quality look of earlier All-Fair items; cover shows pirate and treasure, with three children and ship in background.
$25

PON-E-RUN, ≤1929
$30

THE GAME OF POOR JENNY, 1927
#403; 11½″ × 11½″; bldup bd pictures numerous illust of mischievous donkey and black "Mammy"; four metal riders on donkeys embossed with names "Ned," "Tom," "Bob," and "Jen"; donkeys are the same as the unnamed ones in the 1923 TUTOOM; four colored dice, with the four names on each.
$100

POP AND PLOP SHOOTING GAME, 1928
#306; S&A; 17½″ × 9; 12 linen-finish cardboard animals, gun, cork, two metal strips to fasten box cover as background perpendicular to boxbot, instr in cover.
$50

RACE TO THE MOON, 1931/32
#382; S&A; target game consisting of rocket that flies up when hit by rolled ball.
ref

RADIO GAME FOR LITTLE FOLKS, 1926
Bldup bd, 8 metal radio horn speakers, two dice, dice cup; retail 50¢.
$125

SIMBA, 1931/32
#422; S&A; three targets, rings, gun.
$75

SKIPPY, ≥1936
Card game; 5 × 4; 36 dif. cartoon cards form 12 comic strips of 3 panels each; instr in cover; Skippy card back; ads for BUCK ROGERS and CITIES; game is at least four years later than Bradley's board game SKIPPY.
$75

SKY HAWKS, 1931/32
#377; cardboard pieces are assembled to make an airplane with propeller as spinner and wing as the game board; unique and rare.
$200

SPE-DEM AUTO RACE, 1922, All-Fair
17½″ × 17½″ board, parts box approx 4 × 3 × 2, six 2″ long die-cast metal open cars, each with dif. stamping: Buick, Dodge, Ford,

Maxwell, Paige, Stutz; six wood cubes have first letter of cars' names; cardboard dice cup; instr inside cover.
$135

STOP AND GO, 1928
Gameboard, four metal autos, two 6″ high cardboard pieces are cops holding spinner; amusing game of traffic rules is subtitled "a race for the Baby's milk"; checkerboard on reverse.
$40

STOP AND SHOP, 1930
#417; boxbt bd, 20 die-cut pieces merchandise, 80 pieces money, "Price Today" piece; children's game of trading with and for different commodities; illust of cop similar to traffic cop on cover of STOP AND GO; subtitled A RACE FOR THE BABY'S MILK.
$65

TALES OF THE TEXAS RANGERS. See JACE PEARSON'S TALES OF THE TEXAS RANGERS

TIP THE BELLBOY, 1929
#414; S&A, 12¼″ × 12¼″; bldup board, 9″ high cardboard figure of black bellboy in "Ritz" hat, three metal cups, 12 wood balls, one wood and metal catapult, one metal rod; bellboy dangles on metal pole balancing metal cup on each hand and between legs.
$200

TOONIN RADIO GAME, 1925
Gameboard and parts box 4½″ × 2¾″ × 2; six metal radio speakers 1¼″ high, six wood dice with letters; colorful and attractive gameboard, and excellent radio cross-collectible.
$210

TREASURE HUNT, ±1940
#732; 9¾″ × 7¼″; colored paper sheets were cut up into six objects that were then hidden around the house and pinned to a paper scoreboard when found; instr in cover; part of series with KO-KO THE CLOWN and MONKEY SHINES.
$20

TUTOOM, JOURNEY TO THE TREASURES OF PHARAOH, 1923
Gameboard, small illust part box, four donkeys, same as those in POOR JENNY except without embossed names, two wood dice with numbers, not pips; board path from "Luxor on the River Nile" to large center space of Tut's tomb, superb board illustrations and unusual implements, along with the fact that this was the major entry during All-Fair's second year in business, makes this a valuable item; the small request form in a 1926 *Playthings* magazine for a sample copy was in the shape of a scarab; retail $1.00.
$150 Auc. 10/91 $200

WATCH ON DE RIND, 1931
#502; die-cut bldup bd sets up vertically as target, wood and metal ball catapult, wooden bead balls, stapled boxbot corners; All-Fair catalog admits the title "is really an awful pun"; illust of three black characters, Mose, Sambo, and Rastus, eating watermelon.
$230

(Fink collection)

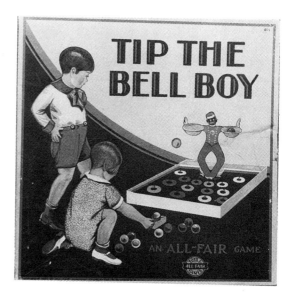

THE WAY TO THE WHITE HOUSE, 1928
#304; U.S. map board, spinner showing state capitals, 72 wood pegs.
$75

WITZI-WITS, 1926
#375; bldup bd with attached spinner is used for fortune telling.
$20

GAME OF THE WORLD FLYERS, 1926
#354; 18 × 9; board, four metal dirigibles, two dice, set of wood checkers, instr in cover; board shows route from N.Y. to Paris (in keeping with Lindbergh's trip), with four players having separate adjacent paths traveling via South America and Africa; use of dirigibles instead of airplanes suggests availability of the tokens from another, earlier game or last minute revision of the gameboard following Lindbergh's successful flight; though most All-Fair items have games only on one side of the board, the bd bk is checkerboard; the cover, which reads "Around the World Flight Air Race," shows ship, city scape, and three dirigibles; the high value of this game comes from the dirigible theme, including the illustrations and tokens; 1926 catalog listing refers to the dirigibles as Zeppelins, instr show © 1928, and box reads 1929.
$200

WPA, WORK, PROGRESS, ACTION, ≥1935
#594-5; 16¾" × 8; board 15¼" × 14¾"; paper shovels, four gloss wood pawns, chance cards, money, instr in cover; board shows bridge, highway, park, and housing projects; WPA title based on the Work Projects Administration, which existed from 1935–1943.
$40

WYNTRE GOLF, 1922/23
ref

X-PLOR-US, 1922/23
Touted as a best seller, still, in 1925.
$50

YATTEAU, 1922/23
ref

ZIPPY ZEPPS
Gameboard shows paths from New York to Paris and Berlin, with picture denoting each city; metal zeppelins, cards picturing zeppelins; box cover shows large zeppelin.
$450

ORIGINAL GAME OF ZOOM, ±1940
#525; 13¾" × 10; board is 23½" × 9½", instrument panel is 9 × 8 with four spinner dials, eight "aeroplanes," four colors each of two shapes, instr in cover; board shows "flattened" U.S. with zones from 5,000 to 25,000 feet on top; cover illust is two-engine plane.
$75

All Metal Product Co.
Wyandotte, MI
early to mid–1900s

As the name implies, this company made games using a metal base or board. The imprint on the base reads "Wyandotte Toys," suggesting the two companies were one in the same.

SPIN 'EM TARGET GAME, ±1930
#2582; S&A.
$40

American Symbolic Corp.
1955 Estes, Elk Grove Village, IL 60007

Though this may be only a one-game company, its well-conceived political parody may make this game a hot collectible in the future.

THE WATERGATE SCANDAL, 1973
#007; Card game; 5 × 7; black on white card box; some card illustrations and titles are phone tapper, big contributor, White House Aide, plus event cards such as "You were exposed by the press"; instr sheet informs that "Cover-up and deception . . . add zest to this game. . . . Players have been known to bribe the dealer, stack the deck, remove and destroy important cards, and 'bug' other players"; enjoyment of the game may be "enhanced by playing it . . . under a table, behind closed doors, and on dark street corners . . . playing in hushed voices and with furtive glances"; in this game "there are just losers. . . . The loser with the least amount of penalty points is therefore the winner"; retail price $2.99.
$18

American Novelties (See **Baker & Bennett**)

American Toy Mfg. Co.
Salem, MA
±1920
7 Chatham Square, New York, NY
±1932

It is not known for certain whether the Mass. and the N.Y. addresses signified two different companies, two concurrent offices of the same company, or a move by one company from Salem to New York; the similar box styles and themes of the MOTOR TOUR and MOTOR BOAT RACE suggest they are the same company; the Chatham square address was taken from a company listing in the NYC directory. See also **American Toy Works.**

(McFarland/Boyea collection)

BOSTON-NEW YORK MOTOR TOUR, ±1920 (Salem)
#121; 9¼ × 11¾; boxbot bd with built in spinner; pawns; instr in
cover. Board and box illust show spiral path passing by Mass. cities
of South Framingham, Worcester, Palmer, and Springfield; Conn.
cities of Enfield, Hartford, Meriden, New Haven, and Norwalk; and
the N.Y. city (out of place on the path) of New Rochelle.
$150

MARBLE MUGGINS, ±1920 (Salem)
S&A; 7x7; partial bldup bd is die-cut to allow marbles to be rolled
into slots in the mouth of Muggins character.
$100

AN EXCITING MOTOR BOAT RACE, ±1932
11¾ × 9; boxbot bd with built in spinner; pawns; instr in cover.
nva

American Toy Works
51 Bowery St.; 56 Allen St.; 7–8 Chatham Square (±1932)
Long Island City, NY
41–59 Wyckoff Ave., Brooklyn (±1947)
1895–1940s

The company was founded in the 1930s by Adolph Wein and
brother Max Wein, who sold their interests in 1944; by 1947 the
firm was located at 41–59 Wyckoff Ave., Brooklyn. Though around
for a long time, the company is known for games primarily in the
1930s and '40s. Their logo is ATWO. Many of their games are
marked with the name Arthur Dritz, an inventor who provided
products for other Long Island City companies, such as Game
Makers Inc. and Vitaplay Toy Co. The American Toy Mfg. Co. was
also listed at 7 Chatham Square in 1932, so it could be the same
company. ATWO games that can be found for around $25 include
the LIBRARY OF GAMES (1938, #403) and MAGNETIC TREASURE
HUNT.

AERO-CHUTE, ±1940
#532
$50

CHECKERS & AVION, ±1925
#8
$35

FLIP IT, ±1925
#13; 11½" × 9¼"; boxbot movement bd plus track board on cover;
four metal cars, four markers, two tongue depressers (flippers), instr
sheet; tongue depressers are used to flip marker into box bottom
to indicate number of spaces the metal cars should be moved on
the box cover board. **Deluxe Games** (see listing) used the identical
box for a different game.
$30

OPPORTUNITY HOUR, ±1940
$35

PINOCCHIO, ±1938
#510; S&A; target game; cover shows Pinocchio water skiing on
sled; good Disney item.
$150

SNOW WHITE AND THE SEVEN DWARFS, 1938
S&A, 19 × 13; © Walt Disney Enterprises, Hollywood; game by
Arthur Dritz; one-piece board has attached wood slide onto which
the seven dwarfs are placed, each dwarf being a die-cut cardboard
figure glued to a wood block; game includes wood dart with rubber
tip and feathers at other end and is made for being thrown by hand;
two wood stands hold board upright; board illust shows Snow White
leaning over and talking to the dwarf lowermost on the slide—when
that dwarf is shot, it falls off the board and all the dwarfs slide down
one place; excellent, colorful Disney illust also shows prince, deer,
and other animals in forest, plus an inset of the witch; cover illust
shows all the characters. Scarce, exceptional Disney piece.
$250

YUMPH, 1930
#308
ref

Amsden & Co.
14 Broomfield St., Boston, MA

THE MOST LAUGHABLE THING ON EARTH, ≤1865
A story game with cards, "comprising Endless Transformations of
Wit and Humor."
ref

THREE MERRY MEN, 1865
Conundrums; 6 × 2½"; 24-page instr booklet with story, numerous
cards with phrases used to fill in blanks in the story; touted as a
game "developing strange adventures, laughable scenes, witty sayings, grotesque appearances, droll misunderstandings, humorous
events, and comical transformations"; cover illust of three smiling
characters; instr booklet also advertises THE MOST LAUGHABLE
THING ON EARTH. Value stems from the game's antiquity more
than anything else.
$65

Animal Town Game Co.
P.O. Box 2002, Santa Barbara, CA
1976–1990
P.O. Box 485, Healdsburg, CA 95448
1990–present

Animal Town was started in 1976 by the Kolsbun family, a group
committed to environmental awareness. The games made after the
first two, NECTAR COLLECTOR and then BACK TO THE FARM, were
all cooperative (not competitive) games, and include DAM BUILD-
ERS and SAVE THE WHALES, which are both likely to become future
collectibles. The gameboard graphics of SAVE THE WHALES (1978)
are excellent, and the implements include eight pewter whales
(each one different), a pewter boat, a gold barnacle, and a "Protect
Our Whales" pin; it retails for $34. Games no longer in production
and now collectible include the ±1979 game MADISON AVENUE
(concerned with how goods are sold whether we need them or not,
and containing a cardboard headband with blinders) and THE
PETER PRINCIPLE (1978 author authorized version), which was
sold to Avalon Hill.

(McFarland/Boyea collection)

A CHICKEN IN EVERY PLOT, ±1980
Board game contains miniature metal tools (for turning off man-made noise) and a real chicken feather, and was designed to teach the importance of the chicken in the ecological system; the artwork was done by the family's 11-year-old daughter.
$30

Animate Toy Co.
31 E. 17th St., New York, NY
early 1900s

Predominantly a toy company, Animate made few games (or only one). It is noted for little metal "beetles" with a rolling wheel mechanism underneath that propels the animals forward at a very slow pace; these toys are sometimes seen for sale separately; however, since they are not mechanical but seem to work on a rubber band principle of unwinding resin, the devices no longer operate because of deterioration of the rubbery material over time.

BUGVILLE GAMES, 1915
Boxbot bd plus additional paper and cardboard boards, four metal "beetles," small cardboard box which is a soccer ball, two ad sheets; good "bug" cover illust; interesting and amusing.
$75

Anti-Monopoly, Inc,
P.O. Box 2427, San Rafael, CA 94902
1973–present

Game of Anti-Monopoly was subject of lawsuit brought by Parker Brothers; Parker won, thousands of games were buried in a landfill, then the decision was overturned in a landmark trademark infringement ruling. The U.S. Supreme Court, overturning lower court findings, concluded that: "(1) the District Court's finding that, as a game trademark, 'Monopoly' primarily denoted its producer was clearly erroneous, and (2) as applied to board game, the word 'Monopoly' had become 'generic,' and register of it as trademark was no longer valid . . . . Moreover, the court's reference to Darrow as the inventor or creator of the game is clearly erroneous." The game is still being made and sold internationally.

ANTI MONOPOLY, 1973,
Standard size box, four plastic tokens, punch-out cards, mailbox cards, social credit loan notes, money, dice; © Ralph Anspach; cover quotes the Sherman Anti Trust Law.
$25 for the earlier versions

ANTI ___ 1970s
Same as ANTI-MONOPOLY, but with the MONOPOLY name left out after the courts ruled in favor of Parker, disallowing Ralph Anspach's use of the word.
$35

Archarena Co.
Peoria, Ill.

Manufacturer primarily of wood Carrom boards. At one time the company was Carrom-Archarena.

ARCHARENA COMBINATION BOARDS, ±1900
$45

FLAG TRAVELETTE, ±1895
18 × 18 board with 7¼" × 4¾" parts box with paste-on litho "Outfit for No. 1"; wood pieces include two tops, eight pegs, and four carrom rings; folded heavy cardboard instructions with ad, instr booklet for 27 games, large spinner; subtitled FLAGS OF THE NATIONS; unusual cardboard adaptation of games that Archarena Co. put out with wood boards (similar to Carrom); retail: "imitation cloth bound, $1.00; cloth bound, gold embossed, $1.50."
$75

The Archer Toy Co.
Jeannette, PA
early 1900s

There is probably a connection between the Archer Toy Co., the Jeannette Toy & Novelty Co., the M.H Miller Co. and the T.H. Stough Co., since they were all from Jeannette, PA, and all made metal gameboards; some of the boards (if not all), including the one listed below, were manufactured by McDowell Mfg. Co. of nearby Pittsburgh. Both Jeannette and Miller produced "Brownie" games.

THE AIR MAIL, ±1930
14½ × 11½; metal board with raised sides and attached spinner; cover shows biplanes over global view of U.S.
$125

Arl-Hi Co.
302–304 North Evergreen Ave., Arlington Heights, IL

I-QUBES, 1948
4½" × 3¼" leather snap case containing seven letter dice. Exact same game was produced by Capex Co. (see listing), dated the same year.
$15

Arrco Playing Card Co.
Chicago, IL
mid 1900s

Arrco made small card games, usually for children. The value depends primarily on the theme. Games (all ±1950) include GO GO GO ($10), SKEETER ($10), and TRAIL DRIVE ($15).

Atkins & Co., Publishers
Philadelphia, PA
early 1900s

GRANDE AUTO RACE, 1920s
Gameboard 24 × 12, parts box 3¾"" square, four metal cards, top, spinner; after the top is spun, players spin the spinner in succession and move their cars as indicated, the race ending when the top stops spinning; earlier boards are not marked with the company name.
$85

CORTELLA, ±1915
Gameboard and parts box 6½" × 3, four wood dice cups, eight small bone dice, sixteen metal-rimmed cardboard disks (similar to early PARCHEESI pieces).
$35

(Mautner collection)

ATWO (See **American Toy Works**)

Austin & Craw
South Norwalk, CT

TIT-TAT-TOE, THREE IN A ROW, 1896
S&A; 5½" × 5½"; cardboard ring die-cut with nine holes (tic-tac-toe style) is attached to box bottom; nine wood marbles; metal piece attached to small grooved wood block can be snapped to propel ball; cover illust of cat head, winking; game is unique in that it might be the only game where the cover illustration is on the diagonal.
$75

Automatic Toy Co.
early 1900s

CROSS COUNTRY RACER, ±1940
10½" × 10½"; 10" diameter metal board with track around outside, 3" metal wind-up car, three plastic car markers; where mechanical metal car stops after moving around the outer track indicates which car marker is moved on inner path.
$75

Auvid, Inc. (See **The Ungame Company**)

Avalon Hill
4517 Harford Road, Baltimore, MD 21214
1952–present

Avalon Hill makes games for the game player. AH games that can be found for $25 or less include ACQUIRE, AIR EMPIRE (1961), BEAT INFLATION, D-DAY (1961), DIPLOMACY (1976), and LUFT-WAFFE (1971).

DISPATCHER, 1958
Railroad theme board game.
$35

GETTYSBURG, 1960
#501; 14 × 11; multi-fold board opens to 27 × 21, two combat results table, Union and Confederate mapboard charts, Combat Factors attacker and defender sheets, pad of time record sheets, uncut range cards, multiple cardboard units, 24-page instr book © 1960 includes historical summary of Battle of Gettysburg; box © 1958; one of the company's earliest games.
$30

TACTICS, 1958
The company's first game; rare and highly collectible to simulation and strategy collectors; any wear reduces value considerably.
$1250

TACTICS II, 1961
$30

TWIXT
Two-player strategy game is based on the knight's move in chess, and requires a player to build a wall from one side of the board to the other before an opponent connects the other two sides; invented by Alexander Randolph for 3M in 1963.
$20

WATERLOO, 1962
$50

B&B Toy Mfg. Co.
177 26th St., Brooklyn 32, NY
mid–1900s

Logo: two bees

RACEWAY, 1950s
$30

Baker & Bennett Co.
873–875 Broadway, New York, NY
early 1900s

Logo: behive with "B&B"; company noted mostly for Wonder Blocks and Wonder Toys; also listed as "American Novelties, Baker & Bennett."

PSYCHOLOGY OF THE HAND, 1919
Puzzle piece makes up five cardboard hands that correspond to five 9 × 8 charts; palm reading (fortune telling) theme with game system; © Gertrude Ann Lindsay.
$30

Baldwin Mfg. Co.
114–120 Forrest St., Brooklyn, NY
mid–1900s

Makers of metal action and skill and action games and toys, primarily around WWII.

KING PIN DELUXE BOWLING ALLEY, ±1947
#390
$20

PAR-A-SHOOT GAME, ±1947
#891
$25

The Bambino Products Co.
105 S. Jefferson St.
Chicago, IL
1934

This may have been a one-game company, but the concept was repeated by others.

BAMBINO, 1934
12 × 14 metal board on a wood frame with four attached score indicators; a 10" metal rod with a ball on top was attached to the base (and perpendicular to it) with a spring mechanism; the player would hit the ball with a small bat and the metal rod would slam against the board, pushing a string into one of many slots—though the movement was faster than the eye could see, the slot where the string was indented corresponded to a particular baseball play; game was marked "pat. pend." and "World's Fair Wonder, Chicago 1933–34"; the same game (same title) was made by the Johnson Store Equipment Co. of Elgin, IL, and other companies.
$125

Fred Beach
 Frederick H. Beach
 Beachcraft
 11 W. 42nd St., New York, NY
 ≤1936–≥1943

Beach was the king of the parlor games, many of his game products coming in a bound booklet form, others being boxed sheets of paper with up to eight games per box and enough sheets to hand out to a number of people at a party; the games included stunts, observation and memory puzzles, identification of photographs and logos or advertising slogans, word quizzes, mystery whodunits, etc.; a number of his games pictured and were geared to military personnel. Most of the games are more noted for their fun and play value than their value as collectibles, and most are valued under $20, including AFTER DINNER (1937), BALLOONIO (1937, includes balloons), FUN KIT (1939), OLDTIMERS (1940), SCRAMBLES, and STUNT BOX (1941, 6½″ high cone container).

CRIME & MYSTERY
$25

SIPPA FISH, 1936
Colored tissue paper fish, straws.
$30

TAKE IT AND DOUBLE, 1943
This game was based on the radio quiz show that was the forerunner of the *$64 Question,* which became the *$64,000 Question* .
$35

J.P. Beach
128 Fulton St. (upstairs), New York, NY
1851

THE JOLLY GAME OF GOOSE, 1851
One of the earliest known of the popular European GAME OF GOOSE published in the U.S.; lithographed by Perkins Sun Lith. Establishment.
$1250

Beacon Hudson Co.
80 Boylston St., Boston, MA

OPEN CHAMPIONSHIP GOLF GAME, ±1930
$75

WORLD'S CHAMPIONSHIP BASEBALL GAME, ±1930
ref

Bettye-B Company
1954–1957
932 Broadway
New York 10, NY

Though in business for only four years, the Bettye-B Company made two significant contributions to the game industry. The company was one of the first to produce a game licensed from a television game show or quiz show, and Bettye-B was also the first company to manufacture three-dimensional plastic vacuum form boards. BREAK THE BANK, based on the NBC program hosted by Bert Parks that began on ABC in 1948, was brought out in 1955, just after Lowell's 1954 game of BEAT THE CLOCK. The company used three-dimensional (relief) boards in the games B.T.O, TRAPPED, and ROBIN HOOD. Most Betty-B games also had unusual variations of spinners.

Bettye-B was founded by Robert Whiteman, a successful New York business entrepreneur. His wife's name Bettye and the "B" for Bob made up the company name. After reviewing Lowell's BEAT THE CLOCK (the first game based on a television quiz show), Whiteman contacted the producers of "Break the Bank" and "Masquerade Party" and told them he had developed games based on their programs. He got a positive response from the producers, but

he had not yet designed either game. He then contacted an associate and had the games invented and drawn up in time for a meeting the following week. Both TV games were successful and led to the development of other licensed games, such as ROBIN HOOD and Ellery Queen's TRAPPED.

Though successful in the game business, Whiteman learned that after designing, manufacturing, advertising and selling his product, he made nearly the same amount of money as the person who did little more than allow him the license to the property. He discontinued the game business in 1957 to devote all his time to his other licensing concerns, including Ripley's Believe It Or Not! Whiteman met Robert Ripley in 1946, worked for him, and eventually became the worldwide director of licensing for Ripley's Enterprises, Inc.; he was responsible for the agreement with Milton Bradley Company that led to production of Bradley's RIPLEY'S BELIEVE IT OR NOT! game in 1984 (which, incidentally, was invented by this author).

Whiteman, working out of offices in Rye, New York, also owns Liberty Library, having acquired all the rights to the writings that appeared in Liberty Magazine between 1924 and 1950. Though only dabbling in games now, he is still active in numerous licensing projects.

The games listed represent the entire line of the Bettye-B Company.

ADVENTURES OF ROBIN HOOD, 1956
Three-dimensional vacuum form board with built in gravity spinner, 8 magic windows, 8 wooden window covers, 4 plastic playing men, 10 chests of gold, 10 horses, 10 shields and armor, 10 bows and arrows, 2 steel balls; based on the CBS-TV show, cover photo shows Richard Greene; retailed at $2.98.
$75

BOTTOMS UP, 1956
Game board with hidden magnets beneath used to play different games where metal playing piece placed on board by player will either stick or flip over to show opponent's color.
$25

BREAK THE BANK, 1955
Build-up board, question booklets, automatic color selector (spinner), 150 pieces of money, 12 gold coins, 6 wood playing pieces. Cover shows Bert Parks. Advertises Dodge automobiles and Alka Seltzer. One of the first games tied-in to a television quiz show. Retailed for $2.98.
$60

B.T.O, 1956
Three-dimensional plastic board with built-in "gravity" spinner, 28 property ownership certificates, 200 pieces of play money, 280 property value cards, 6 automobiles, 2 steel balls, 20 property price holders. Retailed for $2.98. B.T.O stands for "Big-time operator." Similar to MONOPOLY, using New York City locales; players "shrewdly manipulate to monopolize . . . famous New York landmarks."
$45

HAPPY BIRTHDAY, 1955
Children's game. Rare.
ref

HIGH DICE, 1954
The first Bettye-B game. Special dice included, one with a horse's head and one with a horse's tail; different combinations allowed for adding or subtracting points. Rare.
ref

MASQUERADE PARTY, 1955
21½″ x½″, 16 cardboard figures of famous people, wooden stands, clue cards, instr. in box cover; though many collectors are unaware of it, the game can command a high price because it contains such costumed photograph characters as Pee Wee Reese, Jack Dempsey, and Leo Durocher.
$75

TRAPPED, 1956
13½″ × 20″. Ellery Queen license. Three-dimensional plastic board with built-in "gravity" spinner, 6 bodies, 6 fingerprint cards, 6 motive chips, 6 clocks, 6 playing pieces, 2 steel balls. Mystery game. Retailed for $2.98.
$60

R. Bliss Manufacturing Co.
Pawtucket, Rhode Island
1832–1914
games: ≥1871–1914

Rufus Bliss started a company in 1832 that manufactured wood screws and clamps for piano and cabinet makers. He invented various machines, including one that cut wood screws more rapidly than by hand—a process used to produce the "turned men" or shaped wooden playing pieces advertised in early catalogs. Bliss retired in 1863, years before the company produced its first known toy; an 1871 advertisement is the first known to mention Bliss toys. The company incorporated in 1873, and Rufus Bliss died in 1879. The company produced fish pond, parlor ring toss, floor and table croquet, and target games during the 1870s and 1880s, and probably made its first folding board game in 1889 or shortly before then. In 1914 Bliss was bought by Mason & Parker of Winchendon, Mass., a company that continued the manufacture of some of Bliss's toy items.

Bliss was noted for paper litho on wood; most of these items were toys, but some were skill and action games in which a ball or marble was rolled or shot at a target; he patented the first spiral drop marble game in 1889. Bliss also made extraordinary board games with superb lithography; the titles were often incorporated into the box design, a design that often used separate, sectioned-off images (insets). Bliss games, because of their exceptional lithography, are almost as sought-after as McLoughlin games. Most of the prime Bliss pieces were made between 1889 and 1900.

ARENA, 1896
#183, 18x9; gameboard 36x9, track game, box cover litho of two charging knights on horseback; retail 50¢.
$200

ATTACK (T.G.O.), 1889
#87; S&A; 19 × 9½″; board, parts box, 4 wood and wire shooting sticks, 4 projectiles, 56 illustrated wood rectangular soldiers, 40 cardboard markers, instr sheet; ads for WILD WEST and DETECTIVE; "a novel game of war designed expressly for children," illustrates American battles and officers; retail $1.
$500

THE GAME OF DETECTIVE, 1889
18½″ × 9½″, heavy folding board, litho on wood marble box ("the Robber Box"), two heavy cardboard spinners attached to figural wood posts placed in wood stands, one marble (the robber), four cardboard detectives and four assistant detectives, eight wood stands, instr. sheet; instructions title the game THE DETECTIVES, OR, THE DIAMOND ROBBERY; board path meanders around over one dozen character illustrations (newsboy, counterfeiter, organ man, etc.) and geometric designs, perimeter shows man's face in moon/sun; exceptional illustrations throughout, Bliss at its best.
$2,000 Auc. 11/91 $2,700

GAME OF THE DUDES, 1890
9¾ × 12; board unfolds to 19¼ × 9¼ four turned pawns, 20 large markers, two dice and dice cups, instr sheet; box with metal reinforced corners; exceptional litho cover; the instructions indicated the game was "arranged" for 2, 3, or 4 players, listed "four leaders" and cube counters as part of the components, and included one misspelling, "opponant's man."
$375

FANTASMA GAME, ≥1889
#70, S&A game; 17x7½″ litho on wood target game with ball; any one of five heads with score on back flies into air when corresponding post is struck by rolling ball; retail 25¢.
ref

FISH POND GAME (T. Improved), ±1880
wood poles with lines and hooks, lithographed fish on bases, in hinged box;
#1= 6 poles, 36 fish, retail $1
#2= 4 poles, 20 fish, retail 50¢
#3= 4 poles, 10 fish, retail 25¢
ref

FLY AWAY, ≥1889
#62, S&A game; 8x7 setup, rubber-band action litho on wood target game with marble; rolled marble hitting weight suspending by rubber band from upper plank dislodges it from lower plank and sends it flying; illustrations of five clowns; retail 10¢.
ref

FROG POND (G.O.), probably 1890
#114, 13½″ × 13½″; one-piece or boxbot or bldup board, 20 frogs, 6 poles; played like FISH POND; improved version ≤ 1896; retail 25¢.
ref

LAWN AND PARLOR RING TOSS, ± 1880
Jointed stake, chestnut wood box, 6 rattan hoops.
$60

LEAGUE PARLOR BASE BALL, 1889 10x14 litho wood board with scoring discs on attached metal rods, pegs, pawns, and number cube dice, dice cups, paper parts box; no game box.
$1,000

LIFE IN THE WILD WEST, ±1894
#166; multiple-fold gameboard is 18x18; box cover litho shows scout, Indians, children, and cabin; based on more expensive WILD WEST from 1889; retail 25¢.
$500

MAN IN THE MOON (T.), ±1885
#58, S&A game; 12x13 setup, spring-action litho on wood target game with ball; shows face in half moon and owl reading book with descriptive card atop wood post.
ref

MILK MAID
ref

NEWSBOY (G.O.T.), probably 1890
#104, 9¾ × 12; gameboard, cards, playing pieces, dice, dice cups; box litho shows newspaper delivery boy on the run; retail 25¢.
NVA Auc. 6/92 $2100

OPEN SESAME (G.O.), probably 1890
#126, vertical format box; gameboard 14x16½″ in checkerboard pattern; box shows knight on horseback by castle; retail 25¢.
ref

PARLOR FLOOR CROQUET, ±1880
Standard croquet set for four players.
#1= "A Fine Set, fancy-painted" with extra stripes, retail $1.25
#2= "A Good Set, plain painted," retail $1
ref

RUNAWAY SHEEP (G.O.T.), 1892
7 × 15¼″; one-piece board, 3¼″ high Little Bo Peep stands upright on wood and metal stand that pops into die-cut gameboard and acts as spinner; two cardboard sheep on wood bases, instr sheet; geometric board pattern has perimeter illust of sheep, birds and two children; board illust shows girl sitting on haystack, image of spiderweb above, inset below of sheep sitting up reading books.
$275

SHOPPING (G.O.), probably 1891
#124, 18x9; gameboard, cards with descriptions of purchases, dice; box cover litho of crowd in period dress; retail 50¢.
$1200 Auc. 6/92 $1500

STANLEY IN AFRICA, 1891
#164, large, nearly square box; gameboard depicts men and animals; paper dice cups, dart, target; improved version ≤1896; retail 50¢.
$700

TABLE CROQUET, ±1880
#1= eight polished, painted boxwood mallets and 1½″ balls, 2 stakes, 10 enameled weighted wickets, screw clamps and belt, black walnut box.
#2= same as #1 except in maple, no enameling, and hinged pine box.
#3= same as #2 except in hardwood and slide cover pine box.
#4= same as #3 except 6 balls and mallets and smaller box.
ref

VISIT TO THE FARM, Bliss, 1893
179; 7½″ × 15¾″; one-piece bd, four die-cut cards with illust of children stand upright on wood stands, 40 cards, teetotum, 3-D wood house with wood and cardboard roof and paper on wood chimney; exceptional setup.
$275 Auc. 11/91 $500

WILD WEST (G.O.T.), 1889
#86, 18x9; gameboard, path game, box cover shows 4 separate images: scout and three Indians; cross-collectible for western and Indian themes; retail $1.
$650 Auc. 6/92 $350 (taped; no instr)

WORLD'S COLUMBIAN EXPOSITION (G.O.T.), 1893 or 1894
#165, large "album" box, nearly square with geometric design; gameboard depicts buildings and grounds of the Exposition at Jackson Park, Chicago; "fancy-turned men," counters, 4 leather dice cups; retail 50¢.
$750

Bowers & Hard
211 State St.
Bridgeport, CT
±1906–≤1907

This virtually unknown company produced at least two games of exceptional quality.

TEDDY'S BEAR HUNT, 1907
18 × 12½″; gameboard, six metal hunters, one metal bear, six tiny bone dice, two wood dice cups, ad for VANDERBILT CUP RACE. Cross-collectible, "Teddy" theme. Rare.
$650 Auc. 6/92 $900

VANDERBILT CUP RACE, ±1906
17 × 8½″; three-fold gameboard opens to 30 × 16 and shows race course through various towns on Long Island; six detailed metal race cars, two bone dice, two wood dice cups, instr in cover. William K. Vanderbilt II raced with Louis Chevrolet and was associated with Dusenberg and Ford; the race in his name was held in central Long Island between 1900 and 1910, predating Indianapolis and Daytona, but was cancelled because it caused too many deaths. Cross-collectible, automobile. Rare.
$650

C.E. Bradley Corporation
Brattleboro, VT
±1910s–±1920s

This small company that made playthings, toys, and some games is no apparent relation to the Bradley family an hour away in Springfield, MA. Items were often marked only "Bradley of Brattleboro."

DIVING FISH, ±1920
S&A; 10 hand painted wood fish 4½″ long weighted in the rear, fishing line, instr in cover; this could be the only FISH POND variant designed to actually be played in water; instr read, "Mother may let you use the bathtub for a pond as a reward for good behavior." Unusual; rare.
$30

Milton Bradley Company
Springfield, MA
East Longmeadow, MA
1860–1984, family owned
1984–present, owned by Hasbro

Like many early game manufacturers, Milton Bradley was a lithographer (his portrait of Lincoln before he grew his beard is probably worth more to the right collector than most of Bradley's games are). In 1860, as a sideline to his new printing business, he published THE CHECKERED GAME OF LIFE, his first game. Following that success, he issued game kits for soldiers during the Civil War (the games could be considered the country's first commercial "travel" games). In 1866 he patented the first croquet. By 1876 he was producing gameboards of the exact size still used in standard games today. According to a 1947 *Playthings* magazine, by 1876 Milton Bradley "had attained a position of leadership in the nation's game business." He became involved in the Kindergarten movement and saw games as an avenue for education; in 1876 the company was awarded the Medal of Excellence at the Centennial Exposition—"the first award ever made for ethical teaching of children through play."

Bradley incorporated in 1884 and opened a New York office in 1892; by 1903 he had offices in Kansas, Atlanta, San Francisco, Philadelphia, and Boston.

With advances in lithographic processes, Bradley was able to "mass produce" his games. By the time he died in 1911, his company was probably the most prolific game company in the United States.

Milton Bradley Co. purchased McLoughlin Brothers in 1920, and for a short time Bradley reproduced a few McLoughlin games under the Milton Bradley label; in some cases, the cover of the game was changed but the board remained exactly the same. What is interesting is that collectors will pay almost four times as much for a game with the McLoughlin name as for the identical game with the Milton Bradley logo.

The company survived the depression well (games, like movies, were inexpensive diversions). But the restrictions of war forced the company to cut the game line in 1941 from 410 different items to 150. The post-war boom was encouraging, however, and Bradley produced the first television-based game (Hopalong Cassidy) in 1950, starting a trend that would change the game industry.

Bradley continued to be a major force in the industry until the company was bought out by Hasbro in 1984; the plant in Springfield now makes the games of Bradley, Parker, Selchow & Righter, and others, all under the umbrella of Hasbro.

Many of Milton Bradley's early games were dexterity or skill-and-action games, like tiddley winks or ring-toss games. Bradley's games were aimed more at children, whereas many of the games of competitors, such as Parker Brothers, seemed also suitable for adults. Most early Bradley games were not dated, and the four-digit numbering system is unreliable for determining original dates of manufacture. The best resources for learning about the Milton Bradley Company (in addition to an examination of the games) are company catalogs and the book *All in the Game* by James Shea (see Bibliography). The listing below can serve only as a very small representative sampling, since the company produced thousands of game titles over the last 130-plus years.

A.D.T. MESSENGER BOY, ±1915
#4033; 15¼ × 16¼; bldup bd with parts tray, four wood markers, spinner; path game similar to MESSENGER BOY games, with "ambition" and "bright & active" as cause for advancement, and "indifference," "carelessness," and "dissipation" sending the player back; same box size and style as ≥1911 CHECKERED GAME OF LIFE suggests same time period.
$70
$50 for #4017, 7½" × 7½" with boxbot bd

GAME OF AIR MAIL, 1920s
#4021; S&A; 12¼ × 6¼; bldup bd die-cut with holes representing U.S. cities ("Deadwood"), weather conditions ("cyclone"), or events ("shot at by bandits"); six ceramic marbles; one of the largest hand-held dexterity marble roll games requiring the player to tilt the box, rolling the marble across the board, avoiding the hazards.
$35

AUTO RACE GAME, ± 1925
#4289, 17 × 8¾; two versions: one-piece boxbot and bldup with lithoed parts tray, and folding gameboard; four metal cards, four cardboard block spinners 2 × 2 × 1¼; board shows b&w half track around illust of roadster, cover shows racing car; exactly the same as AUTO RACING GAME, which was probably an earlier title; often seen priced much higher than accepted value.
$145

AUTO RACE GAME, ±1930
14½ × 8¼; boxbot bd, spinner, four markers; same series in terms of size, implements, and graphic style as GLIDER RACING and ENDURANCE RUN.
$45

BAMBOOZLE, OR THE ENCHANTED ISLE, 1876
One of the first large folding game boards; exceptional illustration.
$175

BARNEY GOOGLE AND SPARK PLUG GAME, 1923
17x9, gameboartd, four cardboard characters, two metal dice and dice cups; excellent color litho cover and board.
$90 Auc. 6/92 $200

THE BEATLES FLIP YOUR WIG GAME
The only Beatles game (and one of very few "rock and roll" theme games) is less valued than might be expected because it is so common and most of the serious Beatle collectors already have one.
$75

BLACKOUT, 1939
#4605; 19 × 119½; board, printed bldup with parts tray, blackout cards, two dice, instr in cover.
$60

BULL IN THE CHINA SHOP, 1937
#4097; S&A; wood sided box, metal windup top, four wood pins.
$30

THE CADET GAME, 1905
#4036; 8½ × 12; boxbot bd, four wood markers, spinner; simple luck path game, with path spaces consisting of 200 numbered squares laid out 13 per row, illust of West Point archway at top; cover shows cadet with two cadets and cannon in background, illustration marked "Trophy Point, West Point, N.Y." The rare West Point theme ads considerable value to this game.
$80

CALL MY BLUFF, 1965
Based on the 30-min., NBC TV show that ran during 1965 only.
$20

CANDYLAND, 1949
Classic children's game.
$20

CAPTAIN VIDEO, ±1952
#4235; gameboard plus setup control panel with two large spinner dials, printed die-cut bldup with three attached spinners and holes for pawns, 16 wood pawns, instr in cover; superb-looking game with multiple components incl bldup and two-fold piece illustrated to look like space control panels; cover shows two rocket ships and photo of Captain Video; based on TV show.
$125

CENTIPEDE, 1983
Board game invented by the author, based on one of the highest-grossing video games; possible future collectible.
nva

CHARLIE CHAN (see THE GREAT CHARLIE CHAN DETECTIVE MYSTERY GAME)

CHECKERED GAME OF LIFE, 1860, 1866, ±1911
Milton Bradley's first game. *Playthings* magazine said this game "was the first 'game with a purpose' and taught a lesson of success through integrity and right living." The original game is rare, as is the version issued in game packs for soldiers during the Civil War; the 1866 and later versions are much more common.
$1000 (and up), 1860 version with spinners attached to the gameboard
$600, red/yellow/black version
$400, 1866 version
$95, ±1911 #4452; 15¼ × 16¼; bldup bd with parts tray; Auc. 10/91 $138; 6/92 $160

CHUTES AND LADDERS, 1943
Classic children's game based on an early morality game from India called SNAKES AND LADDERS.
$20

CINDERELLA, ±1905
#4111; card game; 6¾ × 5½; 33 color illust cards (eight of Prince, Slipper, God-mother, and coach, plus Cinderella), instr card; cover shows barefoot girl on stool in front of hearth.
$30

COMBINATION TIDDLEDY WINKS, 1910s
#4404; S&A; 9¼ × 12½; bldup board with parts tray, die-cut board is 7½ × 8¾, bone disks: 4 large and 12 small, wood counters of 3 colors (dif color counters have dif point values, so one can't determine exact number that came with game), glass cup, two cardboard mats; great McLoughlin-quality cover litho shows two cats, one pitching disk into gold pot, board litho is two dif cats with four target holes in each.
$40

CONETTE, ±1890
S&A; 10 × 6½; wood box 6 × 6¼ has strings across top making grid pattern that will hold paper cones, with scoring litho underneath; approx. 27 paper cones and cardboard cone holder, four wood catapults; cover shows three well-dressed adults playing the game.
$30

A DAY WITH ZIGGY GAME, 1977
#4722; gameboard, bldup with attached spinner, four cardboard Ziggy pieces with dif color feet stands, cards; good and colorful Tom Wilson cover may not help future collectibility of this game since the comic is read mostly by adults (the game is for children), and the hot cartoon characters are those from collectors' childhoods.
$20

DR. BUSBY, 1937
#4184; card game; 5½ × 6¾; 20 cards (five families of four) incl grotesque animal people such as the Bull family where all members have human bodies and large bull heads; coachman family depicts four black stereotypes, two cutting or eating watermelon; instr in cover shows 1905 date; cover is stylized angular doctor taking two pills.
$40 for #4184; more noteworthy for contents than cover.
$50 for #4425; cover shows black character peering from corner.
$30 for #4183A; cover shows bearded gent selling potion to crowd.

DURAN DURAN GAME, 1985
Gameboard, three sets of cards, four plastic pawns, instr booklet; printed bldup with photo and history of the rock group; cards show band members and album covers; one of few games based on a music group—may become hot collectible of the future.
$25

ELLA CINDERS, 1944
#4483; 15 × 9; Bldup bd, four wood markers, wood die, instr in cover; based on cartoon series by Charlie Plumb; cartoon cover shows Ella and nine other characters from strip; aprons also illust with characters; less popular than other cartoon character games.
$45

ENDURANCE RUN (G.O.), ±1930
14½ × 8¼; boxbot bd, spinner, four markers; same series in terms of size, implements, and graphic style as AUTO RACE and GLIDER RACING; cross-collectible, running; uncommon.
$55

FAMILY FEUD, 1977
Based on the 30 min, ABC TV show that premiered 1976.
$15 for the first edition

FAST MAIL RAILROAD GAME, ±1930
#4570; 21 × 14; bldup bd with parts tray, six wood markers, large spinner; train illust shows "NYC & NRRR."
$85

FIRE DEPARTMENT (G.O.), ±1930
#4247; 16 × 15; bldup bd with parts tray, four large wood markers, spinner.
$80

FLAGSHIP AIRFREIGHT, THE AIRLINE CARGO GAME, 1946
#4144, 16½ × 13½; 21 × 16 board, four celluloid planes on wood bases, two packs of destination cards and one pack of cargo cards, two wood dice, instr in cover, ad for THE RICKENBACKER ACE GAME, KEEP 'EM FLYING; board shows plain U.S. map; cover illust shows American Airlines cargo plane and loading truck, and instr indicate "The Special Package Cards used in this game represent the types of merchandise actually carried by Airfreight in the planes of American Airlines System . . . the first flight with freight cargo having been made . . . on October 15, 1944 . . . from LaGuardia Field in New York to Love Field, Dallas, Texas."
$70 Auc. 10/91 $118 (some box damage)

THE FLIGHT TO PARIS, 1927
#4010; 17 × 8¾; two metal open-wing airplanes, spinner with lead base is placed directly on board; board shows path from NY to Paris, capitalizing on Lindbergh flight without using his name; cover shows yellow prop plane with over-the-cockpit wing on purple background with sea and ship across lower section.
$100 Auc. 10/91 $142

FLIP YOUR WIG (see BEATLES FLIP YOUR WIG)

FLIVVER GAME, 1920s
Board game with early auto theme cover; name comes from slang word for inexpensive car; metal cars, spinner is cardboard auto with wheels that turn.
$125

THE NEW ADVENTURES OF GILLIGAN, 1974
Small gameboard, 3-D setup; based on the 1974 cartoon version of the TV show *Gilligan's Island* (1964–67).
$20

G-MEN, 1936
Card game; 5½ × 4; 52 cards (4 × 12 plus 4) with "logo-style" illustrations; instr sheet; based on works of author Carolyn Wells.
$30

GOLLIWOGG, 1907
Card game; 39 cards; instr on partial bldup; cards incl many black characters; the odd-looking black character on the cover is in keeping with the definition of golliwog(g) as "a grotesque black male doll"; based on the character in books by Bertha Upton. Rare black collectible.
$150

GOOD OL' CHARLIE BROWN GAME, 1971
Gameboard plus 3-D setup; based on the cartoon character by Schultz; cute, but not highly valued as a collectible.
$20

GO TO THE HEAD OF THE CLASS, 1938
Classic children's board game; common.
$40 first edition (1938)
$25 other editions through WWII
$15 post war editions

THE GREAT CHARLIE CHAN DETECTIVE MYSTERY GAME, 1937
22½ × 11½; 50 each of four colors of wood buttons, 73 Charlie Chan cards, 10 murder cards, 32 yellow movement cards, two dice, four wood colored discs with holes in center; superb-looking mystery game has cards with interesting "Confucius" type sayings; wonderful and detailed box illust shows Chan entering room; cross-collectible, character, mystery.
$110 Auc. 10/91 $130

HALMA, 1885
For description and history, see HALMA under "Horsman."
$45 for earliest version.

HOWDY DOODY'S T.V. GAME, 1950s
#4240; 19 × 9¾; © Kagran; board shows all characters plus Airodoodle, Peanut Gallery and NBC TV cameras, six cardboard characters on wood stands range to 3″ tall and include Howdy, Flub-a-Dub, Mr. Bluster, Dilly Dally, Clarabell, and Princess S/F/W/S,

four gloss wood pawns, large spinner with Howdy Doody face; illust bldup sections, instr in cover.
$75

HURDLE RACE, 1905, Milton Bradley
#4076, 16 × 11; boxbot bd, four wood markers, large spinner, instr in cover; cover illust of three boys jumping over wood-post hurdles in park setting while other children sit on fence and watch; exceptional board illust is not at all related to cover graphics in style or artistry, but includes many cartoon characters such as Buster Brown, Happy Hooligan, and Foxy Grandpa, two blacks, and various animals in track game hurdle race.
$100

ILLYA KURAYAKIN CARD GAME, 1966
Based on the MAN FROM U.N.C.L.E. TV show. Somewhat common.
$25

GAME OF INDIA, ±1910
#4292, 21¼ × 14¼; bldup bd with parts tray, 16 markers, spinner, instr in cover; PARCHEESI board illust with elephant silhouettes; cover shows great tiger attacking elephant carrying hunters in basket.
$30
$20 for 1932 version #4208, 14¾ × 14¼; bldup bd with parts tray, four metal dice.

JEOPARDY, 1964
Based on the 30-mins, NBC TV show that premiered 1964.
$15

THE JETSONS GAME, 1986
#4514, 15½ × 8, board, cardboard tokens of Jetson family die-cut from bldup, cards. Possible future collectible.
$15

JOLLY TUMBLERS (See TURN OVER)

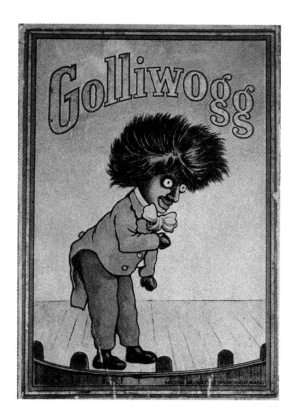

LE CHOC, ±1919
Gameboard showing territory, 48 wood alphabet blocks, with two styles of 8 letters (A through H), each letter having a capturing value higher than the subsequent letter; instructions in English, Spanish, and French; forerunner of STRATEGO, Bradley's war strategy game from 1961; LE CHOC is valued for historical importance, war strategy theme, and outstanding examples of box apron illustration.
$85

LI'L ABNER'S SPOOF GAME, 1950
#4032; card game; 7¼ × 5; four cards for each of ten Al Capp characters, large wood pawns (called "bones"); cover shows Abner, Daisy Mae, and Shmoo playing game. Uncommon.
$65

LITTLE ORPHAN ANNIE GAME, 1927
17x9; gameboard path is concentric circles; cardboard cut-out characters on wood stands, dice; one of few character games where excellently illustrated board and box feature characters talking (cartoon dialog boxes).
$85

GAME OF THE LOST HEIR, ±1910
#4374; card game; 32 cards.
$35

LOTTO, 1932
12 × 8½ × 2½.
$10

GAME OF MAIL, EXPRESS OR ACCOMMODATION, 1895
#4361; 22 × 14½; one-piece buildup and boxbot board with lift-up flap covering parts tray, wood sides box bot; four wood markers, 2 large spinners, cards representing states, cities, and commodities, instr in cover reads "BY MAIL, EXPRESS, OR ACCOMMODATION TRAIN; OR INTERSTATE COMMERCE"; cover litho of speeding locomotive, board is U.S. map.
$225

MAN FROM U.N.C.L.E., 1965
Common card game based on the TV show.
$20

MEN INTO SPACE, 1960
#4003, 19 × 9¾; board is 16 × 18¾; 16 plastic rocketships (four each of four colors), 22 fact cards, spinner and instr on illust bldup; board shows two rockets blasting off from Vandenberg Air Force Base and Cape Canaveral; cover shows men in rocketship XMP-13; based on Ziv productions CBS-TV show starring Bill Lundigan.
$40

MR. BUG GOES TO TOWN, 1955
#4310; 16½ × 8½; path board, bldup spinner with parts tray, eight wood pawns.
$25

MY SHIP COMES LADEN WITH, ±1880
7¼ × 7¼; boxbot bd with letters of alphabet, two sheets of articles (such as Knapp Guns, Guano, Mace, Yolks, Kingfishers) cut up to make little cards; cover shows sailing ship, with design border, all in muted colors.
$50 Auc. 10/91 $50

MYSTERY DATE, 1960s
One of the games most frequently asked for by non-collectors, presumably for nostalgia reasons.
$50

GAME OF THE NEBBS, 1930s
card game, #4041; 5¼ × 3¾; 45 cards include 9 win and lose cards all with dif. illust., and 36 × 4 suits of Nebbs, Potts, Slider, and Max with same illust in each suit.
$30

ON THE MID-WAY, ±1925
#4098, S&A, 15½ × 11½; bldup board with parts tray and die-cut cardboard target stand, 13" long gun, six corks, three cardboard targets , instr in cover with ad for BABE RUTH'S BASEBALL GAME; targets incl black African native; board includes illust of "nine of the popular freaks found in the sides show of a big circus," incl black African Siamese twins.
$75

OUTER LIMITS, 1964
This is a game with great graphics, a TV base, and science fiction theme—all of which make it one of the most desired games of the post-war period.
$180

THE OVERLAND LIMITED, 1920s
#4248; 16 × 15; bldup bd with parts tray, four wood markers, spinner, score card, instr in cover; board shows path with no illust; cover is excellent illust of speeding train engine spewing smoke as cowboy standing near horse waves; orange background and aprons.
$75

PETER CODDLES TRIP TO NEW YORK, 1937
#4378; cover shows silhouette of head.
$25

PINOCCHIO, 1939
19 × 10; based on Walt Disney film; track game; gameboard, large wood pawns, printed buildup.
$95

GAME OF PUSS, ≥1911
#4035; 15¼ × 16¼; bldup bd with parts tray, four wood markers, spinner; same box size and style as ≥1911 CHECKERED GAME OF LIFE suggests same time period; cover shows large illust of open-mouth cat (with written copy that the game "Would Make a Cat Laugh"), two cats boxing, cat couple with him in top hat and her in dress, hat and parasol, and two cats and mouse; board shows four mirror image black cats; exceptional, large cat-lovers' piece.
$125

RACE FOR THE NORTH POLE, ±1909
Thin cardboard box, almost monochromatic; game instructions take up almost one-third of the cover; box aprons stapled together; box-bottom board consists of concentric segmented circles drawn in a single color; excellent example of one of the cheapest games in the Bradley line; cross-collectible, polar theme.
$25

RADIO GAME, 1920s
#4548; 14 × 8; boxbot bd, spinner, four disks.
#4625; 15 × 9 boxbot bd; board is U.S. map showing radio station call letters, time zone spinner, four disks.
$45 either one

GAME OF SCOUTING, 1930s
#4648; 5½ × 7½; wraparound litho, illustrated aprons; 52 cards, all different, illustrating merit badges, patrol signs, scout laws, mottos, oaths, honors, medals, badges, etc.; produced under license of Boy Scouts of America.
$90

GAME OF SKIPPY, 1932
#4836, 14½ × 10½; unusual two-fold board unfolds to 42″ × 6″, with illust throughout of the five Percy Crosby characters; four cardboard playing pieces on wood stands include Skippy, his pal, the policeman, and the Truant Officer; four fancy wood tops; partial die-cut bldup; instr in cover.
$75

GAME OF SNAP, ±1910
#4073; card game; 4¼ × 5½; 20 cards of ten matching pairs, each with phrase using word "snap"; incl illust of dog biting seat of pants of black character; instr in cover; colorful cover shows boy with cap and tie eating from box of ginger snaps.
$35

SNUG HARBOR, ±1930
#4343; 8½ × 16½; 20 tiny metal ship tokens plus two metal submarines tokens, two dice, instr in cover; in the model examined, all the ships are the same color, and some of the ships had thread tied around the mast, probably to distinguish one player's ships from the others, but it is not known if this complicated process was used in all the games; cover shows two-masted boat in harbor at night; board shows harbor scene at two sides, with paths through water from harbor to harbor.
$85

SPIDER AND FLY GAME, ±1925
#4734; 9 × 9; bldup die-cut bd, two wood top spinners, instr in cover; cover is great animated drawing of spider and fly.
$50

SPIN IT, ±1910
S&A #4198, 7¾ × 11; die-cut bldup bd, two wood acorn-shaped tops; cover shows two children playing.
$25

SPY VS SPY,1986
#4600, board, 96 cards, 13 plastic bombs, four pawns, bomb die, four tile racks, label sheet, instr sheet; printed bldup. Based on *Mad* magazine feature; item may increase greatly in value over time.
$15

SQUAILS, 1877
S&A; unusual nomenclature for pieces and moves.
$60

GAME OF THE STATES, 1940
Classic children's board game; common.
$25 for pre-war editions
$15 for post-war editions

THE GAME OF STEEPLE CHASING, 1920s
#4965; 19½ × 10¼; boxbot bd, four wood markers, spinner; track game with excellent illust of horses jumping over long hurdle; cover shows three horses and riders, two jumping bush and one getting stuck in it.
$65

SWING A PEG, ±1890
#4149A; S&A; 9½ × 5¾; wood base and two-part dowel on metal support rod, four cardboard rings; colorful cover illust shows eight people playing game, instr in cover.
$50

TALES OF WELLS FARGO GAME, 1959
#4041, standard size; board is 15¾ × 18¾; six metal horses (two each of three colors), 6 cards with die-cut reward disks, paper money, illust bldup (showing stagecoach robbery) with attached spinner, instr in cover; board shows robbery, western scenes, and Dale Robertson; cover shows train robbery, with inset of Dale Robertson as Jim Hardie; based on TV program.
$85

THREE BEARS, ±1910
#4770; card game; 5½ × 4½; 19 cards incl nine pairs and one Goldie Locks; illust in keeping with classic story; instr card; cards are poorly cut, so part of some illustrations overlap onto other cards; bright color cover shows three dressed bears, Papa with pipe and walking cane.
$35

TIDDLEDY WINKS, ±1920
#4284; S&A; 6½ × 5¼; die-cut bldup bd, glass cup, four celluloid tiddles and 16 winks, two felt pads; cover shows two children and dog, with boy taking his turn; background is colored circles.
$15

TOONERVILLE TROLLEY GAME, 1927
17 × 9; based on Fontaine Fox comic strip; cardboard character cut-outs on wood base; very desirable, difficult to find near mint and complete.
$200

TOY TOWN TARGET WITH REPEATING PISTOL, 1911, Milton Bradley
#4585, S&A target game, 10¼ × 7¼; Foxy Grandpa and two other cartoon characters 3″ high on metal rod attached to two wood posts attached to wood base, six-inch long wood and heavy metal handle gun, 9 wood dowels as ammo; cover shows father and son playing game.
$95

GAME OF TRAFFIC
15¼ × 10¼; bldup bd, large spinner, four wood pawns.
$75

TRIP TO WASHINGTON, 1884
Card game; 3¾ × 4½; subtitled THE WEDDING TRIP OF JEROME AND ELVIRA TO WASHINGTON.
$75

TURN OVER, ±1910
Exact same game as JOLLY TUMBLERS which has a cover that looks as though it is made up of two illustrations from other games. (This practice was not uncommon; in one case three Bradley games have similar covers that seem to all come from the same larger piece of artwork.) The gameboard for the two games (the boards differ in size but the graphics are the same) has nothing to do with *either* cover—the board illustration shows Foxy Grandpa and the Katzenjammer Kids.
$85 for TURN OVER
$50 for JOLLY TUMBLERS

THE TWIGGY GAME
$30

TWISTER, 1966
This game owes its fame primarily to Johnny Carson and Eva Gabor—the game, requiring various body-bending feats, was demonstrated by the well-endowed Gabor on the "Tonight" show, and the public couldn't get enough.
$10

UNCLE WIGGILY'S NEW AIRPLANE GAME, 1920s
#4496; separate board and parts box 6½ × 5¼; rhyming red and white cards, instr in box cover.
$45

VIDEO VILLAGE, 1960
Classic Bradley game is one of the most popular for noncollectors, appreciated as a nostalgia item.
$25

WALKING THE TIGHTROPE, ≥1920
This game uses the identical board from McLoughlin's TIGHT ROPE, which was sold at least fifty years earlier in 1870.
$70

WYHOO, 1906
#4049; card game; 6 × 8½; 110 cards (ten each of ten numbers, plus 10 Wyhoo cards), instr in cover; great litho cover shows costumed elfin character riding grasshopper.
$45

Built-Rite Toys
  Warren Built-Rite
  Lafayette, IN
  ±1934–±1975
  Warren Co.
  ±1975–1990s

Warren Paper Products Co. was founded in 1921 as a paper box manufacturer and produced a line of toys in the 1930s; a 1934 patent might have been the first year of the paper toys, some of

which were "toy-games," such as the OLD TIME SHOOTING GALLERY.

OLD TIME SHOOTING GALLERY, 1940
Rubber band-shooting wood gun with stand-up folded animal cardboard targets that sit on 3-D stand; instr in cover; company name, date, and copyright info were printed on the end of the wraparound litho and are therefore located on the inside of the boxbot and cover aprons.
$25

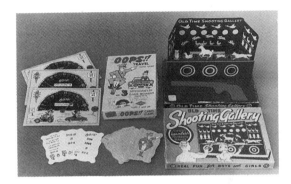

OOPS!! TRAVEL CARD GAME
$15

POPEYE'S SLIDING BOARDS AND LADDERS GAME, 1958
$40

300 MILE RACE, ±1955,
18 × 13; bldup bd with corner parts tray and attached spinner, 30 cardboard numbered cars, wood marker (though instr say plastic), two wood dice, instr on board; board is track with charts, no illust; cover shows cars racing with stadium in background, one car crashing and in flames, full illust is within profile outline of large car, "30 stock cars run at one time." EX, car pieces uncut, contents unused, cover has orig. price sticker,½″ apron separated, aprons taped.
$50

Lorenzo Burge
MA
±1844

THE NEW GAME OF THE AMERICAN REVOLUTION, 1844
Folded board, sold by J.C. (or "G") Hovey, lithography by Thayer.
$1600

THE MERRY CARDS
ref

Alfred Butts
10 Park Ave., New York, NY
1931–1948

The inventor of SCRABBLE, born in 1899, produced a few games before one of them turned into what was to become the country's most popular word game. More than 25 years after Selchow and Righter first made SCRABBLE, Butts contacted the company and was given the opportunity to do another game, ALFRED'S OTHER GAME, which came out in 1981; his picture appears on the box.

LEXIKO AND NEW ANAGRAMS, 1932
11 × 4 × 2; tile game where score was based on length of word and bonuses depending on letters used; letter tiles were made by gluing blueprint paper onto wood; the game was offered to Milton Bradley and Parker Brothers in 1934, but they turned it down; between 150 and 200 sets were made.
nva

CRISS-CROSS, 1937 or 1938
First SCRABBLE prototype; drawn with india ink on tracing cloth and then made into a blueprint, so these games are white letters on blue; number of tiles of each letter and places of premium squares on the board are different from SCRABBLE. Rare.
nva

CRISS CROSS WORDS, 1938
Refined version of CRISS-CROSS, with varied starting spaces (not in the center) and different counts and values of the letter tiles; approximately 125 sets were made, 25 of which were distributed through a Connecticut bookstore owner and are marked " © 1942 Chester Ives" or "C.B.I."; no copyright was obtained, and Ives was drafted in 1943, ending that business association. Scarce.
$150 and up

Cadaco Ltd.
San Leandro, CA (1935–36)
Oakland, CA (1937)
    Cadaco-Ellis
    Cadaco
Chicago, IL (1938–present)

Cadaco (which was originally Cadaco Ltd. and became Cadaco-Ellis upon its move to Chicago) has been a major, prolific producer of games in the U.S. for over fifty years, providing a range from inexpensive, low end items such as PARTY PACKAGE to highly collectible licensed products such as MARLIN PERKINS' ZOO PARADE; it is noted for its long run of ALL STAR BASEBALL (see ETHAN ALLEN). The company name comes from brothers Charles *and* Donald (Mazer) *and* company; Cadaco is now a division of Rapid Mounting and Finishing Co.
    The most valuable games are those few Cadaco Ltd. games that were made in California. Games that can be found for around $25 or less include ALL-AMERICAN FOOTBALL (1961; based on system of ALL STAR BASEBALL but without named players), AMERICAN DERBY (1945), HOOKEY (1940s S&A FISHPOND game that retailed for $1.60), PARTY PACKAGE (1939), SKIP-A-WORD (1953), SPACE PILOT (1951), TREASURE HUNT (±1942, which retailed for $1.40; and 1950), WHODUNIT (1959), and YANKEE DOODLE (© 1940 by Crandall & Ellis).

CHUTZPAH, 1967
One of few games from a major company based on a Jewish theme; "Chutzpah" translates into "unmitigated gall."
$15

ELMER LAYDEN'S SCIENTIFIC FOOTBALL GAME, 1936
20 × 10¼"; two-fold board with four attached dials and die-cut to hold sliding football and 10-yard marker; instr in cover; cover illust of Layden plus letter from him dated Feb. 24, 1936, to Cadaco on stationery from the University of Notre Dame, where he was the athletic director.
$175

ETHAN ALLEN'S ALL-STAR BASEBALL, yearly since 1941
Classic baseball game using cardboard disks that fit over block spinner attached to bldup bd; each disc has name of player and various sized sections relating to the player's ability in different areas; STRATEGIC ALL-STAR BASEBALL has additional plays and is more complex, but did not sell well; inventor Allen was Major League outfielder from 1926–1938; game value depends on players included, with Hall of Fame players more desirable; common, and not highly desirable, but likely to show higher-than-average increase in value over time.
$60 for the most desirable sets from the 1950s
$15 for later, less desirable editions
$50 for STRATEGIC ALL-STAR BASEBALL

FOTO-ELECTRIC FOOTBALL, 1930s and 1965
$75 for early all-wood box version with electric light
$20 for later versions

FOTO WORLD, 1935
Possibly the first Cadaco game.
$150

JINGO, 1942
Combination jigsaw puzzle and bingo; indiv die-cut bingo style boards, puzzle pieces; $1.90 retail.
ref

LITTLE BLACK SAMBO, 1952
Instructions in cover read 1945, boxwrap reads 1951, board reads 1952. Four large wood pieces, spinner; illust cover is Sambo under umbrella with four tiger heads looking on; great board has Sambo with tiger and other animals.
$70

MARLIN PERKINS' ZOO PARADE, 1955
$90

SKIP-A-CROSS, 1953
Cadaco licensed this SCRABBLE copy directly from Selchow & Righter.
$15

TOP-OGRAPHY, 1941
Bldup board, pegs, alphabet top, hour-glass timer; a top and map (geography) game; $2.55 retail.
$40

TOUCHDOWN, 1937
26 × 15; boxbot bd; one of the earliest Cadaco games; excellent cover litho of football player with ball getting tackled.
$110

TRANSPORT PILOT, 1938
$40

WIZARD OF OZ, 1974
Board game based on the MGM movie.
$25

Capex Co. Inc.
615 South Bend, Evanston, IL
1940s and '50s

THE EGG AND I, 1947
10¼" × 7; one-piece board, wooden houses, wooden "egg" spinner, cards; it may seem strange that this game is based on "the thrills and hardships of starting a chicken ranch . . ." until one realizes the game is based on a lesser-known Claudette Colbert/Fred MacMurray movie based on the bestselling Betty McDonald story.
$50

GALLOPING GOLF, 1950
ref

I-QUBES, 1948
Word game; seven letter dice in a leather snap case; exact same game as that produced by the Arl-Hi Co. of Arlington Heights, IL, and probably purchased from Arl-Hi.
$15

Cardinal Industries
Brooklyn, NY, 1945–1976
Long Island City, NY 1976–Present

Cardinal began on the corner of Keep and Hope Streets in Brooklyn in 1945 and is one of the oldest family-owned game companies in the U.S. today. Before its game manufacturing the company made large wooden carnival wheels for carnival booths and church bazaars. Its first game product was plastic dominoes, distributed mostly in Texas. The company manufactured basic mass market staple games such as checkers, chess, and backgammon; Omar Sharif is shown on one of the backgammon games, and chess champion Victor Korchnai is shown on a chess box from around 1980. The company has also produced dice, Mah Jongg, Pachisi, and Labyrinth for decades.

In the early 1950s, owner Les Berger acquired an old plastic fabricator to make molded plastic. The company moved to Long Island City in 1976. Around that time it produced RUMMY-O, which predates Pressman's RUMMY CUBE. The company started acquiring licenses around 1980, and produced such games as THE $25,000 PYRAMID and GENERAL HOSPITAL (1981/82); in 1991 it came out with THE SIMPSON'S MYSTERY OF LIFE board game. Les Berger said his greatest competition during the early years was from E.S. Lowe. Cardinal's early, traditional games have little value to collectors; the few licensed products and more unusual items are of more interest.

GENERAL HOSPITAL, 1981/82
Based on the long-running TV soap, which began in 1963.
$20

THE SIMPSONS MYSTERY OF LIFE, 1990
Gameboard, four cardboard Simpson characters on plastic stands, cards, agenda.
nva

$25,000 PYRAMID, 1981/82
Based on the TV quiz show that began as the *$10,000 Pyramid* in 1973 and became the *$50,000 Pyramid* in 1981.
$15

The Carrom Co.
Carrom Industries
Ludington, MI
1889–1980s

The company, known mostly for its large wooden Carrom boards (square boards with corner pockets played with small, rounded wood pieces instead of balls), also produced bagatelle games and a few board or S&A games, such as DRIVE 'N PUTT, FOX HUNT, KIKIT, and SPIN BOWL (all ≤1947). The Carrom boards range in value from $75 for the oldest, most intricate designed boards to $25 for the newer boards; the boards are generally easy to find but hard to sell, as most collectors of boxed games do not collect these larger items. The company now operates under the name Merdell. (See also **Archarena Co.**).

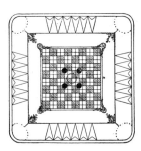 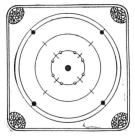

THE BIG GAME HUNT, ≤1947
Dart board.
$25

GUSHER, 1946
15½ × 8; 15 × 15 wood frame board,½″ thick, with die-cut peg holes, metal oil wells 1⅛″ high, wood markers, money, cardboard disks, parts box, instr. sheet.
$75

JOCKEY, 1920s
S&A; box with 6½ × 30 wood board with four cardboard race strips, each strip jumping forward and back as four strings are pulled, causing four metal horses to jump forward along straight track.
$60

NOK-HOCKEY, ≤1947
Popular table game during the '50s worth more for its nostalgic and play value than anything else.
$35

N.D. Cass
Athol, MA
1895–present
games: 1920s and '30s

This company produced mostly children's furniture and playthings and very few games, primarily wood skill and action items.

BOWLING ALLEY, ±1921
$20

H.B. Chaffee Mfg. Co.
451/455 W. 125th St.
New York, NY
±1880–≥1903
Chaffee & Selchow
±1897–±1899
New York, NY

Herbert B. Chaffee operated his own company in the late 1800s and joined forces with Fred M. Selchow for about two years just before the turn-of-the-century. Chaffee & Selchow, prolific for such a short period of operation, produced both board and card games, including an 1899 series of card games based on the Spanish American War (The Starry Flag Series). The company's board game covers were often of exceptional beauty; almost assuredly a connection exists between the company and McLoughlin, partially because of the similar standard and quality, but also because some games have been found (such as THE YOUNG ATHLETE) with the Chaffee & Selchow name on the cover and the McLoughlin name on the instructions.

The connection between Chaffee & Selchow and E.G. Selchow/Selchow & Righter is evident, as H.B. Chaffee was the only other company to publish PARCHEESI (under that exact spelling), the game trademarked by Selchow; in 1897 and 1898 Fred Selchow and Elisha Selchow lived at the same address (see also "Selchow & Righter").

Chaffee & Selchow box covers are noted for the gold outline surrounding figures in the illustration.

H.B. Chaffee

BATTLE FOR THE FLAG, 1887
ref

PARCHEESI, ±1880
Standard game with attractive illustrations of maidens (including one with uncovered breasts, rare in early games) in each corner.
$150

SNAP DRAGON, 1903
24 × 23½″ cloth board is a pin-the-tail variant requiring the blindfolded player to pin the cloth "Chinamen" as close as possible to the dragon's mouth.
$225

Chaffee & Selchow

Games include THE GAME OF CAT, THE OLD WOMAN WHO LIVED IN A SHOE, and TIDDLEDY WINKS and THE MERRY GO ROUND (1898), which sold at auction in 1992 for $3000.

THE ABCDARIAN, 1899
Word-building and spelling game with small letter cards as in ANAGRAMS; cover illust of children playing the game.
$55

BASKETBALL, 1898
22½ × 13½; cover shows women playing the game. Scarce and highly valued.
nva

THE BELL BOY GAME, 1898
Large board game; exceptional cover litho shows hotel front desk with black character peering in through doorway.
$700

BEN HUR
nva

THE BICYCLE RACE, 1898
Standard-size board game.
$550

THE COWBOY GAME, 1898
Standard size board game; cowboy and Indian on cover.
$350 Auc. 6/92 $325 (taped)

DEWEY AT MANILA, 1899
Card game.
$65

LEE AT HAVANA, 1899
$90

MILES AT PORTO RICO [*sic*], 1899
$80

OLD MAID, 1898
Board game.
$45

OLD MOTHER GOOSE, ±1898
8 × 16; excellent litho cover shows elderly woman with broom flying on back of large goose, with landscape beneath.
$175

PARLOR GOLF, ≤1897
$90

GAME OF POOL, 1898
23 × 15; extraordinary lithography
$750

(Krim collection)

GAME OF RED RIDING HOOD, 1898
Small board game.
$85

ROOSEVELT AT SAN JUAN, 1899
Card game.
$85

SCHLEY AT SANTIAGO BAY, 1899
Card game.
$80

SILVERLOCKS AND THE THREE BEARS, 1898
nva

GAME OF TIGER HUNT, 1899
Large board game.
$450

TURNOVER, 1898
Gameboard 17¼" square shows children playing and frogs jumping; strategy game.
$85

THE VASSAR BOAT RACE, 1899
22 × 13; exceptional box cover lithography showing nine women rowing.
$700

WAR AND DIPLOMACY, 1899
Card game; 5¼" × 4¼"; 65 cards incl 32 letter cards (8 × 4), 16 War Pennant cards, and 17 Diplomacy Flag of Truce cards (though instructions call for 17 and 16 respectively); instr sheet; © 1898 J.C. Meem, 201 Warren St., Brooklyn; cover shows officer on horse during battle; gilt lines in drawing bring out the horse and rider.
$85

THE YOUNG ATHLETE, 1898
Large board game; bldup bd with parts stored under lift-up section of board (McLoughlin style); wonderful illust shows men in old fashioned gym attire working out on gymnastic equipment.
$700

Championship Games Inc.
P.O. Box 1000, Southport, CT 06490
1960s

This sport game company by Tod Lansing produced such titles as CHAMPIONSHIP BASEBALL (1966), CHAMPIONSHIP BASKETBALL, CHAMPIONSHIP GOLF, and PRO QUARTERBACK; the games, valued under $20 each, are of interest to players rather than collectors.

Cincinnati Game Co.
Cincinnati, OH
1900–±1924
games: 1900–1905

(See **U.S. Playing Card Co.**)

ASTRONOMY, 1905
$25

GAME OF FORTUNES, 1902
$75

FRACTIONS, 1902
$15

MYTHOLOGY, 1900
$25

C.M. Clark Publishing Co., Inc.
Boston, MA
1900s

Though it is not known whether Clark produced more than one game, STAGE, it is one of a very few games based on the theater.

STAGE, 1904
Card game; 7½″ × 2¾″; 66 cards include seven picture cards each of seven areas: Grand Opera, Tragedy, Drama, Comedy, Comic Opera, Vaudeville, and Farce; cards picture stage actors of the period, including Edwin Booth and William Gillette.
$50

E.O. Clark
±1898–±1900
Clark & Sowdon
≤1892–±1897
New York, NY

E. (Edgar) O. Clark was the successor to Clark & Sowdon. Most of its games were marked "Tokalon Series." The large board games from both companies usually offered exceptional box cover art.

E.O. Clark

THE CHARGE, ±1898
19 × 10; boxbot bd with wood sides, two wood pawns (kings) and 24 wood pawns (soldiers); classic strategy game pitting the two against the 24, the object being for the soldiers to trap the kings before the kings eliminate too many of the soldiers; cover shows attacking soldiers on horseback, American flag waving.
$300

FISH POND, 1890s
#325; S&A; 13 × 11; boxbot bd, bent cardboard fish that stand up on bd, wood poles with string and hook; bd illust shows nice lake scene, two boys fishing; cover shows three boys in boat in lily pond.
$50

THE HIPPODROME, ±1900
$175

THE OWL AND THE PUSSY CAT, ±1900
$350

POSTAL TELEGRAPH BOY, ±1900
$150

GAME OF ROBINSON CRUSOE FOR LITTLE FOLKS, ±1900
Card game; 4½″ × 3½″; 21 cards (7 × 3), instr in cover; seven dif illust include animals, Crusoe, Friday, and a Cannibal.
$45

ROUGH RIDERS, ±1898
Based on Teddy Roosevelt's band of horse soldiers during the Spanish American War.
$200

THE SCOUT, ±1900
$175

Clark & Sowdon

Games include COONIES, MOUNT THE DONKEY, THE OWL AND THE PUSSYCAT, SING A SONG OF SIX PENCE, and THREE LITTLE KITTENS.

AUTHORS ILLUSTRATED, 1893
Card game; cards have exceptional illustrations of the authors and, more interestingly, scenes depicting their works; cover illustration is intricate as well, making this one of the best AUTHORS game published.
$45

THE GAME OF BROWNIES
$300

CHESSINDIA, ±1895
#300, 15½″ × 15½″; boxbot bd with wood sides, 16 wood markers, spinner, instr in cover; PARCHEESI style gameboard has interesting illust of cannons in corner start areas and fortress towers in center; cover illust, which is unrelated to board illust, shows tiger attacking back of elephant with elephant driver and three men in carriage on top.
$40 Auc. 6/92 $90

HIDDEN AUTHORS
$20

HUNTING THE RABBIT, ±1895
#326, 15 × 7¾″, one-piece board, two dif shape pawns, two markers, illustrated spinner, instr in cover; cover and track board show two dif scenes of hunter, two dogs, and rabbit in field; two or three-player game.
$115

JUMBLES, 1893
#104
ref

GAME OF OLD MAID AS PLAYED BY MOTHER GOOSE, 1892
$30

PAWS & CLAWS, ±1895
#203; card game; 5¾″ × 4½″; 29 cards (14 pairs and one odd), instr in cover; 29 dif illust of costumed animals in pairs (Mr. Peter Pig, Mrs. Peter Pig); unusual cover illust of three dressed animals (owl, cat, rabbit) riding a donkey being stopped at toll house by a bird.
$60

PETER CODDLES DINNER PARTY
#103; card game; cover shows animals around table.
$35

RIP VAN WINKLE, ±1890
#350, 10¼″ × 19½″, boxbot bd with wood sides, four wood pawns, spinner, instr in cover; path board is country scene, cover illust is old white-bearded man with gun and mountain scene background; Tokalon series; advertises CHESSINDIA.
$125

RONDAMEE
ref

TETE-A-TETE, 1892
$75

GAME OF WANG, 1892
$45

YACHT RACE, 1890s
#427, 25 × 12¾″, boxbot bd with wood sides, parts box 5″ × 5″ has yacht picture, title, and Clark & Sowdon name, four cardboard yachts 2½″ high and 2½″ at base, wood stands, spinner; notable in size and beauty; (there is also a smaller version).
$225

(Krim collection)

Clover Games
New York, NY
1940s
BAGDAD, THE GAME OF THE EAST, 1940
#324; 17 × 12; one-piece bd 12″ × 12″ with attached 6″ diam.
spinner wheel, 16 wood pawns, instr. sheet; not PARCHEESI-style,
but mostly lucky number game.
$40

T. Cohn Inc.
(Game Gems)
New York, NY
1960s
BEWITCHED, 1965
Gameboard, four cardboard Darrin figures and stands, two spin-
ners, cards; cover shows Elizabeth Montgomery on broom and
Agnes Moorehead; based on the 1964–72 TV show.
$35

KENTUCKY JONES, 1964/65
Based on the TV show that prompted star Dennis Weaver to leave
Gunsmoke . Scarce.
$40

GILLIGAN'S ISLAND,1965
Based on the original TV show. Scarce and in demand; subject to
large price fluctuations.
$200

L.J. Colby & Co.
3226 Forest Ave., Chicago, IL
GAME OF AMERICAN BIRDS
ref

Game of American Birds

Ornithological Lore

By RUTH A. CRAPO.

Every line in this game shows the love
of the author for

"Great nature's happy commoners,
That haunt in woods, in meads and flowery gardens,
Rifle the sweets and taste the choicest fruits,
Yet scorn to ask the lordly owner's leave."

Every child should be acquainted with a
game which cannot fail to awaken an
interest in the appearance, habits and
preservation of our feathered songsters

Published by L. J. COLBY & CO.,

3226 Forest Ave., Chicago.

GAMES OF CHARACTERS, ≤1889
Series of question and answer card games about people, places,
and events.
$25 for any game in the series except BIBLE CHARACTERS ($15)

LITERATURE GAME, 1897
This game was © by A.W. Mumford (see listing) whose company
produced the GAME OF INDUSTRIES.
$25

Colorful Creations
Box 125, Station F, New York 16, NY
1940s

This relatively unknown company may not have made a significant
contribution to the industry, but it did produce one of the smallest
boxed games ever made.

VEST POCKET QUOITS, 1944
S&A; 1¾″ × 2¾″; six bone rings, 3″ high wood post, post stand
attached to box bottom; this miniature ring toss was touted as "the
world's smallest, streamlined version."
$45

Colorful Products, Inc.
NEW FRONTIER, 1962
Envelope 11 × 19½″; thin cardboard board, 12 cardboard markers
(4 × 3), 56 cards, paper money, pad to make additional money,
two dice, instr sheet; Deed cards range from "Distrust Saving-Loan"
to Billie Sol's Grain Stockpile"; MONOPOLY-style board and game
shows covered wagon in center with "New Frontier, JFK & Bust!"
and "Go" space is replaced by "Move Fawhwad"; envelope shows
empty rocking chair marked "Seat of Government" and money is
referred to as "Jack"; subtitled "The game nobody can win"; good
satire, good political/Kennedy collectible that may rise quickly in
price.
$50

Morton E. Converse Co.
Winchendon, MA
late 1800s, early 1900s

Morton Converse was born in New Hampshire in 1837, served in
the Civil War, served on the State Senate of Mass., and died in
1917. His 1883 game was possibly the first patent for a bean bag
game in the U.S.

FABA BAGA OR PARLOR QUOITS, 1883
22 × 17 wood board with two holes, pat. #285,396 "which covers
any board supported in an inclined position, having any opening
through which an object may be tossed."
$65

Corey Games
Everett, MA
late 1930s–40s

Corey was an active game company during the late 1930s and
1940s; some games had themes of patriotism and war victory.
Games include AIR ATTACK, PIRATE'S ISLAND, SPINO, SUFFOLK
DOWNS RACING GAME, and THING A JIGS (all ≤1947). In the early
'40s, Corey was a division of the Quality Paper Box Co., Boston. A
1947 listing shows a factory at 8 New St. in East Boston.

AL DJEMMA, 1944
Parcheesi-style board game.
$45

BARAGE, 1941
$30

BLOCKADE, 1941
20¼ × 15; one-piece boxbot and buildup grid pattern showing two
islands and land around board perimeter;12 × 6 cardboard piece

with four attached dials; two small parts boxes, one containing 20 cardboard discs indicating food, oils, metals, and arms, and one with 20 metal pieces: six warships, six cargo ships, four subs, and four planes; instr in cover; subtitled A GAME FOR ARMCHAIR ADMIRALS.
$50

HIPPETY HOP, ≤1947
$40

QUESTO, 1939
Word game with boards with 36 squares and letter cards to be placed in the squares to make words in various directions.
$15

RAFFLES, 1939
14¼ × 3¾; linen paper board, plastic markers, three dice; gambling game.
$30

STRATEGY, GAME OF ARMIES, 1938
Gameboard, 40 pawns, two dice, instr in cover; some sets may have original instr sheet © Nathan Reinherz.
$30

YANKEE TRADER, 1941
Board game with ships.
$40

Charles M. Crandall Co.
Montrose, PA
games: late 1800s

Crandall was noted mostly for building blocks and the PIGS IN CLOVER game (1889), which was distributed under the Selchow & Righter name. Crandall games (not blocks) are rare.

MOTHER GOOSE BOWLING GAME, 1884
S&A; 18¼″ × 10½″ × 5½″; litho on wood; five adjoining nursery tale houses (Jack Spratt, Dame Trott, Mother Goose, Tom Tucker, Jack Horner) with the respective characters on top. In this exceptional ball-rolling target game, when the ball hit a pin protruding from the front of one of the houses, the character would pop up.
$850

The Cracker Jack Co.

Noted for "surprise in every box" toys, Cracker Jack occasionally offered a game premium in its caramel-coated popcorn.

MIDGET AUTO RACE, ±1930
$15

THE GOLD RUSH, ±1930
Card game; 1¼″ × 1¾″.
$15

Craig Hopkins (See Hopkins)

Creative Designs, Inc.
Creative Ideas, Inc.
Gatesville, TX
Creative Products
508 East. Howard Ave., Decatur, GA

Creative Designs/Creative Products:
WA-HOO, ±1950
$25

Creative Ideas:
MYSTERY CHECKERS, ±1950
$20

Wm. Crosby
Boston, MA
1840s
GAME OF THE RACES, 1844
$1300

THE STRIFE OF GENIUS, 1840s
Invented "by a lady."
$150

Cutler & Saleeby Co.
Springfield, MA
±1910–≥1927
There is no listing for this company in city directories between 1890 and 1930 and no information is known about either of the two names.

ANAGRAMS
$25

INDIA BOMBAY, ±1910
#4020; 11 × 10; one-piece bldup boxbot bd with parts tray, 16 wood markers, two dice; Parcheesi variant showing four animals in start squares and Indian temple in center; cover is excellent illust of two tigers attacking an elephant.
$40

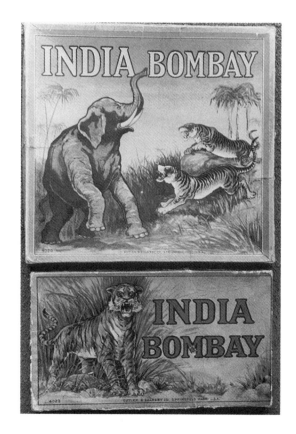

INDIA BOMBAY, ±1920
#4023; 10¾″ × 6; board is 10¼″ square; box has wraparound litho and printed aprons; cover shows roaring tiger.
$30

SKI-HI, NEW YORK TO PARIS, 1927
#2117; cover shows tip of Manhattan and Eiffel Tower across the ocean, with biplanes overhead; theme capitalizes on Lindbergh flight.
$80

Charles Darrow
40 Westview St., Germantown, PA
1933–34

DARROW MONOPOLY, 1934
20½″ × 10¾″; gameboard has © 1933 Chas. B. Darrow in corner of jail space, no patent numbers or pat. pending on board; instructions are on the buildup, marked "1934 Rules" and with Darrow's address; money has no lettering, just geometric design in denominations of $1, $5, $10, $20, $50, $100, and $500; 17 white Community Chest cards, 16 tan Chance cards; 28 property cards including utilities and railroad, all solid color printed one side only; assorted wood houses, hotels, dice; box is white box with blue-lettered "Monopoly" written in red stripe across the cover; this is one of the earliest commercially produced MONOPOLY games, before it was sold to Parker Brothers; though Darrow's MONOPOLY has brought high prices at auction, it is felt there are few collectors willing to pay that price and the actual value of the game is considerably lower. (Darrow prototypes, printed on oilcloth and sometimes with circular boards, are rare and are worth tens of thousands of dollars.) Scarce.
$2,500 Auc. 9/88 $2,400; 11/91 $4,000 (aprons torn off, one missing)

F.G. Decker and O.F. Decker
Buffalo, NY
late 1880s, early 1890s

Makers of educational card games, mostly question and answer style in the areas of history and geography; games include GAME OF CITIES, GAME OF THE STATES, GAME OF THE WORLD (all ±1890).

BIBLE CHARACTERS, ±1890
$35

A GAME OF CHARACTERS (AMERICAN/FOREIGN), 1889
Card game; card pack with 100 cards, with a total of 700 questions.
$40

James L. Decker Products Co.
8509–15 Higuera St
Culver City, CA
1940s

The company manufactured primarily plastics and S&A games such as ZOWIE HORSESHOE GAME, and PUT-N-TAKE SPIN GAME (both ≤1947, both valued under $20).

Degen, Estes & Co.
22 Cornhill
Boston, MA
1860s

H.V. Degen and his son Henry Dutton Degen took on as an apprentice Dana Estes (who later became co-publisher of the famous "Zigzag" and "Chatterbox" book series) and formed a partnership with him after the Civil War. The partnership disolved in 1867 when the Degens moved to New York. An early ad read "publishers of TOY BOOKS AND GAMES" [sic]. Some of their products included THE CHECKERED GAME OF LIFE, MODERN HIEROGLYPHICS, PATRIOT HEROES, and WHAT IS IT?, OR THE WAY TO MAKE MONEY, all of which are scarce or rare.

PUCKS PORTFOLIO, 1866
Card game.
$100

Deluxe Game Corp.
New York, NY
mid-1900s

One of Deluxe's games, FLIP IT, was marked "ATWO," suggesting a tie in with American Toy Works (see below).

FLIP IT, ±1940
#27; boxbot bd plus second board on box cover, two metal cars, die, instr sheet; box cover is the same as game of the same name by American Toy Works (see listing), but the game is completely different and doesn't match the box (for instance, the box cover reads "no dice," but a die is included, and the S&A flipping action of the original game has been eliminated).
$30

ZIP-TOP, ±1940
#42; action game; wood sided box, eight pins, one metal windup top, typed instr sheet; of greater value to top collectors than game collectors.
$55

Dexter Wayne (See **Wayne**)

The D.M.R. Co.
404 Deerfield Lane, Louisville, KY 40207
1960s

Maker of sports games such as LET'S BOWL A GAME and LET'S PLAY GOLF.

LET'S PLAY BASKETBALL, ±1965
Card game.
$15

Geo. B. Doan & Co
300 Wabash Ave., Chicago, IL
early 1900s

Most games were listed as "Chicago Game Series." Games produced in or before 1907 included AMERST (a three-in-one game with circular board divided into 20 sections; retailed for 50¢), BANZAI (a word game with embossed wood letter tiles), BASE BALL (retailed for 25¢), NAVAL BATTLE (retailed for 35¢), PUTTING ON THE LID (a skill and action game), and the TWENTIETH CENTURY FUN BOX, which contained four of the above games and retailed for $1.

WORTHWHILE, 1907
Card game; 6½″ × 3¾″; 68 cards, 60 of which have sayings/quotations; 32-page instr booklet lists seven games to play, incl "Dodo," "Dicker," "Privilege," "Show Me," "Tryo," and "Union."
$40

Wallie Dorr Co.
35 Murray St., New York, NY
early 1900s

FOOLISH QUESTIONS, 1931
Card game; 5¼″ × 3¾″; 52 illustrated answer cards are comical answers to questions on instr sheet (for example, Foolish Question No. 45, on which answer card pictures children playing marble game in field, "Morning, children; playing marbles?"; answer, "No, you old mummy, we're studying Greek in a Chinese laundry"); numbered joker card; red box with black lettering has man asking, "What's this—A game?"; cover and card illustrations by famous illustrator Rube Goldberg, and game is based on his cartoon strip of the same name.
$45

TOURING, 1906
The famous TOURING games by Parker Brothers were taken from the Wallie Dorr Co., holders of patent # 836532 for TOURING.
$40

Wm. F. Drueke & Sons
Grand Rapids, MI

Drueke is known for traditional items and for reissuing other companies' games. Games in its line were often given Volume numbers. The games, often sold in gift shops, are sought more for their play value than collector's value. A company called Metro sold the same games as Drueke, though they were given higher volume numbers, suggesting Metro took over some of Drueke's line.

Sarah H. Dudley
Berlin, Mass

OUR BIRD FRIENDS, 1901
Card game; 2¾″ × 4½″; 56 cards, each illustrating (in b&w) and listing facts about dif bird; instr sheet containing many testimonials.
$30

Durable Toy and Novelty
8 Morris St., Paterson, NJ
New York, NY
1940s

HUNTER'S SHOT, ≤1947
ref

ROL-A-LITE, ±1947
10″ diameter metal tin 2½″ high with 12 holes for marbles in the top; tin opens for marble storage; litho on metal shows flags of 24 countries, world map, and PUT AND TAKE game; other games that could be played include "Hi Lo," "Odd or Even," "Play the Flags," "Play the Marbles," and "Roulette."
$75

S.O.S., ±1947
Bagatelle; 23 × 14; title stands for "Stay Off Street, Stay on Sidewalk"; great litho on metal.
$70

Ed-U-Cards Mfg. Co.
248 W. 23rd St., New York 11, NY
Long Island City
1940s through the '60s

Manufacturer of small card games for children; at one time a division of KPB industries in Bethlehem, PA. Games include ABC, PARKS, and STORIES (all ≤1947), and low value games OLD MAID (≤1947), and TRACKS (±1950).

COWBOYS & INDIANS, 1949
$25

NEW YORK WORLD'S FAIR CHILDREN'S CARD GAME, 1964
Card game; 4¾″ × 3¾″; 36 cards with nine color illust of exhibits at the 1964 World's Fair in New York.
$25

Educational Card & Game Co.
New York, NY
1920s

BILD-A-WORD, 1929
Common game using cardboard letters to make words—(note the phonetic spelling in the title of this educational word game); game came with dictionary, which is often missing (and the absence of which lowers the game's value by 50%).
$35

HEROES OF AMERICA, 1920s
$35

Einson-Freeman Publishing Corp.
Einson-Freeman Co. Inc.
30–28 Starr & Borden Avenues, Long Island City, NY
±1933–1935

Morris M. Einson was a lithographer and a pioneer in window and store display advertising (he created an early cardboard robot that sharpened razor blades in drugstore windows). His company began producing cardboard advertising jigsaw puzzles in 1932 and was a major puzzle manufacturer into the '40s; game production, however, appears to be limited to the mid-1930s. Einson-Freeman also acquired licenses to such figures as Dick Tracy, Popeye, and Walt Disney characters. In 1935 Einson relinquished control of his firm to the younger men in his employ. Leo Einson was the company treasurer; the company's capital in 1933 was just over $633 thousand.

The company logo pictured a book and the word "Funland," and is similar to the logo of another Long Island City company, Stoll & Einson, which operated during the same period and used the word "Playjoy" with its logo; the Einson of Einson-Freeman may be the same Einson as the one of Stoll & Einson, but this has not been confirmed. (See also **Stoll & Einson and Stoll & Edwards.**)

DICK TRACY DETECTIVE GAME, 1933
#203; unicolor box cover is blue on blue; four cardboard tokens, spinner; Famous Artists Syndicate, similar to POPEYE THE SAILOR SHIPWRECK GAME.
$75

(Fink collection)

GAME OF LITTLE BLACK SAMBO, 1934
#207
$60

MACY'S PIRATE TREASURE HUNT, 1942
Macy's premium consisting of a 10 × 15 envelope with the board drawn on it and the implements inside, including four ships and a spinner, and a pirate's hat, eye patch, and periscope; coloring the enclosed parrot might entitle the purchaser to a $10 gift certificate in Macy's Toy Dept.
$35

PIONEERS OF THE SANTA FE TRAIL, 1935
$40

POPEYE THE SAILOR SHIPWRECK GAME, 1933
#202; two-color box shows blue ink on red background; King Features, similar to DICK TRACY DETECTIVE GAME
$75

ROLD GOLD PRETZEL TOSS, 1935
S&A; advertising game by The American Cone and Pretzel Company; ring toss game using cardboard cutouts of their product, pretzels.
$20

THE GAME OF SOCKO THE MONK, 1935
Advertising premium for Socko Insect Spray.
$25

STAR RIDE, 1934
$25

STOP & GO, 1936
$25

STOP THIEF
Bldup board with interesting geometric village scene illustration same as the cover, with cardboard disks of four policemen and one thief; strategy game.
$45

THREE LITTLE PIGS GAME, 1933
Gameboard 19¾" × 14 features numerous illustrations of the Walt Disney characters.
$95

TOM SAWYER ON THE MISSISSIPPI, 1935
#212; 12" × 12"; bldup bd, four disks with faces of Tom Sawyer, Huck Finn, Aunt Polly, and the black character, Jim; spinner.
$80

Elastic Tip Co.
370 Atlantic Ave., Boston, MA
1890s

This company made variations of the same product—a dart game. What is noteworthy is that the company was one of the first to advertise a game extensively.

THE GREAT FAMILY AMUSEMENT GAME, ≥1889
S&A; 8¼" × 11; target game with "harmless rubber tipped arrow"; box forms target that attaches to wall plus tray underneath; cover shows mother and seven children, two rifles and two targets; inside cover shows two illust of family playing, plus price list for different versions; "thoughtful parents will not let their children grow up without it"; retail from 50¢ for the small game to $1.65 for the deluxe; the most advertised game of the period.
$35

Electric Game Co.
Jim Prentice Electric Game Co.
Holyoke, MA
1934–±1963

Jim Prentice set himself up in the game business in 1934, a year after graduating from college, refining an electric baseball game he invented while in high school. His big break came when he got a good order from Macy's, and when he started getting responses to ads he put in comic books. During the company's zenith in the 1940s he employed 150 people and advertised extensively, and the company earned around $1.5 million per year. The company that bought him out around 1963 closed up shop about a year later.

Though the Electric Game Co. put out different types of games, the majority were electric sports games and ELECTRIC QUESTIONER type games that used two probes, one of which was placed on a question or object, the other on the answer or matching object—a correct connection in this battery powered game would cause a buzzer to go off and a light to go on. Prentice's first and favorite game was ELECTRIC BASEBALL; other games include ELECTRIC BASKETBALL, ELECTRIC FOOTBALL, ELECTRIC HOCKEY, ELECTRIC JACK STRAWS, and HOLE IN THE HEAD.

AIR-BASE CHECKERS, 1942
$30

COMIN' ROUND THE MOUNTAIN, 1954
18¾" × 13¾"; wood frame on pressed wood board with litho, cards, light, buzzer device; required two batteries; cartoon-like cover illust shows "mountain family."
$50

ELECTRIC BASEBALL, 1935–1950s
Prentice's first game was manufactured by him and sold to Parker Brothers under its name for approximately one year around 1934. When Parker dropped the item, Prentice began selling his own wood-frame, battery-operated sets.
$60 early versions only, with all colored lightbulbs intact.

LETS GO TO COLLEGE, 1944
Card game; 6 × 9¼"; designed to look like a book; printed bldup, many cards, square paper chips, decorated dice cup, card frame.
$45

The Elten Game Corp.
202 E. 44th St., New York, NY

BALANCE THE BUDGET, 1938,
card game, 52 cards with exceptional parody cartoon illustrations in great color, score sheets, instr sheet with cartoon illust; card categories are Labor, Commerce, Relief, WPA, FHA, FCC, TVA, AAA, and an assortment of Tax cards; the instructions read, "Every hand emphasizes the fact that Americans live in a true democracy. For only in this grand and glorious country . . . where it is possible to 'kid' established institutions and leading political figures, could you play this daring, hilarious game." Cross-collectible, political.
$45

Embee Distributing Co.
41–155 E. 25th St., NYC.

BRINGING UP FATHER GAME, 1920,
Envelope 9¾" × 18¾" holds standard size board, four counters, large spinner with b&w illust of father, instr sheet; bd back litho 7 × 7 is same as litho pasted on envelope, with signed cartoon illust of mother singing to piano accompaniment of daughter while father holds head; board has numerous comic illustrations based on comic strip of George McManus.
$75

The Embossing Co.
23 Church St.; 58 Liberty St., Albany, NY
1870–1957

The company produced blocks, dominoes, checkers, and other small wood products with raised (embossed) designs or lettering. Advertisements from the 1910s show that the company made (or distributed) Meccano (metal building sets) and Plasticine (clay-like material). The driving force of the company was Edward C. "Schoonie" Schoonmaker (1857–1947), who was the company's

major sales person from 1884 to 1932. The company was bought by Halsam is 1957. Most of the collectible games other than ANAGRAMS, checkers, and dominoes were produced from the late 1920s through the early 1940s.

ANEX-A-GRAM, 1938
Word/tile game; 11¼ × 11¼; wood racks 10½" long, embossed Anagram tiles; SCRABBLE style crossword game, the object of which is to get rid of all the tiles in your hand.
$25

BOTTOMS UP, 1934
Wooden checkers are embossed on one side with a pig's bottom.
$35

FLAPPER FORTUNES, 1929
$30

FRISCO, 1937
$45

JACK-BE-NIMBLE, 1940s
S&A; a quick reaction (fun to play) game with a ball on a string, a rubber ring, and a cup, plus dice, requiring a player to jerk the ball out of the ring only on certain dice counts before being trapped in the cup by the opponent; the game was "reinvented" around 1991 and produced by Talicor under a different title.
$35

NECK AND NECK, 1929
4¼" × 2⅛"; one-piece thick wood board 3⅝ × 1¾" ×½", six dif color pegs, 2 mini dice; one of the smallest horse race games.
$40

RING-TOSS, ±1940
#609; S&A; 10 × 10 × 2 box, blue drawing on red; nine 2 × 2 embossed blocks with 2¾" peg on each makes multiple ring toss stands; rubber rings.
$30

SNIFF, 1940s
28 dominoes, cribbage board, pegs; "A revival of a Grand Old Embossing game of the eighties"; litho shows a melodrama scene.
$30

TIT-TAT-TOE, 1929
3½" × 3½"; one-piece wood board 2⅛" square with nine wood marbles.
$25

VEST POCKET CHECKER SET, 1929
3⅜ × 2½"; one-piece wood board 2⅛" square; two dif color pegs for checkers, additional color pegs for kings; one of the first "travel" game sets.
$25

Empire Plastics
Bronx 56, New York
Pelham Manor, NY
late 1940s, 1950s

Manufacturer of small games and solitaire puzzles with plastic board and/or pieces.

EMPIRE AUTO RACES, 1950s
Three-fold cardboard race track 24" × 6½", five plastic race cards, each different, built-in spinner, instr on board.
$30

ZINGO, 1950s
S&A; mini-badminton game.
$20

Evangelical Pub. Co.
Chicago, IL

Manufacturers of series of religious card games.

BIBLE AUTHORS, 1895,
Card game; 5½" × 4; 56 cards (14 × 4), instr; illust of 14 characters from Bible; cover illust of Christ and Sunday Series of the Holy Bible.
$15

Ewing Mfg. & Sales Co.
Pasadena 10, CA
1950s

Ewing may not have done much more in games than handle the Davy Crockett items it had license to during the height of that character's TV popularity.

DAVY CROCKETT RADAR ACTION GAME, 1955
S&A; 14¾" × 10¼" × 3½"; magnetic bldup board; player uses steering wheel to move magnet under board and propel men on horses around gameboard along path and through hoops as Crockett "fights his way from Tennessee to the Alamo."
$85

E.E. Fairchild (See **All-Fair**)

Fireside Game Co.
Cincinnati, OH
1895–1900
(See **U.S. Playing Card Co.**)

CHESTNUT BURRS, 1896
$25

ELECTION, 1896
$35

MAPLE GROVES, 1896
$25

OAK LEAVES
$30

OUR UNION, 1896
$40

THE PINES, 1896
$25

Fishlove Industries
712 North Franklin, Chicago, IL
1940s

This company's name means little to most collectors, but it produced the first product ever to carry Bing Crosby's name and picture.

THE CROSBY DERBY, 1947
Board game; horserace theme.
$65

Fitzpatrick Bros.
Chicago, IL
1930s and '40s
MEET THE MISSUS, 1937
Board and card game in an envelope.
$30

WHO IS GUILTY?
nva

A. Flanagan Co.
262 Wabash Ave., Chicago, IL
1889s–early 1900s
Manufacturers of educational card games.

GEOGRAPHY GAME, ±1910
$25

HELPS TO HISTORY, 1885
$35

Flinch Card Company
Kalamazoo, MI
1902–1936

The company published the famous game of FLINCH in 1902, then issued other games after the success of the first.

The first game of FLINCH, one of the country's most popular card games, showed a 1901 and 1902 copyright by A. J. Patterson; a 1903 copyright lists Flinch Card Co., and another copyright in 1935 once again lists Patterson. Parker Brothers apparently obtained the rights to sell FLINCH beginning in 1904, though it was still being manufactured by the Flinch Card Company. Parker Brothers' 100th anniversary calendar states, "By 1904 . . . Parker Brothers was also on the move as it introduced . . . FLINCH, which outsold any card game previously published."

However, in 1913, the game of FLINCH, with a revised copyright, still listed the Flinch Card Company as "sole manufacturers," and the 1934 (and possibly 1935) Sears Roebuck catalog picture of the game also showed the Flinch Card Company. Parker Brothers bought the Flinch company in 1936.

The myth of FLINCH continues, now etched in metal. On the plaque along the Toy Manufacturers Hall of Fame in the International Toy Building in New York honoring Geo. S. Parker is the inscription: "Parker revolutionized . . . parlor games . . . with his own intriguing creations such as Rook, Pit and Flinch"; the inscription is adorned with an illustration of FLINCH, a game Parker did not invent but bought from the owner of the copyright, A.J. Patterson, who was most likely also the game's inventor.

Other games that can be played with FLINCH cards include "Go to Store," "Muggins," and "Patience." In spite of its long and interesting history, FLINCH is a very common game that is of value primarily to those looking to play the game.

BOURSE, OR STOCK EXCHANGE, 1903
$30

COMPETITION, OR DEPARTMENT STORE, 1904
$35

FLINCH, 1902
$8

ROODLES, 1912
$15

Frantz Mfg. Co. (See **Hustler Toy Corp.**)

B.L. Fry Products Co.
St. Louis, MO
1940s

BABY BARN YARD, 1943
$25

JACKPOT, 1943
$25

Fuller, Upham & Co.
Providence, RI

Only one game is known to have been produced by this virtually unknown company, but It is perhaps the first game based on an operetta.

PINAFORE, 1879
$75

Funland (Logo for **Einson-Freeman;** see listing)

Sam'l Gabriel Sons & Co.
74 Fifth Ave., New York, NY
    Gabriel Industries, Inc.
    New York NY
    Hagerstown, MD
    Lancaster, PA 17601
    1910–present

Gabriel, publishers of books and games since 1910, was a prolific company during the 1930s and '40s, producing some small, high quality games with good color lithos and illustrations with a European style. However, many of Gabriel's games are not highly valued, and can be had for $25 or less; examples are CHEE CHOW (1939, trangrams, THE MYSTIC SEVEN and SOLITAIRE editions), CLOWN WINKS (±1930, TIDDLEDY WINKS game showing four clowns with mouths open), DUBBLE UP and GOOD THINGS TO EAT LOTTO (both 1940s), MT. EVEREST (1955), OBJECT LOTTO (1940s), POUCHO CHECKERS (1977, cloth pouch and Hagerstown, MD address in a kangaroo theme game), and SNAP-JACKS (1940s).

BALLY HOO, 1931
9¼ × 5½; two packs of 52 cards plus jokers; advertising parody of Brand names, such as "Sprigley's Gum," or "Cream of Whit" (showing black character), and matching parody slogan cards, such as "His Master's Vice," and "I'd run a mile from one." The game was a product of *Ballyhoo* magazine, published by Dell for a few years beginning in 1931, which had cartoons and advertising that was all parody (the magazine is also collectible).
$50

BIRD LOTTO, 1940s
$35

CLIPPER RACE, 1930s
#T248; 14 × 18¼"; map of world board unfolds to 22½" × 17¾", five stand-up metal clipper ships 1½" high and long, two globe-graphics.
$70

IN AND OUT THE WINDOW, 1940s
S&A; as gameboard unfolds, cardboard section pops up in middle making a house for a tiddley winks game.
$35

INDIANS AND COWBOYS, 1940s
#T235; board, 12 metal tokens of cowboys and Indians, instr sheet; cover is cowboy art.
$65

J. FRED MUGGS 'ROUND THE WORLD GAME
Muggs was the monkey mascot on the *Today* show with Dave Garroway.
$75

JUMPING JUPITER, 1940s
#T267; S&A; good cover illus of planets.
$45

PETER RABBIT GAME, Gabriel, 1940s
#T249, 17½" × 12¾", board, four metal rabbits, two spinners, color photo ad sheet.
$75

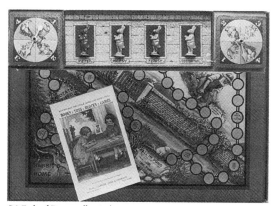

(McFarland/Boyea collection)

PUT IT IN THE BANK, 1940s
S&A; as gameboard unfolds, cardboard section pops up in middle making a house for a tiddley winks game.
$35

SHUFFLE-BOARD (T. NEW G.O.), ±1920
#T21; S&A; 15 × 8¾"; boxbot bd, six wood rings; one of Gabriel's best litho covers.
$85

SPIRO T. AGNEW AMERICAN HISTORY CHALLENGE GAME, 1971
21 × 12, six pawns, spinner, cards, booklet with 750 American History questions; Agnew photo on cover, along with signed letter on letterhead, "The Vice President, Washington"; board shows star path forming a liberty bell; players answers questions and move through states in order of their entrance into the union; retail sticker reads $5.99.
$35

STOCK MARKET GAME, 1955
$30

Game Gems (See **Cohn**)

Game Makers Inc.
44–35 21st St., Long Island City, NY
1940s

This Long Island City company was active during the 1940s and used the talents of inventor Arthur Dritz (see also **American Toy Works** and **Vitaplay Toy Co.);** Dritz did AERO-BALL for Game Makers and AERO-CHUTE for American Toy Works, and research is still being done to see if the companies had more in common than just the same inventor.

AERO BALL
S&A; #37; cardboard airplane and marbles that were flipped by the plane.
$30

BOMBER BALL
S&A; #60; 15½″ long boat is target; four marbles placed on the back of a cardboard plane 10½″ long with a 15½″ wingspan are dropped on to the ship below when a shoot is pulled; good color illust.
$45

Games of Fame
Westfield, MA
1940s

A small company that made a variety of games around WWII; games include BLUFF, JEEPERS, and OLLO (all ≤1945).

BULA, 1943
S&A; toss game with two wood rackets each with an attached cardboard pouch, and a woven cloth ball, all packaged in a lithoed shoe box; subtitled "The South American Game."
$45

FLAGSHIP, 1944
One piece board, 18 wooden pieces of three types, five wood rings; strategy game; © C.H. Taylor.
$35

PICKIE, 1945
S&A; two 15″ wood bats and six 3½″ long diamond shaped wood blocks.
$40

SABOTAGE, 1943, Games of Fame
Card game; 5 × 4; 90 cards, high gloss with bright colors, incl Rubber card depicting black cartoon-style native sitting by tree in jungle, and cards showing materials and factories, and Sabotage, Camouflage, Bomb, and Bomb Repair cards; instr sheet; © C. H. Taylor.
$45

Games Research
48 Wareham St., Boston, MA
1960s & 1970s

This company made a number of strategy games aimed at the avid player; the one most successful in reaching the general public was DIPLOMACY, later bought and popularized by Avalon Hill.

DIPLOMACY, 1961
Military strategy game played over a long period by a large number of players (preferably seven) requiring deals to be made and broken between players before each move.
$35

The Garrard Press
Champaign, IL
≤1940s–≥1950s

Publisher of a series of card games including GROUP SOUNDING (1945), SYLLABLE (1948), MATCH (1953), and KNOW YOUR STATES (1955; © E.W. Dolch; distributed by Gelles-Widmer Co.). All the games are valued under $20.

General Mills
This cereal manufacturer placed games on the back of some of its boxes during the 1930s and '40s; these simple premiums, such as CHEERIOS BIRD HUNT and CHEERIOS HOOK THE FISH, are most often found poorly cut and rarely found with the box intact. For most non-Disney titles, the value would be:
$40 uncut box
$20 gameboard cut cleanly from box
$10 poorly cut gameboard

Glow Products Co., Inc.
New York, NY

TICKER, 1929
16½″ × 2¾″ × 2½″; cloth board 15¾″ × 24 in cardboard tube, tube cover becomes cardboard dice cup, two special dice, 7 market markers, 7 stop loss cards, 7 bear raid cards, stocks certificates incl two each of International Copper, General Steel, United Oil, Premier Utilities, American Railroad, National Equipment, Consolidated Motors; money chips of four dif color denominations (40 white, 24 each of blue and red, 16 yellow); instr sheet; the game offered "all the thrills of the stock market itself" and has increased in value because it was issued in the year of the big stock market crash.
$75

Goodenough and Woglom Co.
New York, NY

This company produced primarily (if not all) Bible and religious theme games. Games include BIBLE LOTTO, BIBLE QUOTTO, BIBLE RHYMES, and HYMN QUARTETS (all ≤1933); most of the games would be valued at $15 to $20.

THE GAME OF TRAITS, 1933
Card game of characteristics found in the New Testament; four each of 15 traits, incl. contentment, diligence, purity, courage, and kindliness.
$25

Gotham Pressed Steel Corp.
133rd St; Cyprus Ave., New York 54, NY
1930s–1950s

Gotham made most games out of metal boards; many were bagatelle games (pinball) or common table games like billiards.

JUNGLE HUNT, ±1940
9 × 16½"; metal board with attached swivel gun shooter; painted litho shows hunter, native, and animals.
$45

RIDE 'EM COWBOY, 1939
Cowboy theme bagatelle.
$45

Wm. R. Gould (See **Snow Brothers**)

A. Gropper
New York City
1920s

HUNTING IN THE JUNGLE, 1920s
S&A; 13¼" × 6½"; bldup bd 9½" × 5, eight linen-finish animals on wood stands, rifle with wood handle and metal barrel, four wood bullets, instr sheet; cover with paste-on litho much smaller than box shows hunter shooting bear with lion and tiger nearby; target game similar to All-Fair's 1928 POP AND PLOP (unusual glossy litho animals may have been made by same company).
$40

Paul K. Guillow (See **Nucraft**)

The Halma Co. (See **Horsman**)

Halsam Products Co.
Chicago, IL
1917–1960s (?)

Halsam produced wood products such as AMERICAN LOGS, checkers, dominoes, and play bricks; most of its items were for building sets and playsets rather than games; Halsam purchased the Embossing Co. in 1957.

Hamilton-Myers
Middletown, PA
1890s

Very little is known about this company, and few of their games have been found, but what *is* known is that the quality of their games is exceptional.

CHEVY CHASE, ±1890
Board and parts box; backgammon variant; four kings, twelve knights, wood pawns, eight dice, four dice cups. Scarce.
$120

(COLUMBIAN EXPOSITION, exact title unknown), ≥1893 Hamilton-Myers
Gameboard 20" × 42½" high, 2" diameter metal ferris wheel that acts as a spinner; unusually long and narrow board represents the Chicago midway (only the board and spinner have been seen by this author—a complete boxed edition would probably be worth well over $1,000). Rare.
nva

THE GAME OF THE TROLLEY RIDE, ±1890
Scarce.
$250

Harett-Gilmar, Inc.
Far Rockaway, NY
1950s

The company produced a small number of well-made board games during the 1950s.

HOWDY DOODY'S 3-RING CIRCUS, ±1950
13½" × 8½" "Electric Questioner" game with three detail-laden interchangeable cardboard sheets.
$75

ROBIN HOOD, 1955
Board game with 3-D setup.
$40

TRAFFIC JAM, 1954
$35

TREASURE ISLAND, ±1954
18½" × 12½"; bldup bd with built-in spinner and wood shaft used for moving magnet under board, two working mini-compasses used as playing pieces, metal ship, two wood pawns, 16 cardboard "pieces-of-8."
$50

Hassenfeld Brothers
Providence, RI
games: 1954–1968
Hasbro Industries
1968–present

The company that started out as Hassenfeld Brothers and then shortened its name to Hasbro, was noted mostly for its toys, especially the G.I. Joe line. In the 1980s and '90s the company purchased Coleco (which owned Selchow & Righter's games), Milton Bradley, Parker Brothers, and part of the game lines from other companies such as Ideal and Lakeside, making it now the largest game company in the U.S.

THE DATING GAME
$50

FIREFIGHTERS
$85

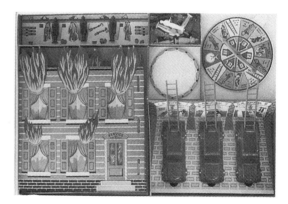

G.I. JOE
$40

MAGIC MILES, 1950s
$25

THE MERRY MILKMAN, 1955
3-D board game; plastic milk trucks, milk bottles, butter and cheese make this game a favorite for collectors and nostalgia buffs.
$65

2 FOR THE MONEY, 1955
$30

WOLFMAN MYSTERY GAME, Hasbro #2717
$200

Willis P. Hazard
178 Chestnut St., Philadelphia, PA

THE CONQUEST OF NATIONS, OR OLD GAMES WITH NEW FACES, 1853
Card game; slipcase card pack; 52 cards incl 13 from suits representing America, Europe, Africa, and Asia, each national suit with illust of male, female, child, dwelling, and map of continent; theme from American suit is Indian family and tepee; invented "by a lady of Philadelphia"; date on card is 1847; predecessor of McLoughlin's GAME OF NATIONS OR QUAKER WHIST, from 1898.
$80

H.G.I. Marketing Service Inc.
1935 Friendship Drive, Suite F
El Cajon, CA 92020
Tel. (619) 258-9393
1989–present

The "Cityopoly" games made by H.G.I. in 1989 and 1990 before the line name was changed to "Metropoly," are good candiates for tomorrow's collectibles.

L.J. Hodges
Worcester, MA
1850s

TRAVELS AND SOJOURN OF ICHABOD SOLO, ESQUIRE, AMONG THE PEE-WEE INDIANS, 1858
Card game; 3½″ × 4½″; instr and story booklet with blanks, 146 cards with words and phrases that are used to fill in the blanks; "a humorous game of tranpositions" (conundrums); printed by Chas. Hamilton; the full title on the instruction booklet reads, "TRAVELS AND SOJOURN OF ICHABOD SOLO, ESQUIRE, A RENOWNED SINGING-MASTER OF QUAVERTOWN, U.S.A., AMONG THE PEE-WEE INDIANS; besides being one of the earlier games of its type, the game is noted for what may be the longest game title known.
$150

Home Game Co.
345 W. Austin Ave.,
Chicago, IL
±1904

Makers of standard card games such as BRIDGE WHIST, CRIBBAGE, FIVE HUNDRED, and PINOCHLE, and the GYPSY WITCH FORTUNE TELLING CARDS.

BIRD CENTER ETIQUETTE, 1904,
Card game; 5½″ × 4; 48 cards (8 × 6), cartoon illustrated instr sheet; cards and cover illust by famous cartoonist John McCutcheon.
$45

BUNCO, 1904, Home Game Co., 345 West Austin Ave., Chicago
Card game; 5¼″ × 3¾″; 115 cards, instr sheet; cards incl. number cards, "Stop" cards picturing policeman, and "Bunco" cards picturing high hat charlatan; editions came in cover box and slip-cover box. This was one of the most highly advertised games of the period.
$25

SOME'R'SET, 1905
nva

C.I. Hood
Lowell, MA
1870–1922
games: primarily 1890s

Charles I. Hood became a partner in one of the earliest companies to promote its products extensively through the use of premiums, including puzzles, dominoes and games, most of which touted the benefits of his elixir, Hood's Sarsaparilla.

HOOD'S SPELLING SCHOOL, 1897
3 × 3; word game; cardboard letters in advertised Prof. Hood's Sarsaparilla on the back.
$35

HOOD'S WAR GAME, 1899
Card game with theme of U.S. vs Spain; each card touted Hood's sarsaparilla as "the best money can buy," and a drink that "purifies the Blood, strengthens the Nerves, sharpens the Appetite, and cures That Tired Feeling."
$50

Craig Hopkins
Chicago, IL
New York, NY
1940s

WATERMELON PATCH, 1940s
Board game.
$45

PENNANT CHASERS BASEBALL GAME, 1946
20 × 11½; bldup die-cut bd with attached spinner, wooden markers, instr in cover.
$35

E.I. Horsman
80 & 82 William St. (corner of Maiden Lane), New York, NY
15 Union Square W., New York, NY (1918)
Manufactory at Valley Falls, RI
≤1880–1918

Edward Imeson Horsman (1843–1927) founded a firm in 1865 that was primarily a toy distribution company. By the 1870s he was importing doll parts & bodies which he then assembled and sold. Though his 1880 catalog did not list dolls, apparently he had a New York showroom full of them—by 1909 he was considered the number-one doll manufacturer in the U. S.

One source indicates that Horsman's company was listed under his full name until 1901, then under his initials until after 1918 when the company became E.I. Horsman & Aetna Doll Co. No Horsman games, however, were marked with his full name instead of initials. Horsman's company was owned by the Regal Doll Mfg. Co. after 1925, then by others, and was bought by Gata Box Ltd. in 1986.

As a manufacturer, Horsman is noted for issuing Halma in 1888, though Milton Bradley claims to have acquired the original game from the inventor in 1885. As a jobber, Horsman sold other companies' games, including Bradley's. The 1880 & '81 Horsman Trade Catalogue contains a full page of "Bradley's Games," as well as uncredited games whose titles include an 1859 game by F.A. Day & Co., an 1875 game by F.A. Wright, and an 1877 game by C.E. Hammett Jr.

The best Horsman games appear to have been made between 1885 and 1895. Many Horsman games are marked simply "E.I.H."

We are all so happy because we play "HALMA," and papa says if we are real good children we shall have "BASILINDA" that new and delightful amusement by the author of "Halma."

Ask for Halma Circular. Free on application.

RULES FOR PLAYING BASILINDA

BY AUTHOR OF HALMA

AN AMUSEMENT FOR CHILDREN

PUBLISHED BY
E. I. HORSMAN, 80 ...am St., N.Y.

BASILINDA, 1890
16½" × 8½"; gameboard with perpendicular center divider, wood cannons, pawns, and stands, instr sheet; interesting strategy game could be forerunner of BATTLESHIP; the game was marked "copyrighted by The Halma Company."
$165

CROKINOLE
$65

DIN, 1905
Card game; 5½" × 4; 80 cards fit together to make ten animals and barnyard fowl; instr sheet has cartoon of six adults playing game as animals look on through window; box is gold letters on blue.
$20

HALMA, 1885/1888
Gameboard and parts box; checkerboard is 16 × 16 spaces, some of which are not used when only two play; 64 wood pawns, 19 each of two colors and 13 each of two colors, as piece count changes depending on number of players; produced also by Parker Bros. as late as 1961; forerunner of CHINESE CHECKERS, also called HOP-PITY; either Horsman or Milton Bradley obtained the rights for HALMA, based on a 1885 copyright; HALMA, which means "jump" in Greek, is the first original American classic strategy game; since it is an unadorned abstract game, it does not command a high value. Somewhat common.
$45 for original version

KLONDIKE
ref

LETTERS, 1878
The box of this game credited to Noyes, Snow & Co was marked "E.I.H."
$35

MAGNETIC JACK STRAWS, 1891
$25

RING-A-PEG, ±1885
$45

SNAP, 1883
Card game; 6¼" × 4¼"; 40 cards with eight odd b&w illust (incl two upside/downside faces), instr sheet with Horsman address and date on outside and 1872 Snow Brothers (Worcester, Mass) copyright on the inside; superb cover with beautiful farm scene sunset shows boy riding pig.
$55 Auc. 10/91 $91

TIDDLEDY WINK TENNIS, 1890
This tiddley wink game played on a cloth board with a tennis net across the middle is the only game known to be marked "E.I. Horsman *Jr.*"
$75

For Sale by Booksellers, and Toy & Fancy Goods Dealers Everywhere. ASK FOR CIRCULAR.

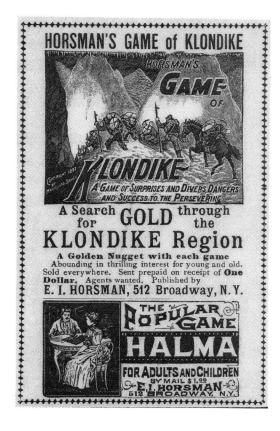

TRILBY, 1894
Gameboard and parts box; board illustrations are from "Trilby," the 1894 book by Harper & Bros., publishers of the Daphne du Maurier novel about a singing teacher's (Svengali) obsession with a female pupil, Trilby; shown are Trilby, Svengali, Trilby's left foot, 3 Musketeers, "Rosemande" of Shubert, and other drawings; bd bk litho 6½" × 4½"; one of the most beautiful of the 19th Century American gameboards. Rare.
$450

Household Words Game Co.
Washington, DC
1916

GAME OF HOUSEHOLD WORDS, 1916
Card game; 2¾" × 3¾"; one of the best advertising games, it contained 48 cards with ads for such well-known companies as Arrow Collars, Campbell's Soups, Carter Inx, Champion Spark Plugs, Colgate's Bouquet (powder), Cream of Wheat, Mobiloils, Morton Salt, Royal Typewriter, Sunshine Biscuits, Victrola, and Wrigley's; different editions carried different local ads as well; the game plays like AUTHORS.
$85

J.H. Hunter

THE GREAT AMERICAN WAR GAME, 1899
25½" × 12 × 2½", boxbot bd, wood box bottom sides, 22 metal soldiers, two wood cannons with 4½" long barrels fit into wood box ends designed as stone walls, four steel balls, instr. sheet pasted inside cover; cover illust over two feet long depicts Civil War battle with cannon fire, smoke, exploding bombs, dead soldiers, and attacking Union armies; deep box bottom has wall graphics only; exceptional cover and contents make this one of the most outstanding pieces by an unknown company.
$800 Auc. 11/91 $1,000

Hustler Toy Corp.
Frantz Hardware/Frantz Mfg. Co.
Sterling, IL

The relationship between Hustler and Frantz is not entirely clear, but both names appeared on most or all of their games. The products were all sports games made out of metal.

THE GREAT AMERICAN GAME, BASE BALL, ≤1923
9¼" × 14½" × 2½" metal board on wood base, with rolling event determinator device, 18 wood pawns for players (which fit into holes in board), one plunger to advance roller; four dials for strikes, balls, runs, and outs; instr on board; good litho of ball players; litho has barn with roof ad "Frantz Garage Hardware"; ad for INTERCOLLEGIATE FOOTBALL inside cover is newspaper story dated 1923. Often overpriced at shows, considering it is common.
$100

COUNTRY CLUB GOLF, 1920s
Scarce.
$120

INTERCOLLEGIATE FOOTBALL, 1923
9¼" × 14½" × 3½" metal on wood base device, with rolling event determinator, two metal rods attached to board to show ball placement and ten-yard marker, three attached score marker arrows, one plunger to advance roller; instr on board; excellent litho of stadium and players; litho has barn with roof ad "Frantz Garage Hardware"; same style as THE GREAT AMERICAN GAME, BASE BALL.
$80

I. B. & W (See **Ives, Blakeslee & Williams**)

Ideal Novelty & Toy Co.
Brooklyn, NY
  Ideal Toy Corp.
  Hollis, NY
  games 1963–1970s

Ideal Novelty & Toy Co. began in 1907 when Morris Michton got permission from Roosevelt to use the name "Teddy" bear for a new line of stuffed bears. Ideal, a major force in the toy industry in the 1950s and '60s, produced its first game in 1963; many of its games were TV related. The company was sold to CBS in the late 1970s; Milton Bradley then picked up some of the Ideal line in 1986.

THE CASE OF THE ELUSIVE ASSASSIN, 1967
This Ellery Queen mystery game developed by inventor Sid Sackson underwent a revision, including the elimination of the gameboard, and, in 1971, became the deductive-reasoning card game published by 3M as SLEUTH; same series as FU MANCHU. Crosscollectible; mystery.
$55

DICK TRACY CRIME STOPPER, 1963
$85

DR. KILDARE, 1962
Based on the TV series; cover shows Richard Chamberlain.
$40

FU MANCHU'S HIDDEN BOARD, 1967
Board game based on Sax Rohmer mystery character; eight plastic men (four different), 40 cards, pad, die, instr booklet; same series as CASE OF THE ELUSIVE ASSASSIN, but less common; cross-collectible; mystery.
$75

HOLLYWOOD SQUARES, 1976
Based on the TV show which premiered on NBC in 1966.
$20

HONEY WEST, 1965
Based on the short-lived adventure TV series starring Anne Francis.
$80

HULK SMASH UP ACTION GAME
$15

IRONSIDE, 1967
Based on the NBC-TV show.
$95

MAN FROM U.N.C.L.E., 1965
Common board game from the TV series.
$30

MOUSETRAP, 1963
This crazy chain reaction game has become a classic in the "mechanical/skill & action" game category; its success prompted the design of CRAZY CLOCK and the more obscure FISH BAIT.
$45

THE NURSES, 1963
Board game based on CBS show that ran from 1962 to '64 before title was changed to *The Doctors and the Nurses* .
$35

SALVO, 1961
The game of BATTLESHIP.
$25

THE STING, 1976
Board game based on the movie; 16 plastic property tokens, 35 cards, pawns; cover shows rendition of Robert Redford and Paul Newman; uncommon.
$45

SUPERMAN CARD GAME
$65

(Oglesby/Stock collection)

SURPRISE PACKAGE, 1961
$20

THE WEIRD-OHS GAME, 1964
$130

International Games
One Uno Circle, Joliet, IL 60435; tel. (815) 741-4000
1972–present

Began as a one-game company with the manufacture of UNO. Success with that game led to a wide and varied line of card and board games.

DUKES OF HAZARD, 1981
$10

G.I. JOE, ±1982
Like all G.I. Joe products, the two games in this series may soon be collectible.
$10

GREMLINS, ±1984
This game, based on the movie, may become a collectible of the future.
$15

UNO, original version, 1972
Green box. rare. Though 80 million UNO sets in their distinctive red boxes have been sold world-wide, the original green-box version is now rare; between ten and twenty thousand were manufactured.
$25

I-S Ultd.
148 E. 38th St., New York 16, NY
1954

Further research needs to be done to determine if this little known company made more than the one good-playing card game, which has become a semi-classic.

BALI, 1954
$20

W. & S.B. Ives
 D.P. & S.B. Ives
 H.P. Ives
 1840s–1890s

Until recently, W. & S.B. Ives were thought to have published the first board game made in America, THE MANSION OF HAPPINESS, but another company's game was discovered to predate the Ives game by two decades. Nevertheless, Ives remains the first major force in U.S. game history, and family members continued to make games for decades. By 1898 Parker Brothers owned most of Ives.

CHARACTERISTICS, 1845
$125

MANSION OF HAPPINESS, 1843
$650 Auc. 6/92 $1000

MANSION OF HAPPINESS, 1864 (Henry P. Ives and D.P. Ives & Co.)
Board opens to 18½″ × 14¾″; hand-colored reissue of W. & S.B. Ives' 1843 original; "an instructive moral and entertaining amusement"; marbleized bd bk with paste-on title litho.
$300 Auc. 6/92 $290

THE NATIONAL GAME OF THE AMERICAN EAGLE, 1844 (W & S.B. Ives)
folded gameboard opens to 17 × 14½″, parts pouch attached to bd bk, two-piece teetotum of bone or ivory, instr sheet, bd bk title litho; this early morality game instructs: "whoever possesses (arrives at) Patriotism . . . (and) Integrity may advance . . . ; whoever possesses Penetration can proceed to Hope; whoever possesses or is guilty of Mendacity or Duplicity must move back." An anti-political message is also clear: "He who sacrifices his principles by becoming an Office-seeker" moves back, as does the player who "gains his notoriety by possessing Party Spirit," whereas "whoever posseses Disinterestedness can proceed . . . " Rare.
$3000 Auc. 11/91 $4,900; 6/92 $3000

THE GAME OF POPE OR PAGAN, OR THE SIEGE OF THE STRONG-HOLD OF SATAN BY THE CHRISTIAN ARMY, 1844
$2500 Auc. 6/92 $1400

THE GAME OF THE STATES, OR, WHO'LL BE PRESIDENT, 1845
$125

Ives, Blakeslee, & Williams
 I.B. & W
 Bridgeport, CT
 ±1891

Few games were produced by this early toy company, which started making toys in the late 1860s. The factory of the father and son team of Riley and Edward Ives was located on the property of Cornelius Blakeslee; Edward married Jennie Blakeslee, and in 1872, two years after the company moved to Bridgeport (where it became known for quality clockwork toys), father-in-law Joel Blakeslee joined the business. Ives, Blakeslee & Co. added (Jerome) Secor to the name of the firm in 1876, and by the early 1880s the company was a major manufacturer and exporter. After the death of Riley in 1895 and Blakeslee in 1896, Edward and his son Harry continued the business until it went bankrupt and was taken over by Lionel in the late 1920s. Three major toy resource books do not mention games or Williams in connection with Ives & Blakeslee, suggesting the association with Williams was brief; the 1891 patent date of PHARAOH'S FROGS provides us with a time period. Ives, Blakeslee & Williams items may be marked only "I. B. & W."

THE GREAT GAME OF PHARAOH'S FROGS, 1891
S&A; metal patented frogs jump into a divided boxbot bd.
$150

TIDDLEDY WINKS
S&A game in wood box.
$65

Jacmar Mfg. Co.
70 Berry Street, Brooklyn 11, NY
115 West Broadway, NY 13, NY
1950s

Jacmar was another company like Jaymar (see listing) presumably setup as a business for a member of the Marx family (possibly Jacob or Julius Marx). The company is most noted for its "Playway to Knowledge Electric Educational Game Series," consisting of ELEC-TRIC QUESTIONNER style games.Most of the titles, such as ELEC-

TRIC QUIZ, ENGLISH, GEOGRAPHY, KIDDIE QUIZ, MAGIC MULTI-PLIER, NATURE QUIZ, TRAVEL AMERICA, and U.S. HISTORY, have the same value, about $25, depending on the illustrations on the cover or overlay sheets. The SCIENCE listing below gives a sample description.

AN ADVENTURE IN SCIENCE, ±1950
10 × 8; two wire probes, built-in bulb, six two-sided die-cut overlay sheets covering such topics as astronomy, atomic terms, birds, chemistry, electricity, the human body, rockets, and weather; battery operated game marked "questions answered by electricity"; instr in box incl ads for twelve other games in series; cover shows science lab; the rocket overlay gives this game increased value.
$30

MICKEY MOUSE, ±1950
$50

ROBOT SAM THE ANSWER MAN, ±1950,
8¼" × 10¼"; buildup bd has six illustrated two-sided die-cut overlays; "Electric Questioner" game has 156 questions on 13 subjects incl American Indians and history of aviation; cover shows old-fashioned robot resembling Wizard of Oz tin man.
$45

SPEEDORAMA
Four one-piece boards have race games for horses, racecars, speedboats, and airships. The space board contributes significantly to the value.
$50

TRAVEL AMERICA, ±1950
#417; 10¼" × 8¼"; similar to ROBOT SAM, with questions about American history; cover shows U.S. map.
$25

WALT DISNEY'S 20,000 LEAGUE UNDER THE SEA, ≥1954
Board game based on the 1954 Disney movie.
$70

Jaymar
Jaymar Specialty Co.
Brooklyn, NY
200 5th Avenue, New York, NY
Lake Success, NY (1984–present)
±1925–present
games: primarily 1930s–1950s

Jaymar was another company financed by successful toyman Louis Marx, setting up his father Jacob in a company designed to produce wood and paper toys (Marx specialized in metal). The firm was taken over by Jacob's son-in-law Howard Kaufman. Jaymar became a successful puzzle manufacturer, but also produced a few games over the years, the better ones (for collectors) being based on licenses the company acquired. Games valued under $25 include CROSSWORDS (1953) and QUIZZICAL QUESTIONS BY PROF. QUIZ (±1940).

BLONDIE AND DAGWOOD'S RACE FOR THE OFFICE, 1950
$45

KATZENJAMMER KIDS HOCKEY, 1940s
S&A, 10 × 7; 19" die-cut board is attached to one end of box bottom, unfolds out of box to make ramp for finger-snapping markers into holes, 12 wood markers; dif board and box illustrations show the seven Katzenjammer characters, board has holes cut in some characters' mouths, cover has mother shooting puck into father.
$65

WHAT'S MY NAME?, 1920s
Based on the radio program featuring Edward Bryant and Joe Cross.
$25

Jeannette Toy & Novelty Co.
Jeannette, PA
1920s

See **Archer Toy Co.**

BROWNIE AUTO RACE, ±1920
S&A; 10" diam. circular metal board, two metal cars 1¾" long, red and blue marble; marble roll game with Palmer Cox's "Brownie" theme.
$125

JHS NY (J.H. Singer, NY; see **Singer**)

JS
The initials "JS" on bagatelle (pin ball) games stand for Joseph Schneider (see listing). When found on boxed board games, the "JS" stands for John Sands, an English manufacturer.

The Judson Press
Philadelphia, PA
±1940

Manufacturer of Bible card games, many invented by Nellie T. Magee (see listing), such as BIBLE BOOKS, BIBLE CHARACTERS, BIBLE CITIES, and BIBLE DRILLS. These specialized products have value only to certain collectors.

BIBLE ABCs AND PROMISES
Card game in card pack; advertised as "Profitable Play Bible Games," "for sale by publishing houses of all denominations."
$15

Kellogg Co.
Battle Creek, MI

Like many cereal manufacturers, Kellogg put games on its cereal boxes and sent them in the mail as premiums.

JUNGLE JUMP-UP GAME, ±1940
Paper board, plastic hunter with small pellet rifle, plastic animals
3½" long.
$45

STORY BOOK OF GAMES, 1931
Series of four books, eight pages of heavy cardboard with heavier
cover stock with back flap containing spinner and punch-out playing
pieces; designed like a comic book, with four colorfully illustrated
board games with fairy tale themes inside. These items have more
value to advertising/premium collectors than game collectors; value
drops 30% if pieces are missing. Retail= boxtop plus 10¢. Somewhat common, but harder to find in Kansas, Nevada, Washington,
and Wisconsin where such merchandising was prohibited.
$35 for book #1 with the "Black Sambo" story
$25 all others

Kenilworth Press
New York, NY

THE GAME OF THE THREE LITTLE PIGS, ±1933, Kenilworth Press,
NYC
10½" × 21½", pat pend, © by special permission Walt Disney
Enterprises, from the Walt Disney *Silly Symphonies* , "The Three
Little Pigs"; thin large board, yellow space, spiral path leading to
space 74 in center showing illust of 3 pigs playing piano, flute, and
fiddle in brick house, 12 pigs and 4 wolf counters, 44 cards incl 2
jokers, act as dice; good, scarce Disney item.
$160

Kenner Products Co.
Cincinnati 2, OH
1947–1967 (private ownership)
1967–present (conglomerate)

Kenner, originally famous for Play-doh, the Spirograph, and the
Easy-Bake Oven, among other products, was purchased by General
Mills in 1967. General Mills purchased Parker Brothers in 1968,
and Kenner-Parker Toys Inc. was spun off in 1985; Tonka purchased
them in 1987 and Hasbro bought Tonka in 1991. The company,
which now also makes action figures and plush, made mostly toys
and very few games.

BEAT THE BUZZ, 1958
S&A; plastic base with bent, curved wire running from one end to
the other is boxed version of carnival/arcade game requiring players
to move metal loop along the wire without touching it and setting
off buzzer.
$30

Kerk Guild
Utica, New York
1930s

This small company produced the earlier (pre-Parker Bros.) Winnie-
The-Pooh games for copyright holder Stephen Slesinger.

THE VAN LOON STORY OF MANKIND GAME, ±1931
7½ × 10 box designed to look like book; opened, book front and
back make one illustration; coated (vinyl?) cloth board 30" ×
29½", with gameboard path spiraling inward; four metal sailing
ships 1½" high, wood disks, two dice; based on Hendrik Van Loon's
book of that name; illustrations by Van Loon.
$85

WINNIE-THE-POOH, 1931
10½" × 15¾"; gameboard, four metal bears, spinner instr in box
cover; good cover illust based on A.A. Milne's story.
$85

Klauber Novelty
845 South Wabash Ave.
Chicago, IL
1920s–'40s

This small company made a variety of sports related games, including AMERICAN SWEEPSTAKES (1931), and SHUFFLETTE (1941),

and items of low collectible value such as BRIDGE KENO (1929),
and HOLD YOUR HORSES (race game in a 27½" × 3" box; valued
at $20).

Knapp Electric & Novelty Co.
  Knapp Electric Inc.
  Port Chester, NY
  Indianapolis, IN
  games: primarily 1920s and 1930s

The company was founded in 1890 (or 1894) by David Knapp and
one employee with $600 and produced primarily electric trains.
They became a division of P.R. Mallory. The company is noted
mostly for its ELECTRIC QUESTIONNER games.

ELECTRIC QUESTIONNER, ±1920
Wood box, two wire and metal probes, die-cut overlay cards,
bell/buzzer, light; various series (each with dif. set of cards); in terms
of dating your set, pictorial series 81–88 was introduced in 1927.
These relatively common games are often seen at shows priced
much higher than the generally accepted value placed on them by
game collectors.
$35

ELECTRO GAMESET, ±1930
12½" × 12½"; four one-sided 12 × 12 cardboard boards fit over
presswood board with 4" diam. metal center with magnetized
spinning needle; playing pieces are colored rivets; games incl Air
Race, Auto Race, Baseball, and Football.
$45

FINANCE, ≤1936
Knapp's version of MONOPOLY. Rare.
nva

GES IT GAME, 1927
One of the few Knapp electric games to have a paper litho box (not
wood) with intricate illustrations.
$35

THE TELL BELL, 1928
Similar to ELECTRIC QUESTIONNER (and less common) but with a
much more interesting illustrated cover.
$50

Kohner Bros
New York, NY
1950s

Minor manufacturer of TV-based games and other games, such as
TROUBLE and TUMBLEWORDS.

THE SKY'S THE LIMIT, 1955
18½" × 13¾"; stunt game with assorted objects to be attached to
string or dowel, spinner, balloons; based on NBC program.
$25

Lakeside Toys Inc./Lakeside Industries
Minneapolis, MN
≤1962–1980s

Lakeside was an active company in the early 1960s, making some quality games, but at a high price; the quality was said to have decreased over time. The company was bought out by Hasbro. Games include ARENA (1962), BEANBAG BUCKANEERS, PLAY IT COOL, QUEST, ROYAL GAMBIT, and TOPPER.

The Leister Game Co.
1320 Dorr St., Toledo 7, OH
9 North St. Clair ST., Toledo 4, OH
26 N. Erie St., Toledo 2, OH (±1947)
1940s and 1950s

The company of Reginald S. Leister specialized in party games and stunts, usually in booklet form, sometimes boxed and aimed at the military during WWII. Included in the series are FUN, GAME KIT, GIMME, KIDDIE KAPERS, KRITTER KIT, LUCK, PARTY CAPERS, and PUZZLE PACK; A BARREL OF FUN (1946) was manufactured and distributed by Hart Vance Co., St. Louis, 3, MO; NEVER A DULL MOMENT (1942) was produced by the National Association Service, 2017 Glenwood, Toledo; Leister games are purchased more for their humorous play value than as collector's items and are valued at $10–15.

AT EASE, ±1945
Military theme card/stunt game shows photographs of uniformed personnel acting out some of the required party stunts.
$40

AUTOGRAPHS, 1945
Card game; 5½" × 4; cards with autographed photos of stars and brief history.
$45

BRIDE BINGO, 1957
12¾" × 6¼"; BINGO cards are marked "B-R-I-D-E," each card containing terms that relate to a wedding and its preparation; this game is collected mostly for its "camp" value, or to use as an unusual shower gift.
$35

TO THE AID OF YOUR PARTY, 1942
5½" × 8½" spiral bound book, photo on one page accompanies parlor game description on the other; answers to quizzes on back page; games include identifying advertising slogans, trademarks, photos of stars, and photos of people in the news.
$25

Jack Levitz
Philadelphia, PA
1949

This "company" may have made only one game, but what is significant is that it is one of the few Jewish theme games to surface in the collectors market. The game was distributed by Malerman's Hebrew Bookstore, 504 Pine St., Philadelphia 6, Pa.

BIBLE QUIZ LOTTO, 1949
8¼" × 6½"; 18 Bingo cards each with eight words or phrases corresponding to a particular book of the Bible, a packet of small cards with quiz questions and answers; covers the Five Books of Moses, "designed to serve as a refresher in the study of the Torah"; cover shows family playing the game, and an illust of a Torah under the word "Quiz."
$30

Lido Toy
New York, NY
1940s and 1950s

This post-war company produced small, inexpensively made games with plastic pieces. What little value the games have is based on their themes.

AIR RACE AROUND THE WORLD, ±1950
$20

ROCKET RACE TO SATURN, ±1950
$25

Lindstrom Tool and Toy Co
Bridgeport, CT
1940s–1950s

Company noted for tin bagatelle games. Games include the pinball style games of AIRWAYS (±1950) and POKER BALL PIN GAME (±1910; a 23" × 15" metal-framed wood board bagatelle game depicting playing cards), both valued at $20.

CANDID CAMERA TARGET SHOT, ±1950
S&A; target game with 9 × 9 one-piece litho covered pressed board with metal stand; illust show 9 airplanes, one of which is printed upside down.
$30

F. & R. Lockwood (see pages 9–11)

E.S. Lowe Co., Inc.
27 W. 20th St., New York 11, NY
1920s–1973

Edmund Lowe was the businessman who made his name (and fortune) with BINGO games in the 1920s. Prior to WWII, his company concentrated on paper dolls. Some of Lowe's traditional games were leather bound and sold through gift shops. In 1956 he promoted a game he played with neighbors called YACHT, later to become Milton Bradley's now-classic (but not very collectible) game of YAHTZEE. Bradley bought E.S. Lowe in 1973.

FOX HUNT, 1930s
$25

HORSE RACE, 1943
#534.
$20

THE JEEP BOARD, 1944
4 × 4; 3½" square two-sided, ½" thick designed to play 15 games and ten puzzles, and aimed at soldiers during WWII; two boards were glued together with a cloth fixed between them, so the game could be tied to the leg when playing (see back cover photo of author with the game); 40 dif. color wood pegs, instr booklet; the game was patented and sold in 1943 by Geo. S. Carrington Co., 2740 Fullerton Ave., Chicago.
$20

Samuel Lowe Co.
Kenosha, WI
1940s

This company produced mostly small games, many with small, thin cardboard gameboards. Games that can be bought for around $25 include the AIRPLANE SPEEDWAY GAME (1941), BASEBALL, FOOTBALL, HOCKEY, BASKETBALL (1942), CROSS COUNTRY (1941), and PIRATE SHIP (±1940).

HORNET, 1941
11 × 11; two one-piece boards, catapult, spinner, wooden markers, instr on gameboards; good war illust cover.
$40

LAND AND SEA WAR GAMES, 1941,
#1296; 11 × 11; two one-piece thin cardboard gameboards (nothing on back), cardboard and wood catapult, four markers, spinner showing dice moves, wax paper parts bag; one board shows various styles of biplanes and single wing aircraft, and is a target game using catapult; the second board shows tanks and anti-aircraft artillery and is a path game; instr on both boards.
$60

Lowell
New York, NY
±1954–1960s

Lowell was one of the primary producers of games, especially those based on TV programs, during its short but prolific run in the 1950s.

BEAT THE CLOCK, 1954
Based on the CBS stunt show that premiered in 1950, hosted by Bud Collier; allegedly Lowell's first game.
$60

BIG TOWN, ±1954
Based on the show that ran from 1950–1954.
$50

DOLLAR A SECOND, ±1955
17 × 14; based on the ABC-TV stunt show starring Jan Murray that ran from 1954–1957; paste-on sticker on box reads "Sponsored by Mogen David wine."
$30

GROUCHO'S YOU BET YOUR LIFE, 1955
18 × 12; bldup bd with parts tray and built-in clock timer, multiple choice question cards, answer card, cardboard letters, instr sheet; © NBC, based on TV show; cover, board, and instr show cigar-smoking Groucho, cover and instr show DeSoto Plymouth name.
$100

JUSTICE, 1954
Elaborate game based on the short-lived TV show contains metal balance scales.
$45

LARAMIE, 1960
Based on the TV western that ran from 1959–1963.
$75

PERSONALYSIS, 1957
$25

SHOW-BIZ
Cover shows 16 stars, incl Jack Benny, Milton Berle, George Burns, Bing Crosby, and Sammy Davis, Jr.
$60

$64,000 QUIZ GAME, 1955
Based on the TV show.
$35

STEVE CANYON
Based on the TV show; excellent cover showing Canyon.
$40

THIS IS YOUR LIFE, ±1954
Based on the show (which had been on radio since 1948) hosted on TV by Ralph Edwards from 1952–1961.
$30

YOURS FOR A SONG, ±1962
96-page song book with instr, cardboard list of song titles, song selector, bldup with two spinners and song board, five wood blocks, rubber squeaker; cover shows three people playing game, two singing, plus photo inset of host Bert Parks; based on ABC TV show.
$35

Lubbers & Bell
721 Second Ave., Clinton, Iowa
1920s

The company is most noted for PUZZLE PEG (1922), a form of an early solitaire peg puzzle that became popular in plastic as HI-Q.

BLOX-O, 1923
Small boxed strategy game for two; retail=50¢.
$15

TOSS-O, 1924
S&A game with marble toss.
$15

ZOO HOO, 1924,
11¾" × 14¼"; one-piece gameboard, die-cut parts board with 15 punch-out disks showing animals and one clown and a card depicting "Wash," the guard—a stereotyped red-lipped black character; the back of his picture card reads, "This disc is never used in playing Zoo Hoo. It is included only for the amusement of youngsters"; the backs of the animal disks explain something about each animal; instr in cover; cover shows animals racing by while astonished guard Wash looks on; a solitaire puzzle; interesting and scarce black collectible.
$55

Madmar Quality Co.
Utica, NY
1914–1950s

Madmar, a name taken from the name of founder Miles Bickelhaupt's daughter, Madeleine Mary, was noted mostly for its puzzles during the 1920s and 1930s; the company was bought by the Foster Paper Co. in the 1950s.

CRICKETS IN THE GRASS, 1920s
#122; tiddley wink variant with two felt pads, two tin cups, and pegs, which were "tiddled"; interesting cover illustrating the title.
$45

Nellie T. Magee
Lincoln, Nebraska
1920s, 1930s (?)

Mrs. Magee produced a series of Bible games, such as COMMAND-MENTS and various titles beginning with the word "Bible," most of which were published by other firms, such as The Judson Press (see listing). The games, which were used "for play, study, gifts, rewards, and entertainment," sold for 15¢ each.

BIBLE CITIES/PROFITABLE PLAY
Game #3, card game; 36 cards from 9 Biblical cities, plus two card backs and box front.
$15

Douglas Malewicki
Los Angeles, CA
1965

NUCLEAR WAR, 1965,
Card game 7½" × 5½"; large pack of Nuclear War cards, picturing bombs, bombers, missiles, and anti-missiles, and propaganda card, plus Secret cards and (smaller) population cards; large spinner showing bomb exploding with red background, instr sheet states that the object is to get opposing powers to "join your superior forces of government" or annihilate them; population is the measure of success or failure in the game; "A player who loses his entire population withdraws from the game."
$30

Marks Brothers Co.
Boston, MA
1930s

No connection with the famous toy family of "Marx," this company had the Disney license for games during the 1930s and made numerous target games.

STAX, 1930s
S&A; 7½" high, 3" diameter cylinder; 7" high cardboard cone with wood tip, numerous wood sticks, instr sheet; object is to stack wood sticks before toppling entire stack; cartoon figure on box looks like "Esqui," the character logo illustration of *Esquire* magazine.
$20

THE INTERNATIONAL GAME OF STAK, 1937
S&A (see above); 14 × 10 × 2¾ box with four cones and rules "for one or more kibitzers."
$25

MICKEY MOUSE COMING HOME GAME, 1930s
Gameboard shows Mickey in the center with Pluto, Minnie, Horace Horsecollar, and Clarabelle Cow in each corner; parts box 2¾" × 3⅛ has five markers and a die; © Walt E. Disney; excellent color illust.
$125 board and separate parts box
$250 full box edition

Martin Co.
North Adams, MA
1890s–early 1900s

This lesser-known company produced a lot of interesting games and magic sets around the turn-of-the-century, mostly skill and action games, often with wood pieces. Their nicely detailed illustrated covers frequently showed people playing the games.

FISHING GAME, 1899
$40

RING SCALING, ±1900
$45

WONDER TIDDLEY WINKS, 1899
5½" × 5½"; wood cup, "celluloid" disks.
$30

Louis Marx
Boston, MA
1950s and 1960s

One of the giants in the toy industry, Marx made a few games, mostly licenced character target games such as DICK TRACY, HOPALONG CASSIDY, and LONE RANGER, and PUBLIC ENEMY NO. 1. Most of these metal character or theme games sell for between $100 and $200. Marx's success allowed him to support the beginnings of two other companies, Jacmar and Jaymar (see listings).

Master Toy Co.
New York, NY
1940s

Most games by this company were approx. the same size, 11½" × 11½", consisted of a die-cut build-up board and pegs, and employed the same simplicity of style in illustration, similar to Rosebud Art. The company's "average" games are valued around $25, including THE BIKE RACE, COAST TO COAST, and ONE TWO BUTTON YOUR SHOE.

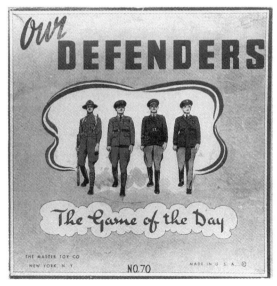

OUR DEFENDERS, ±1944
#70; bldup bd with attached cardboard spinner with wood handle, four dif military men in uniform that match images on the board are cut up into ten-piece puzzle pieces; instr sheet; pure luck game is one of few to combine game play with puzzle.
$35 Auc. 10/91 $66 (corner and apron repairs)

Mattel
Hawthorn, CA
games: 1950s–1980s

Mattel, noted mostly for its Barbie Doll and "Hot Wheels" cars, has periodically tried its hand at games, often unsuccessfully. It produced the classic LIE DETECTOR GAME in 1960, then revised it in 1987, only to close down its game division and sell the product to Pressman.

LIE DETECTOR, 1960
Plastic "detector", multiple character cards; rumors had it that the original characters were modeled after Mattel employees. In the 1987 update, incidentally, the score board was revised (by this author), many of the characters were given fresh faces (not based on any real people), all references to smoking were eliminated (the "ex-smokers" now sport tie pins and lapel pins instead), the "gangster" was changed into a "racketeer," and the "teacher" was replaced by a "psychic reader"! The value of the original diminished considerably with the release of the new version. Because of the unusually large size of the box and the frequency with which this good game must have been played, it is difficult to find the game in very good condition.
$35

MATCH-IT, 1961
A "Beany & Cecil" item that is more a solitaire puzzle than a game.
$35

WORD FOR WORD, 1963
$20

Mayhew & Baker
Boston
late 1850s

Publishers of early card games, including GAME OF THE SCHOOL IN AN UPROAR, and THE GAME OF YANKEE LAND (both ±1858),
and GAME OF THE YOUNG PEDDLERS (1859); Kilburn & Mallory were often their lithographers.

THE NEW GAME OF TOURNAMENT, 1858
$300

McDowell Mfg. Co.
Pittsburgh, PA
1920s, 1930s

McDowell may have made the metal gameboards for the Archer Toy Co., Jeannette Toy & Novelty Co., the M.H. Miller Co., and the T.H. Stough Co., all of Jeannette, PA. There might also be a connection with Wolverine Supply & Mfg. Co., another Pittsburgh based company that produced metal game boards.

WHIRLING AEROPLANE RACE, ±1925
#60; litho metal game with airplane theme.
$90

John McLoughlin
New York, NY
1850s–1858
McLoughlin Brothers
New York, NY
1858–1920

McLoughlin is unquestionably the most desirable name in games from the point of view of collectors of early material. One of the most prolific companies, McLoughlin consistently produced the most beautiful illustrations for its game boxes, gameboards, and cards. The company goes back to 1828 as a book publishing company, founded by John McLoughlin, Sr., who emigrated from Scotland in 1819. John McLoughlin, Jr., took over the business upon his father's retirement and expanded the line to include card games.

John Mcloughlin had one of the earliest assembly lines in the game business, as the handpainted games were traditionally colored by a number of people, each person using only one color.

The company's most outstanding period of production was during the 1880s and early to mid 1890s. In 1920 McLoughlin Bros. was bought by Milton Bradley.

The list of key dates below provides a sketch of the company history and aids in determining the dates of undated games by noting which address was indicated on the game.

1850–1858	John McLoughlin introduces hand colored card games.
mid-1850s	Fire destroys business.
1858	John and brother Edmond form McLoughlin Bros. 24 Beekman Street
1864	30 Beekman St.
1887	623 Broadway
1914	890 Broadway
1920	McLoughlin bought by Milton Bradley Co.

John McLoughlin

CONUNDRUMS, 1853
Rare.
$675 Auc. 6/92 $1300

YANKEE PEDLAR [*sic*], OR WHAT DO YOU BUY, ≥1850
John McLoughlin card game, 5½ × 5¾ , 12 hand-colored cards showing trades/professions ("Poulterer," "Huckster," "Toy Dealer," etc.), instr sheet with conundrums, instr title=YANKEE PEDLAR, OR WHAT D'YE BUY; by Jack Bunsby. Scarce.
$700 Auc. 11/91 $1,200

McLoughlin Brothers

GAMES OF AMBUSCADE, CONSTELLATIONS, AND BOUNCE, 1877
7½ × 14¼ bookshelf game in slipcover; board unfolds to be full board for AMBUSCADE on the outside, and boards for the other games inside; 24 markers, illustrated instr booklet; on bottom of litho on wood double arrow block spinner is notice: "M'Loughlin Bros.' Indicator. A Complete and Unobjectionable Substitute for, and Improvement upon Dice, Teetotums, &c." Inside boards are

geometric, outside one has five illustrated scenes incl Indians and Western motif; when folded, game looks like two books on shelf.
$200

AROUND THE WORLD WITH NELLIE BLY: see ROUND THE WORLD WITH NELLIE BLY

GAME OF BATTLES OR FUN FOR BOYS, 1889
S&A, 24¾ × 21¾; 60 cardboard soldiers 6½" tall nailed to wood stands, 12 wood and metal parts to make two 7" cannons, 30 ammo shells, two heavy cardboard tents, two flags; "the player who first destroys his opponent's army, killing all the men, wins the game"; McLoughlin at its best.
$700

BICYCLE RACE, 1891
$550

GAME OF BOMBARDMENT, 1898
10½ × 8½; boxbot bd, 20 markers (2 colors), spinner (numbered 3–12), instr in cover; board shows soldiers on fort wall firing at ships, cover shows two battleships, one with the U.S. flag firing and the other exploding.
$115

BULLS AND BEARS, 1896
The 1896 McLoughlin catalog said about its game: "Based upon the customary operations of the stock market. The rapidly shifting fortunes of those who dabble in stocks, have been woven into a single game, that for the time being will make players feel like speculators, bankers and brokers." Rare.
nva Auc. 6/92 $28,000

THE GAME C F CAPTIVE PRINCESS, 1899.
14½ × 15; boxbot bd, path game.
$95

CAPTIVE PRINCESS, ±1880
Bookshelf game opens to 14 × 14m with one board outside and two inside; spine is blank cloth; wood sides and inside wood divider; six paper litho on wood playing pieces almost 1½" in diameter, each illustrating a knight in armor, two wood color cubes that act as dice, large wood dice cup; inner boards are geometric in design, outer board for CAPTIVE PRINCESS has illust of knights, winged dragon, and princess.
$210

GAME OF CATCHING MICE, 1888
8 × 8; board opens to 15 × 7½; two large and 32 small wood counters in two colors; double arrow spinner; instr in cover; board has outer track for the two men and an inner track for the 32 mice; colorful board illust shows lots of mice; cover is wonderful scene of three cats peering over frosted cake at two mice; exceptional cat piece.
$200 Auc. 10/91 $264 (repaired aprons)

CHIROMAGICA, OR THE HAND OF FATE, 1901
12¼ × 12¼; one-piece boxbot bldup bd with wood sides, instr on board, one 4½" diam question disk; board illustrations include 24 presidents and heads of foreign states, and the White House and Capitol building; exceptional cover illustration is of wizard in work room, with owl on globe, snake, books, and smoking magic lamp with hand pointing out of smoke.
$325 Auc. 11/91 $375 (cover wear, corner damaged)

CHRISTMAS GOOSE, 1890
19½ × 10½, boxbot bd with wood sides, two wood playing pieces, 24 markers (12 white, six blue, six red), large spinner; oval path with many illust., cover shows jester in white face and high hat holding golden egg and using cane to grab goose.
$600 Auc. 11/91 $850 (missing part apron)

GAME OF THE CHRISTMAS JEWEL, 1899
#5160, Pearl Series; 8 × 17½, boxbot bd, two wood markers, one pawn representing the Christmas jewel, large spinner; two-player game; illust child in hat and with toys in hand.
$350 Auc. 11/91 $600

THE GAME OF CITY LIFE OR THE BOYS OF NEW YORK, 1889
Card game; 6¼ × 4½; 44 cards vividly illustrated with "the scenes, characters, and incidents common to life in a large city"; these characters include: wife beater, cruel woman, strong-minded woman, street gamin, rum seller, defaulting bank cashier, capitalist, dude, and the corner loafer; cards also show officials, fireman, and house on fire; cover shows fireman and girl in runaway horse-drawn carriage; cross-collectible, fire theme.
$80

GAME OF COCK ROBIN AND HIS TRAGICAL DEATH, ±1885
Card game; 6½ × 5; 42 cards include 12 very colorful cards with verse and illust of dif animals, and 30 cards with same color illust of robin with arrow in him, each card with different answer to question of who killed Cock Robin; thick box is embossed gold lettering on red.
$65

GAME OF DAY AT THE CIRCUS, 1898
23 × 16½, one-piece bldup boxbot bd with folding section for parts storage underneath, 12 metal figural pieces: "an elephant, a bicycle rider, a nigger, an Indian"; spinner, instr in cover; extraordinary circus collectible.
$1,000

GAME OF THE DISTRICT MESSENGER BOY, 1886
14½ × 25¾; one-piece boxbot and bldup board, die-cut holes for two spinners, section of board lifts for parts storage underneath, 4 metal messengers, instr on board.
$190

GAME OF THE DISTRICT MESSENGER BOY, 1904
10½ × 19½; boxbot bd, four wood pawns, spinner; path game duplicated on left and right sides, with morality theme sending players back for drunkenness, embezzlement, and dullness, and ahead for ability and affability until player becomes a "respected banker and a good citizen"; cover reads 1896, instr read 1904, but board is same as THE ERRAND BOY, a folding board game from 1891.
$135

THE DOUBLE FLAG GAME, 1904
Card game; 6¼ × 4½; 36 color cards, each showing half a flag, incl those of Persia and Siam; cover shows child in wicker basket as boat, with flag on mast and broom as oar.
$65 Auc. 10/91 $77

THE ERRAND BOY, 1891
11 × 10¼; board 10¼ × 19¾; four wood pawns, spinner, flower pattern box wrap; path game with morality theme similar to CHECK-ERED GAME OF LIFE and MESSENGER BOY games in which such traits as affability and integrity advance the player, whereas inattention and dullness hold the player back; six excellent vivid color illustrations on board include center drawing of smoking youth standing idle with packages afoot while other youth hurries to deliver his packages; cover illust shows one youth hurrying with package while another drops his packages during scuffle with other boy.
$125 Auc. 10/91 $172

FARMER JONES' PIGS, ±1890
8½ × 14¾; boxbot bd, twelve cardboard pig disks in wood stands, spinner with pig illust; cover shows farmer chasing pigs out of yard, board shows path with pig illust throughout, incl center drawing of pigs in cornfield; date is suggested by flowered box wrap, which is the same as for 1891 ERRAND BOY game.
$225 Auc. 10/91 $270

FUN AT THE CIRCUS, 1897
16¾ × 16¾, wood frame, CHUTES AND LADDERS variation, four turned wooden pawns, themed spinner, very colorful.
$600

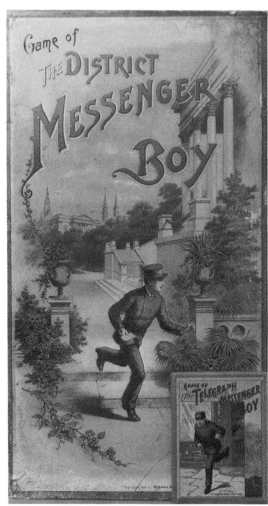

(Krim collection)

GOOSY GOOSY GANDER, ≤1896
8½ × 14½; boxbot bd, four cardboard goose heads each on colored wood stand, spinner, instr in cover title game the GAME OF GOOSEY GANDER; path game with goose eggs as spaces; cover illust shows dressed geese, highlighting one in hat, veil, neck piece, boa, etc. (Ohio sales receipt from 1896 lists price at 20¢.)
$375 Auc. 11/91 $500

GRANDMA'S (IMPROVED) ARITHMETICAL GAME, 1887
Card game; 6¼ × 4½; 119 question card slips, instr booklet with answers; booklet cover shows elderly woman; back cover lists Grandma's series: RIDDLES, GEOGRAPHY, USEFUL KNOWLEDGE, OLD TESTAMENT, NEW TESTAMENT; box cover shows elderly woman on chair watching boy write on blackboard while young girl with dunce cap sits on stool crying.
$40

GRANDMA'S (IMPROVED) GAME OF USEFUL KNOWLEDGE, 1887
Card game (see above); 101 question cards; cover is bright color illust of mother and child in museum with lion, elephant and other animals.
$40

HAND OF FATE, 1901
Fortune telling game similar to CHIROMAGICA; exceptional cover showing bats, black cats, owls. Scarce.
$2,000 Auc. 11/91 $4,000; 6/92 $1800

HEEDLESS TOMMY, 1893
20 × 9½
$400

H.M.S. PINAFORE, ±1880
Card game; 3¼ × 4¼; half-slipcase card pack; illustrated color cards showing the principles and seamen from Gilbert and Sullivan's 1878 operetta, "H.M.S. Pinafore"; cover illust of ship. McLoughlin's game may have been based on an 1879 game of PINAFORE from Fuller, Upham & Co., which had silhouette cards of sailors and cousins and aunts.
$125

THE NEW GAME OF HUNTING, 1904
$600

THE IMPROVED HISTORICAL CARDS, ≤1900
card game, © 1884; 8¾ × 5¼; wood frame box, approx 200 info cards, each with 1884 date, though data on cards goes through the

1889 inauguration of Benjamin Harrison; gold lettering on oxblood box.
$30

THE GAME OF JACK AND THE BEAN STALK, 1898
10½ × 19¾; boxbot bd with wood sides, two dif shape wood pawns, large 4x4 illus spinner, instr in cover; two-player path game.
$500 Auc. 11/91 $900

GAME OF JAPANESE ORACLE, ±1875
Fortune telling amusement; 3 × 4¼ half slipcase card pack; 29 question cards, each with 20 answers; 20 illustrated cards (10 each of two superb gold leaf illustrations) determine which answer applies to the player and depending on whether player is a man or woman; cover shows Oriental with long queue and magic lamp.
$100

GAME OF JUST LIKE ME, 1899
Card game; 4¼ × 5½; dif illust rhyme cards plus response cards of monkey looking in mirror saying, "Just like me"; instr sheet; cover shows three monkeys.
$60

GAME OF LEAP FROG, ±1910
Two editions: #5125; 9 × 11; boxbot bd, 16 wood markers (8 red, 8 yellow), illustrated spinner (1–8), instr in cover; bd litho shows

frogs in reeds, cover shows three boys, one leaping over other; other edition is 8½ × 10¼; McLoughlin name in large writing, title in red, this edition earlier and slightly smaller than the other.
$75 (either one) Auc. 10/91 $144

THE LETTER CARRIER, ±1890
8½ × 14½; boxbot bd, four wood pawns, spinner, seven uncut sheets of 16 cardboard letters (all with New York addresses) for a total of 112; cover shows postman delivering letter to woman.
$135

LITTLE GOLDENLOCKS & THE THREE BEARS, 1890
10¼ × 19¾ , boxbot bd with wood sides, four playing pieces, spinner, instr booklet; exceptional illustration.
$550

THE GAME OF LOST HEIR, ±1890
Card game; 6¾ × 5¼; 36 cards (four suits of eight, representing the police of a city, with an extra card each for New York and Philadelphia, and The Lost Heir card and a "ragamuffin known as the "Wrong Boy" card); other cities are Boston and Chicago; each city card has intricate vivid color illust of the city's shield; instr sheet; exceptional cover shows young boy leaning on hands, with NY cityscape incl Statue of Liberty and Brooklyn Bridge.
$75 Auc. 10/91 $138

GAME OF LOST HEIR, 1893
Card game; 6¼ × 4½; 48 cards (four suits of 11); (see also above for description of cards); cover shows cigarette smoking tough kid and clean-cut boy.
$75

LOST IN THE WOODS, ± 1895
10½ × 20¾, boxbot bd, wood sided box, four wood pawns, wood dice cup, two bone dice; bright illust path game, exceptional cover of two girls in woods.
$700 Auc. 11/91 $1,100

MAN IN THE MOON, ±1901
One of the most talked about McLoughlin games (synonymous with the McLoughlin name) that has been the subject of "auction fever," selling for very high prices.
$3,500 Auc. 9/88 $4,600

THE MANSION OF HAPPINESS, 1895
22½ × 15; boxbot bd with wood sides, six large, ornate pawns, two large illustrated spinners may not be original; spiral path board has circular spaces, many with detailed illustrations; instructions inside cover make reference to the original edition (without mentioning Ives), and explain that "Stocks" and "Pillory" spaces have been removed to modernize the game for children; "The only out-of-date punishment . . . retained is the Whipping Post (because) it has some eminent advocates at the present day . . . "
$750 Auc. 11/91 $850

MOTHER HUBBARD, ±1875
Card game; 3 × 4¼; many cards with a picture of an object and its name on each card; instr booklet includes rules for six dif games; cover shows dressed dog sitting in chair, smoking pipe, and reading the "Sporting News."
$60

GAME OF NATIONS OR QUAKER WHIST, 1898
Card game; 5½ × 7½; 52 cards representing four "Nations": Europe, Africa, Asia, America, each with 13 cards: Map, Man, Woman, Children, and House cards; America cards show Indian family, incl man in full regalia, and tee-pee; Africa cards show native warrior and family and hut; Asian cards show Chinese family and pagoda; European cards show Victorian house and couple in period dress and boy on bicycle; instr sheet.
$80

NAUGHTY MOLLY, 1905
Twelve cards can be laid out to form a bizarre illustrated story of what happened to a little girl who tried to trap some birds.
$75

NAVAL MANEUVERS, ≤1920
23 × 16, one-piece bldup and boxbot bd with parts tray under end section of board, which lifts up, five metal ships, five subs, spinner.
$200

THE GAME OF NOSEY, 1905
Card game; 8¼ × 4¾ × 3½; large nose (4½″ long) with mustache attached to pair of glasses, deck of cards; use of nose in game is similar to that of dunce cap.
$300

GAME OF OLD MAID, ±1870
Card game; half-slipcase card pack; 53 cards consist of 26 pairs, with the unusual inclusion of a *pair* of Old Maid cards—the odd card being the Old Maid/Old Bachelor card, illustrated with the two faces chin to chin; instr read THE MERRY GAME OF OLD MAID AND OLD BACHELOR; cards include "Ching chang chung" with queue down to the floor, and "15th Amendment," a well-dressed black character (the 15th Amendment gave the right to vote); the illustration on the cards represent the best of McLoughlin.
$80

THE MERRY GAME OF OLD MAID, 1898
10½ × 19½, boxbot bd, four wood pawns, large spinner, instr in cover; this is one of the few times OLD MAID has been seen as a board game; the litho on the center of the gameboard and identical one on the spinner is the same illustration as on the McLoughlin OLD MAID card game; cover is old maid in period outfit holding dog, with large heart background.
$300
$65 for GAME OF OLD MAID OR MATRIMONY (±1890; #408, 7½ × 7½, with boxbot bd)

THE IMPROVED GAME PETER CODDLE AND HIS LATEST TRIP TO NEW YORK, ±1900
Card game; cover shows startled man.
$40

PHOEBE SNOW, ≥1900
Board game with good city scenes; the character of Phoebe Snow came from the name of a train on Lackawanna Railroad in which a woman in white was associated with the clean running of the coal-burning engines; cross-collectible, railroad.
$200

THE NEW GAME PICTORIAL AUTHORS, 1888
Card game; cards show drawings of authors with signatures.
$30

GAMES OF THE PILGRIM'S PROGRESS, GOING TO SUNDAY SCHOOL, AND TOWER OF BABEL, 1875
9½ × 18½ bookshelf game with slipcover; 12 round-top wood pawns ("Pilgrims") and six pointed-tip wood pieces (the "Staff"), double-arrow block spinner, instr booklet; illust on slipcover shows man passing through gate guarded by two lions chained to walls

and is entitled "Christian Passes the Lions"; board opens to show PILGRIM'S PROGRESS on one side, with 17 illustrations incl "Faithful is Burnt" showing a burning at the stake; inside are GOING TO SUNDAY SCHOOL, showing four churches and ten illustrations, and TOWER OF BABEL with an extraordinary drawing of the building of the tower; game does not have "book-like" ends when closed.
$400

THE GAME OF PRINCE AND PRINCESS, 1905
Bookshelf board opens to 14½ × 15, with one board outside and two boards inside; spine has geometric design; wood sides and inside wood divider; three wood pawns, 17 red markers, 8 blue markers, large spinner, instr sheet for PRINCE AND PRINCESS, FOX AND GEESE, and SKIP; main board illust outside with giant and gnomes, one inside board with boy, fox, geese, and war scene, other inside board with geometric design.
$225

GAME OF PUSSY & THE THREE MICE, 1890 (instructions are 1891)
19½ × 10½; boxbot bd with wood sides, three small wood pawns (mice), one larger pawn (cat), large double arrow spinner, instr in cover; circuit, two-player game; illust dressed cats and mice on board and box.
$400 Auc. 11/91 $550 (missing cover aprons)

GAME OF RABBIT HUNT, 1870
Bookshelf game opens to 11½ × 9, wood sides and inside divider, plain spine, RABBIT HUNT in color on outside, ARCHERY and MORRICE (NINE MEN'S MORRIS) in black and white on inside, 24 wood markers (four colors: 9, 9, 3, and 3), double teetotum consisting of cardboard hexagon, wood shaft and 3″ cardboard box spinner platform, two instr sheets; good archery illustration, plus dog and rabbits illust; nice early McLoughlin.
$200

THE NEW GAME RED RIDING HOOD AND THE WOLF, 1887
Card game; 6¼ × 4½; instr booklet lists title as GAME OF LITTLE RED RIDING HOOD; illust of red-capped girl in forest picking flowers with wolf.
$85

RIVAL POLICEMEN, 1896
21 × 12¼; board game based on two actual competitive police forces in New York City in the late 19th century.
$1800 Auc. 9/88 $1,600

ROUND THE WORLD WITH NELLIE BLY, 1890
16 × 19½; one-piece bldup and boxbot bd (16 × 16) with two parts trays, four wood dice cups, four large turned pawns, two bone dice; spiral path of 72-day journey depicts sea, city, or a character for each day; beautiful litho board has spiral path depicting sea and city scenes from 72-day journey of real life character Nelly Bly, who beat the around-the-world-in-80-days record of Jules Verne's fictional Phineas Fogg; train marked "Nellie Bly" has caption "Over a mile a minute"; center board illust shows finish in NY with one bridge and Statue of Liberty, ship "speeding across the Atlantic," and illust

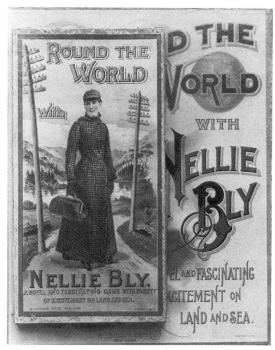

of Bly and Verne; cover shows Nellie Bly with travel bag on roadway; largest of the Nellie Bly games; © J.A. Grozier.
$300

ROUND THE WORLD WITH NELLIE BLY, 1890
8½ × 16½; gameboard, four fancy-turned wood pawns, four spinners, instr booklet advertising LOUISA on back, bldup with gold ribbon attached to facilitate removal of gameboard; bd bk is gold on red with Bly standing on globe; classic cover shows same illust in color of Bly in neck-to-floor coat holding satchel, with country lake and mountain scene and telephone poles in background.
$175 Auc. 10/91 $330

ROYAL GAME OF KINGS AND QUEENS, 1892
20 × 11½.
$625

SKIRMISH AT HARPER'S FERRY, 1891.
16⅛″ × 15″. Bldup bd with parts tray, set of black and set of white pieces; strategy game; board has Civil War scenes.
$550

SKIT SCAT, 1905
Card game. The beautifully illustrated cards, which lay out to make a serial story of the antics of a cat trying to get a fish in a bowl, are either drawn by, or copied from, a famous French illustrator.
$70

SNAKE GAME, ±1890
7¼ × 7¼ boxbot bd, four wood pawns, spinner, instr on cover.
$85

GAME OF SNAP, 1892
Card game; 4¼ × 3¼; 20 cards incl ten matching pairs which illust use of word "snap" (also used to mean a bite or break); one card, "The King of Snappers," shows alligator biting leg of black youth; bright color illustrations; instr in cover; cover shows shark chasing black swimmer; Punch and Judy Series.
$55 Auc. 10/91 $63

SPIDER'S WEB, 1898
This game was almost an exact reproduction of the game of SPIDER & FLY made twenty-eight years earlier.
$85

GAME OF STANDARD AUTHORS, ±1890
Card game; 6½ × 4½; 52 cards, instr sheet; gloss cards show illust of 13 authors; cover is detailed illust of desk with large bust of Shakespeare.
$25

STAR AUTHORS, 1888
Card game; 4½ × 6½; 36 cards, instr booklet © 1887; illust of 18 authors, listing of 54 book titles; cover is illust of Henry Wadsworth Longfellow.
$25

GAME OF THE TELEGRAPH MESSENGER BOY, ±1886
Card; 5¼ × 6¾; Card game version of DISTRICT MESSENGER BOY board game; instr sheet.
$60

UNCLE SAM'S MAIL, 1893
21½ × 9½; three-fold board opens to 35 × 20½, six wood pawns, 144 cardboard letters, four dice, two dice cups; wood box sides.
$350

WALKING THE TIGHT ROPE, 1897
10½ × 8½; boxbot bd, two wood pawns, spinner with tightrope illust; cover shows circus woman directing monkey pulling dog in wheelbarrow across tightrope; board shows men dressed as clowns, sailors, and harlequins crossing river on tightrope stretching from tree to rock, some plunging into water below; board is same as much earlier McLoughlin bookshelf game; style of board graphics is different from box graphics.
$150 Auc. 10/91 $300

WAR OF WORDS, ±1910
#370; card game; 4 × 5; 42 cards incl 35 each with a letter and an illust of a fox holding a goose, and six "prize" cards depicting dif animals, all clothed; instr sheet; cover shows well-dressed cat.
$60

WHERE'S JOHNNY, ±1885
Card game; 6½ × 5; 41 cards incl 22 with dif beautiful color illustrations and verse, and 19 with same color illustrated border and verse; instr sheet shows title WHERE IS JOHNNY? Cover is embossed gold lettering on red.
$75

WHICH IS IT? SPEAK QUICK OR PAY, 1889
Card game; 6¼ × 4½; 52 cards incl 17 animals, 18 birds, and 16 fish, plus one card of "Mr. Crowley," an 'Orang Outang' or chimp from New York's Central Park zoo; instr booklet has story which names all the animals; instr lists title as WHICH IS IT? BIRD, BEAST, OR FISH? Extra card advertises LOUISA in full color; cover shows fish in stream, inset of bird and cat.
$70

WHIRLPOOL GAME, ±1890
7½ × 7½, boxbot bd, 12 wood pawns (six of two colors), illustrated spinner; spiral path with illus in corners and center; game where slowest player wins (two players use one pawn at a time, fast-moving pawns get drawn into whirlpool and player enters new piece).
$35

YOUNG FOLKS HISTORICAL GAME, ±1890
Card game; 6¼ × 4½; 36 with headings of one or more persons, places, and events, and one or more questions for each listed event; example of "Brooklyn Bridge" heading followed by question, "What great bridge was completed in 1883?" provides clue to game's time period. Common.
$25

Merchandisers Inc.
250 Park Ave., New York, NY

ADMIRALS, THE NAVAL WAR GAME, 1939
19½" × 10½", two heavy die-cut cardboard gameboards each 15 × 10, 16 heavy metal die-cast ships (eight different types, including battleship, aircraft carrier, destroyer, and sub), pegs, instr sheet; BATTLESHIP style game; cover illlust is same as gameboards, depicting battleship firing.
$125

Metro (See **Drueke**)

M.H. Miller Co.
Jeannette, PA
1920s

See **Archer Toy Co.**

BROWNIE HORSESHOE GAME
$60

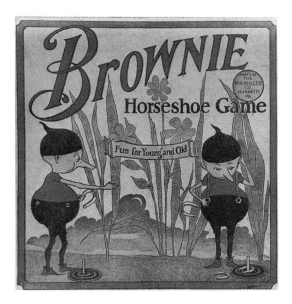

BROWNIE KICK-IN TOP, ±1920
The game is of interest to top collectors as well as collectors of Palmer Cox's Brownies.
$60

BROWNIE RING TOSS, ±1920
$50

Morris Systems Publshing Co.
550–559 Lafayette Blvd., Detroit, MI (1930s)
New York 10, NY (1940s)

THE 400, ARISTOCRAT OF GAMES, 1933
Trivia game with eight books with 400 questions in each; spinner, score sheets, instr sheet; book subjects include American History, Cooking & Food, Etiquette, Famous Sayings, Love & Marriage, Riddles, Spelling, and World Events.
$25

GAMEVELOPE, 1944/'45
5½" × 5½" envelope, wartime premium compliments of the National Jewish Welfare Board; six puzzle/games on four cards include the standard checkers, plus "zany puzzles."
$35

A.W. Mumford Co.
Auditorium Bldg., Chicago, IL
±1897

Mumford held the copyright on L.J. Colby's 1897 LITERATURE GAME (see listing), providing us with a time period for his company, and suggesting he may have started his own company after the success of the Colby game.

GAME OF INDUSTRIES, ±1897
Card game; 3½" × 2½"; cards with four questions on each, instr sheet.
$25

National Association Service (See **Leister Game Co.**)

National Games, Inc.
91 Church St., corner Union, West Springfield, MA
1946–≥1947

National is listed in city directories for 1946 and 1947 only, though some of its games look to be later, and one, CROSSWORDS, is dated 1954 (the only game to show a date, and one possibly made by a different company). The company was founded by James K. Makrianes in 1946 as an offshoot of his National Paper Box Co., which was first listed in 1943 and advertised "cardboard toys" by 1944. His son was vice president, and Mrs. Clara A. Makrianes, presumably his wife, was the treasurer. The company made predominantly standard board games with ordinary implements, but with unusually high-caliber illustrations on the box covers; the value of the games is governed primarily by the cover illustration; boxes were smaller than average standard boxes (about 17" × 9"). Traditional games such as CHINESE CHECKERS (#2005; bldup bd., 18 marbles) and GAME OF INDIA (#2003) are valued under $25.

GAME OF ARABIAN NIGHTS
$45

BIG GAME
#3021; 9¼ × 15 box; two versions: folding board 17 × 14½ with four wood markers and regular dice, and bldup bd die-cut to hold

dice cup, with four wood pawns and amber dice; instr sheet; box and board drawn by Gillette French.
$30

CROSSWORDS, 1954
This game, which does not have the same style of construction or illustration, may be by a different "National" company.
$20

FORTY NINERS
#5016; thin gameboard, four plastic pawns, two dice, instr sheet; cover shows prospector with riders chasing stagecoach in background; good cross-collectible for western theme.
$50

JACK AND THE BEANSTALK
$45

Newton & Thompson Mfg. Co.
Brandon, Vt
±1920s

The company made mostly traditional skill and action games plus MAH JONGG sets under different titles; all the games were predominately wood and came in thin cardboard boxes. Most of the games can be found for between $15 and $30, including CHING-CHONG (±1920; MAH JONGG game, wood tiles, wood box), JUNIOR OUTDOOR CROQUET (±1900; #554, croquet game for four), LUCKY STRIKE TEN PIN BOWLING SET (±1920), and TILES, THE OLD CHINESE GAME (≥1923; MAH JONGG game in wood box with 144 wood tiles, many wood stick counters and bone dice).

New York Toy and Game Co.
7 W. 22 St., New York, NY
1930s

Since New York was one of the centers of the game industry, the name of the company suggests more games should be available than have been found; a number of non-game items have been located.

TOY FISHING OUTFIT, 1930s
#108; 23½" long tube, 3½" in diam., with a handle in the middle, holds a 22½" long fishing pole, with metal shaft and reel and wood handle, plastic fish and float, string, 8-page instr booklet; the rod was designed to be used for actual outdoor fishing as well as for playing indoor games of FISHPOND.
$50

Noble & Noble, Publishers
New York, NY
games: 1920s

The company, noted mostly for books, made its own games as well as boards and cards for other companies, including Stoll & Edwards (see listing).

DEFENDERS OF THE FLAG, 1922
Card game; 8 × 6; cards have pictures of soldiers in uniform from various wars and various branches of service.
$45

THE THREE BEARS, 1922
Card game; cross-collectible, bears.
$35

Northwestern Products Co.
2721 Spruce St.; 2714 LaSalle St., St. Louis, MO

Northwestern is noted mostly for its "Poosh-M-Up" series of bagatelle games, all with cute cartoon illustrations. The average bagatelle should be valued at around $35, though prices at shows usually seem to be set much higher.

DIRECT HIT, ±1950,
15 × 10½" box comes with separate one-piece 16 × 19 double-thick board; four dart tipped plastic bombs over 3" long, 9½" painted wood plane with plastic mini-cockpit attaches to 8" wood shaft with metal rod attachment that moves to release bombs hanging from plane's underside; target has illust of town building with positive scores shown for acceptable targets incl two blimps and negative scores for targets such as hospital and museum; © Whe-gro Co.; cover shows plane and two children playing game; the large model plane, an unusual working device, makes this game much more desirable than the box might indicate.
$70

HAPPITIME BAGATELLE, 1933
Bagatelle; 17 × 11 wood "pin ball" with glass cover carries Northwestern's "Poosh-M-Up" logo, though the name "Northwestern" does not appear anywhere; the "Happitime" name is followed by "Sold only by Sears Roebuck and Co."; cartoon illust shows men on a construction site, but the game is also used to play baseball; pat. 1925018; the Sears name gives this bagatelle greater desirability.
$45

KING ARTHUR, ±1950
Bagatelle; 11 × 17 glass-covered "pin ball" with marbleized painted wood frame, and board illust of King Arthur theme.
$40

SUSPENSE, ±1950
An all-plastic version of HANGMAN, where plastic body parts are connected together hanging from a scaffold.
$20

TACTICS, 1940
"Game of World Strategy" consisting of gameboard with multiple squares, battleships and planes, wood markers, cardboard gold coins, two packs of chance cards.
$45

Novel Toy
159 W. 25th St., New York, NY
showroom: 208 N. Wells St., Chicago, IL
≤1940–≥1950

CONEY ISLAND PENNY PITCH, ±1950
S&A game with attractive 3-D setup, good color litho.
$55

MYSTIC WHEEL OF KNOWLEDGE, ±1950
12½" × 12½"; cardboard wheel, six two-sided quiz cards, spinner, instr on wheel.
$25

WISE OLD OWL, ±1950
#1500; magnetic CHIROMAGICA style game with composition owl on plastic base, five two-sided quiz sheets; illust shows owl, stars and moon.
$35

Novitas Sales Co.
Waltham, MA
1920s

Not only have just two games been found by this company, but the games are almost exactly the same except for the title.

CHIN-CHOW, and SUM-FUN (both ±1925)
10 × 3¼", MAH JONGG games, with 144 cardboard tiles, four racks (metal in SUM-FUN, cardboard in CHIN-CH0W), colored toothpicks for scoring, two tiny bone dice, folded instr sheet; boxes read "Known in China as MAH JONG, PE-LING, MAH-CHUCK," but the "MAH JONG" has been crossed out, possibly in keeping with import and manufacturing laws governing use of the word MAH JONGG.
$10

Noyes & Snow
1876
Noyes, Snow and Co.
1876–1879
Worcester, MA

(See **Snow Brothers**)

LETTERS IMPROVED FOR THE LOGOMACHIST, 1878
Card game; alphabet cards with picture of dog on each card, picture of crown on J, K, Q, V, X, and Z.
$35

Nucraft Toys
Wakefield, Mass.
1927–1928

Inventor Paul K. Guillow, a former U.S. naval aviator who made gliders and flying models, put out the LINDY game in 1927, the same year as Parker Brothers. He claimed ownership rights, and allegedly sued Parker, but Parker won. Guillow later invented and sold the board game CRASH.

CRASH, THE NEW AIRPLANE GAME, 1928
14 × 7½"; gameboard, 12 open body metal monoplanes, spinner, instr in cover; board and spinner hand lettered.
$50

THE NEW LINDY FLYING GAME, 1927
Card game in card pack; 75 cards incl 39 mile cards, 10 Take Off, 10 Favorable Weather, one Lucky Lindy card, and 15 hazard cards, including Motor Trouble, Storm, Heavy Fog, and Forced Landing; instr sheet; this "New York to Paris" game is the same concept as TOURING and basically the same as Parker Brothers' LINDY, THE NEW FLYING GAME. The Guillow game should be valued more highly than the more common Parker game.
$45

Offset Gravure Corp.
New York, NY
1930s

MERCHANT PRINCE, 1937
Board game.
nva

TRAILER TRAILS, 1937
Board game with comical theme of journey across the U.S.; good cartoon cover includes illust. of motorcycle cop which increases the game's value (motorcycles are desired and rare); "a trailer full of fun for adults and children."
$60

J. Ottmann Lith. Co.
New York, NY
1890s–early 1900s

Ottmann is one of the more desired manufacturers of card games from the late 1800s into the early twentieth century. The box cover and card illustrations were usually excellent. Some of its games were marked "St. Nicholas Series." Their common games, such as DR. BUSBY and PETER CODDLES, can be found for $25 and under.

COMIC CONVERSATION CARDS, 1890s
Card game; 6¼" × 8¾"; cut up question cards and strips of answer cards, instr on half bldup; excellent cover illust shows well dressed couple playing cards in parlor.
$40

COMIC CONVERSATION CARDS, 1890s
Card game; 5 × 7; see description above. The unusual, excellent cover illust on this version shows a well dressed black couple playing cards in parlor, with a dog like Buster Brown's "Tide" under the table; this is one of few games to show blacks in a positive light, comparable to the way in which the white couple was depicted in the companion game; since the two similar games exist, it would be interesting to know whether this game was specifically targeted to a black audience.
$90

FOXY GRANDPA AT THE WORLD'S FAIR, ≥1904
This is one of Ottmann's best card games because of the "Foxy Grandpa" cartoon license, the St. Louis Exposition theme, and the quality of the cover illustration; it is also an uncommon game.
$250

THE GAME OF JAPAN, 1903
$300 Auc. 6/92 $225 (taped, dirty)

THE LITTLE DRUMMER
13 × 13; boxbot bd, four wood markers, spinner; illust suggests Civil War scene; this unusual board game for Ottmann has no company identification on the cover.
$100

REX, ±1920
Card game; 5 × 6½" × 1½"; 151 cards incl 10 each of 15 numbers plus Rex or King card; instr sheet; cover shows King on throne being offered a jewel by kneeling servant.
$40

Ottoys (See **Valley Novelty Works**)

Geo. S. Parker
135 Bridge St., Salem, MA
(Store rooms at Derby Wharf)
1883–1888
Parker Brothers
Salem, MA
1888–1968 (family ownership)
1968–present (sold to General Mills in 1968, to others, and then to Hasbro in 1991)

The story goes that when George S. Parker was 16, he spent $40 to print 500 copies of a game he invented called BANKING. After three weeks' travel around Massachusetts he had sold more than 450 of them. With such success, he founded Geo. S. Parker & Co. in 1883. In 1885 his first catalog listed eight games, most of which he designed himself. He purchased the rights to the games of W. and S.B. Ives, and started selling the games of J.H. Singer (see listings); because of this, he was able to list 125 items in his 1887 catalog. In 1888, his brother Charles Parker joined the firm, and the company name was changed to Parker Brothers. Ten years later another brother, Edward H. Parker, signed on, and in 1901 the company incorporated.

Parker Brothers brought PING PONG to the U.S. in 1902, and introduced three classic card games between 1902 and 1906— FLINCH, PIT, and ROOK. Three years later production was devoted almost entirely to puzzles. By 1935 Parker had negotiated to produce MONOPOLY, and by 1936 the company was making some of the most substantial games of the twentieth century. Parker Brothers kept pace with Milton Bradley throughout the 1900s, gearing some of its line to adults while Bradley focused more on children.

This American giant of the toy industry (along with Bradley) was bought by General Mills in 1968 and spun off as Kenner-Parker Toys Inc. in 1985. They became a division of Tonka in 1987, and then Tonka was bought by Hasbro in 1991. Production of all games was moved to the Hasbro-owned Milton Bradley factory in Springfield.

The prime pre-war period for Parker Brothers as far as collectors are concerned are the 1880s and '90s. Geo. S. Parker games are difficult to find and eagerly sought after, but, except for the rare pieces, they don't have as much value as the oversized Parker Bros. board games from half a decade later. Many of these large, exquisite games consisted of a one-piece board on a solid wood frame, with a patented sliding drawer in which the implements were kept; some of these historical treasures are valued as highly as McLoughlin games.

With over a century of games to its credit, Parker Brothers has produced a wide range of items for America's education and leisure, a very small sampling of which is shown here.

Geo. S. Parker

BAKER'S DOZEN, ≤1885
Extremely rare.
nva

BANKING, 1883
Parker's first game. Extremely rare.
nva

BILLY BUMPS VISIT TO BOSTON, 1888
Card game has advertisement for George Parker's favorite game CHIVALRY on the bottom of the box.
$35

CHIVALRY, 1888
Strategy board game—one of Geo. Parker's favorite games; became CAMELOT in 1927 or 1930.
$100 (original only)

THE GOOD OLD GAME OF OLIVER TWIST, ≤1888
Card game; 4¾ × 6¼; incl 19 pairs of cards (8 pairs illustrated) with character and quote (Mr. Grimwig: "I had serious thoughts of eating my head to-night."); Oliver Twist card and an Artful Dodger card; instr sheet; cover illust shows Oliver standing with spoon and plate in front of "Master of the Workhouse," saying, "Please, Sir, I want some more."
$115 Auc. 10/91 $153 (apron missing, some box wear)

GREAT BATTLEFIELDS, 1886
Card game. One of Parker's earliest games. Rare.
$120

IVANHOE, 1886
Card game "founded on the famous story of Sir Walter Scott." Somewhat common.
$50

JOHNNY'S HISTORICAL, 1888/1890
Card game; 4¾ × 6¼; cards with names of one or more people, places, events on each followed by one to five questions; there are at least three dif. versions, each with dif. number of cards and dif. subjects; there are dif color boxes of this game, and one printing where the color was out of whack; some boxes read "Geo. S. Parker" but instrs read "Parker Brothers"; © Harry J. Phillips; most common Geo. S. Parker game; values of all editions are equal.
$30

SPECULATION, ≤1885
$65, depending on the market

WHEN MY SHIP COMES IN, 1888
Card game; 5½ × 4; 80 cards strips divided into four categories; parlor game similar to conundrums with no competetive play or winner; instr sheet; cover shows ship in full sail with seaside village background.
$45

Parker Brothers

ABC, ±1902
Card game; this colorfully illustrated children's educational game matches an animal with each letter of the alphabet. "X" illustrates the "X-mas Turkey.")
$40

ACROSS THE CONTINENT, ±1910
18 × 16¾; red box version of game first produced in 1891 (1890 pat. #439089); gold lettering and gold train; four large wood pawns, four bone dice, two packs of destination tickets, instr pasted in cover names games later than the © 1901 shown on the gameboard, which is large, colorful topographical map of U.S. showing characteristics of the country pictorially (such as cotton fields, mining, cattle raising) and principal railroad routes.
$50

ACROSS THE CONTINENT, 1922
18 × 11¼ (see above); two-fold board opens to 32 × 17; cover is one of best transportation covers showing speeding train, roadster, and motorcycle, passenger ship in the bay, and train on bridge in background.
$130

ADMIRAL BYRD'S SOUTH POLE GAME, LITTLE AMERICA, ±1930
17 × 13; bldup bd; four cardboard microphones are attached by string to playing pieces; based on establishment of Little America base at the South Pole by Byrd in 1928.
$200 Auc. 10/91 $260

ALICE IN WONDERLAND, 1930s
15¾ × 13; boxbot bd, 20 letter cards spell A-L-I-C-E, others name characters such as The Walrus, The Mock Turtle, etc.; instr sheet; illustrations in each corner of board show Mad Hatter, White Rabbit, Dodo, and frog; tea party illust in center; cover shows Alice and five inset illustrations; cross-collectible.
$70

AS THE WORLD TURNS, 1966
Based on the CBS TV show that premiered 1956; Parker issued this game ten years after the show began, just as it began to slip from its spot as the number one daytime program.
$40

AUCTION LETTERS, 1900
card game; 7½ × 5½; 56 letter cards, $24 in cardboard coins, a 5 × 3¾ money box, instr sheet; cover shows dressed rabbits auctioning cards with letters on them; players bid for letters to make four-letter words.
$35

THE GAME OF AUTHORS, ±1890, 1896, 1897
±1890: #372; 4½ × 6; 30 cards illust 10 authors; cover illust of Oliver Wendell Holmes. 1896: 6½ × 5; 52 cards (gloss-finish, probably made by Cincinnati Card Co.), 2 ad cards for WATERLOO and CHIVALRY, instr sheet; cards have illust of author or beautiful detailed illust of scene depicting author's work. 1897: 9½ × 6½; wood frame box divided into four compartments, 56 cards, instr sheet; gilt-edge cards have illust of 14 authors; colorful cover shows family playing game.
$20 for ±1890
$25 for 1896
$20 for 1897

BARBER POLE, 1908
S&A; tiddley wink game with litho on wood pole; game was in production 1908–1933.
$25

THE BARON MUNCHAUSEN GAME, 1933
Letter cubes; 5 × 3½ × 2; five wood cubes that could spell B-A-R-O-N; 3" high cardboard dice cup and box cover show Baron playing game; illustrated box aprons; based on NBC radio's "The Jack Pearl Show."
$30 Auc. 10/91 $57

BATTLE OF MANILA, 1899
19 × 15; one-piece bldup and boxbot bd with parts drawer, four intricately designed metal battleships, wood "shells" (ammo) in four colors plus smaller "Spanish" shells, wood dice cup, three bone dice, spinner; box cover illust of battleships and Dewey, path board through ocean shows Manila, Cavite, and Corregidor Island; "A Game Commerorative [*sic*] of Admiral Dewey's Famous Victory, May 1, 1898."
$65

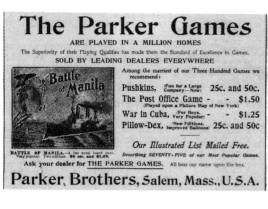

THE NEW BICYCLE GAME, 1894
21 × 12; boxbot bd has wood sides, spinner, 4 cardboard bicyclists on wood stands, destination cards, inst in cover; cross-collectible.
$575

THE BLACK CAT FORTUNE TELLING GAME, 1897
Card game; 6½ × 5; 24 cards; instr sheet titled BLACK CAT FORTUNE TELLING CARDS; this game generates an unusual amount of interest and draws higher prices than might be expected; cross-collectible as fortune telling and one of the best illustrated cat games.
$110 Auc. 10/91 $150

BLOCK, 1905
Card game; 53 cards consisting of eleven cards each of five suits "A" through "E," with the exception of the "A4" and "A9" cards) one of few games to have such an odd card count); listed as having been awarded the Grand Prize at the 1904 World's Fair in St. Louis; patented June 13 in "U.S.A. (and) Great Britain . . . ," four months before QUIT, an identical game, received its patent in "the United Kingdom, (and) America . . ."; it seems, then, that BLOCK and QUIT were identical, the latter title possibly originating in England and the former in the U.S.; the rules for BLOCK, listed as "copyright Geo. S. Parker," have an extra paragraph (beyond those of QUIT) for clarification. Valued more for play than collectibility.
$20

BOAKE CARTER'S STAR REPORTER, 1937
Gameboard, six airplanes on tall stands, six telephones, six colored pins, cork for pins, cards incl 63 news items, 9 disaster, and 8 catastrophe, two dice, instr sheet; game was in production 1937–1963. This game and STAR REPORTER (sans Carter) are among the games most often requested by players and collectors alike.
$90 Auc. 10/91 $178

BOOM OR BUST, 1951
15½ × 15½; bldup bd has posts to hold smaller board overlay, which changes "Normal" board to "Boom" (on one side) or "Bust" (on the other), affecting property values around the board; original version has board die-cut with small slots next to property spaces, plus numerous cardboard color "T"s to identify property ownership by player; popular playing game of the 1950s sought after by noncollectors and priced higher than similar games because of its demand; not uncommon (but getting increasingly harder to find); well-played, it may be difficult to find with a box in good condition.
$85 (original with "T" pieces)
$70 (other editions)

BOTTLE-QUOITS, 1897
S&A; 10 × 3¾ × 4; 9" wood base with 3½" high posts connected with wire that passes through wood bottle; five cardboard rings; instr in cover; rings tossed onto bottle may tip bottle, dumping previous rings; cover shows only a woman playing the game—unusual for the period and type of game.
$70 Auc. 10/91 $87

BOWLING, 1896
15½ × 11½; boxbot bd, spinner and playing pieces, instr in cover.
$135
$40 for smaller (5¼ square) game of same title from 1900.

THE GAME OF BOY SCOUTS, 1912
5½ × 4; five patrols of ten cards each; box stamped "Royalty paid to Owners of U.S. Patent No. 952939, Patented March 22, 1910"; cover shows boy scout climbing rock.
$50

THE BOY SCOUTS' PROGRESS GAME, 1926
Gameboard, four wood pawns, metal bust of Abe Lincoln, two dice, cardboard disks, wood dice cup, instr sheet; box cover identical to bd back litho.
$145
$110 without bust of Lincoln

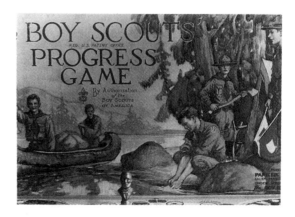

BUFFALO HUNT, 1898
5¼ × 5¼; boxbot bd, four wood markers, die, instr in cover; tiny board game is simple path game from and to Indian camp; cover shows two cowboys chasing buffalo; game was in production 1898–1906.
$35

THE CAKE WALK GAME, ≤1900
15 × 9; the box for this Parker game reads "Anglo-American Game Co., Montreal"; boxbot bd, four playing pieces, spinner, instr in cover; illust. shows seven blacks on cover and four on the game-board; the "Cake walk" was a popular dance of the period; unusual piece, prime black collectible.
$750

(Krim collection)

CALLING ALL CARS, ±1938
#34; 16 × 7¾; board 14½" square, four metal race cars with drivers, 11 × 6¾" card with two spinners, instr sheet; orange box with illust of police cars. Somewhat common.
$45
$25 for later versions, especially larger box.

CAMELOT, 1930
Board game based on CHIVALRY, said to be Geo. S. Parker's favorite game, and eventually marketed in abbreviated version called CAM. Common.
$30

THE GAME OF CAMOUFLAGE, 1918
Card game; 6¾ × 4; pack of cards with intricate card back illust of soldiers and large anti-aircraft gun; camouflage cards have geometric design, other illust cards are Bomb, Howitzer, Mortar; special spinner; instr sheet; cover is gold lettering on brown box.
$40

CAPER, 1970
11 × 23; gameboard with 3 platforms, 4 pawns, 3 plastic cars, 4 jewels, metal tools and ladders, cards, instr in cover.
$30

CATS AND DOGS, 1929
17¼ × 9; four 2½" tall painted celluloid dogs and cats in wood stands, large spinner with cat as the dial, instr in cover; cover shows dog and cat on path in flower garden; the celluloid pieces are unusual and exceptional.
$125 Auc. 10/91 $260

THE CENTURY RUN BICYCLE GAME, 1897.
$350

CHIVALRY (See listing under Geo. S. Parker)
Many editions were made of this game after Geo. S. Parker's introduction of it in 1888, until the manufacture of CAMELOT between 1927 and 1930.
$50 pre WWI and deluxe editions
$25 later editions

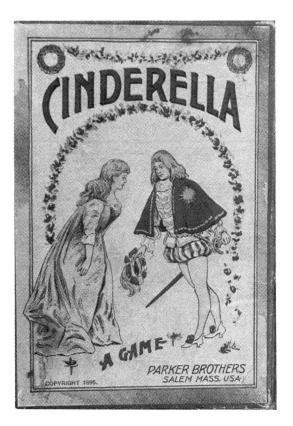

CINDERELLA, 1895
Card game; 4 × 5½; 33 cards include 15 pairs (depicting scenes from the story) and three singles: the Prince, Cinderella, and a slipper.
$55

CLUE, 1949
Board with separate parts box; five metal implements (weapons: knife, candlestick, revolver, lead pipe, wrench) and *real* rope (as found in only the earliest editions), cards of suspects and locations.
$50 for edition subtitled THE SHERLOCK HOLMES GAME
$40 for other earliest editions (real rope)
$20 for later full-box editions

COCK ROBIN, 1895
Card game; 5½ × 4; 27 cards (13 pairs plus killer Sparrow); instr sheet; multicolor drawings of animals of the "Who Killed Cock Robin?" story.
$40

COMICAL HISTORY OF AMERICA, 1924
Card game; game was in production 1924–1930.
$30

CONFLICT, 1940
Gameboard and 48 metal implements (battleships, airplanes, and anti-aircraft guns); one of Parker's most popular games; the wartime version substituted composition pieces for the metal implements. Common.
$40 (metal pieces)
$50 (composition pieces)

CONTACK, ≥1939
Six-sided domino tile game, originally produced in 1939 by Volume Sprayer Manufacturing Co. of Tulsa, Oklahoma. Very common.
$20 hexagonal box
$10 rectangular box

THE COON HUNT, ≤1904, Parker Brothers
15 × 9½; boxbot bd, wood block spinner, four pawns, instr in cover includes error crossed out and hand written over (may not be on all copies); cover illust shows four blacks with exaggerated big lips, each with gun, cane, club, ax, with raccoon looking down from tree unnoticed; path board shows hunting dog and black character "Uncle Rastus."
$550 Auc. 11/91 $750

THE GOOD OLD GAME OF CORNER GROCERY, ≥1901
Card game; 6½ × 5; "New century edition" of game © 1887 by Geo. S. Parker; 40 cards (some illustrated) "marked with names of articles usually sold in grocery stores" and money box with 112 pieces of money totaling the value of all the groceries.
$45

THE GAME OF COTTONTAIL AND PETER, 1922
16 × 16½ board, parts box 4 × 3 × 2, two die-cast metal rabbits, two die-cast metal foxes, wood dice cup, two dice, instr sheet; colorfully illust with foxes chasing rabbit in center, animals looking on around perimeter; bd bk and box wrap illust with rabbits collecting eggs.
$40 Auc. 10/91 $120

THE COUNTY FAIR, ±1895
Card game; 6¼ × 4¾; cards illustrating dif characters, incl those too poor to buy at the fair: "Small Dirty Boy," "Jim The Beggar," "Old Man From the Poor-farm," and "George Washington Whitewash," a black character.
$45

CRAZY TRAVELLER, 1908
S&A; 12½ × 12½; thick, finely polished wood box bottom and sides with eight fixed wood pins, six movable wood pins, metal top with winder, instr in cover; cover shows odd character (shaped like animated top) and illust of buildings, bird, and tiny dog holding umbrella with tail.
$60

CROW HUNT, ±1940
S&A; 17½ × 15; target of four cardboard crows and Elmer the duck on fence; repeating rifle shoots six rubber bands in rapid succession; hitting Elmer is worth more points since "he . . . shouldn't be there anyhow."
$50 ($25 with gun missing)

DOMESTIC ANIMALS, 1903
Card game; 5½ × 4; 56 cards picturing a dif animal on each card with statements about the animal; instr booklet from the United States Playing Card Co.; plain cover illust shows two horses and fence.
$15

THE DRUMMER BOY GAME, ±1890
9 × 15; boxbot bd, four markers, spinner; spiral path board leads players from rank of drummer boy to attaining rank of colonel; board shows illustrations of soldiers in formation, cover shows drummer boy during battle, with head bandaged.
$125

EAST IS EAST AND WEST IS WEST, A TRIP AROUND THE WORLD, 1920s
16¾ × 11¾; board shows photographs of major cities and sites; cover shows ocean liner with insets of street scene, incl Flatiron Bldg in New York City and Arab market scene entitled "Streets of Cairo."
$100 Auc. 10/91 $95 (missing aprons)

EDDIE CANTOR'S "TELL IT TO THE JUDGE," 1930s
10½ × 34¼; bd bk litho and cover have illust of Cantor holding up cards from game; money has illust of Cantor; the game was made with two gameboards: the first, ±1933, showed an angular path; it was replaced ≤1939 by a rounded colorful path with cartoon illustrations superimposed over photo of Cantor.
$45 (earlier edition with no face on gameboard)
$65 (version showing Cantor's face on gameboard)

FINANCE AND FORTUNE, 1936
19¼ × 9¾; six wood figural pawns (each dif shape and color), 48 wood houses (eight each of six colors) plus many same color houses, chance cards, money, rent card, two dice, instr sheet; has Chance spaces and four railroads (Union Pacific, New York Central, Santa Fe, and Boston & Maine); players collect $200 when passing starting space marked "Cash Here," players buy unowned property and place their house on the space (there are no deed cards) and subsequent players landing on the space must pay rent to owner; the object is to survive while opponents go bankrupt; no patent # on gameboard; one of the MONOPOLY style trading games based on Elizabeth Magie Phillips' 1904 LANDLORD'S GAME; Parker originally bought rights to FINANCE from the Finance Game Co. (see listing), published FINANCE AND FORTUNE in 1936, then changed the name to FINANCE and issued another game called FORTUNE, which "was published merely to secure its trademark"; amazingly enough, all four games, MONOPOLY, THE LANDLORD'S GAME, FINANCE, and FORTUNE, were offered in 1939 (and possibly earlier); FORTUNE was unsuccessful and gone by 1940. FINANCE AND FORTUNE was again produced under that title ≤1947; there was a © 1958 edition as well. The subtitle HOUSE AND LOT was also used to protect the name from competitive use.
$45 (1936); $20 (1940); $10 (1958)

FINANCE, ±1937 (See FINANCE AND FORTUNE)
$40 (1930s); $30 (1940s)

THE FIVE WISE BIRDS, 1923
S&A; 17½ × 8; target game; five cardboard birds on wood fence attached to wood stand (sign reads, "No shooting allowed"), 19" long wood-handle, metal-barrel rapid-shooter rifle; cover commentary: "It is wrong to shoot real birds but these imaginary comical birds from the Island of Woozoo cannot be hurt with the toy gun"; game was in production until 1964.
$45 for original; $15–$30 for later editions

FLINCH, 1902
One of the country's most popular card games; licensed from the Flinch Card Co. and purchased outright in 1938. Very, common.
$5

FLYING THE BEAM, 1941
18½ × 9½, four heavy die-cast metal tokens, large 7" × 7" spinner, instr sheet; game designed by army pilot Cpt. William J. Chapman, based on actual blind flying conditions.
$85

FLYING THE UNITED STATES AIR MAIL, 1929
18 × 14¾; thick, large board showing "Air Mail routes over the United States," 36 thin cardboard typed and handwritten letters (2¾ × 3½), four metal planes on tall stands, four dice, four wood dice cups, map board shows specific scenes in dif regions; letters include personal notes, such as "Sorry to hear you were delayed . . . . remember it takes gas to run a car—Always Your Loving Mother,"

and business letters, such as to "Messrs. James Kodak & Co., Inc., Rochester, NY; cover shows twin engine aircraft on ground and night scene with searchlight beams.
$115 Auc. 10/91 $126

FORTUNE, ±1938 (See FINANCE AND FORTUNE)
$70

FUN AT THE ZOO, 1902
21 × 11; boxbot bd with wood sides, four pawns, spinner, instr in cover; path board illustrates various zoo animals; cover, however, illustrates a circus setting.
$200

GAME FOR EVENING PARTIES, pb±1910
22¾ × 10¾; compendium of games including: pads for CONUN-DRUMS, THE TROLLEY CAME OFF, PILLOW-DEX, WHO?, PUSHKINS, SPOON & EGG RACE, PEANUT RACE; box bot separated into four sections with wood dividers, painted peanut shells, wood balls, metal spoons, instr sheet, ad for AUCTION LETTERS and PING-PONG; rare and interesting multi-game set.
$300

THE GUINESS BOOK OF WORLD RECORDS GAME, 1979
Though it is a good licensed property, this game is not likely to appreciate much in value because it contains no information about actual world records.
$9

HEADS AND TAILS, ±1900, ≥1901
Card game; 4½ × 3½; 19 cards (nine pairs plus lion card); good color illust of jungle animals.
$30 Nickel Edition, instr in cover
$25 Regular edition post–1900 (by Parker *Inc.*), instr sheet

HEY WHAT?, 1907
Card game; 6½ × 5; 36 cards incl 18 "Hey?" cards with five questions per card and 18 "What" cards with name and drawing of a different animal; sample question: "What has ears like your own?"; sample answer: "A mud turtle"; instr sheet; the object of the game is to keep from smiling or laughing; same flowered box wrap as GOOD HUNTING, CORNER GROCERY, and BLACK CAT FORTUNE TELLING GAME (1897).
$20

HIDDEN TITLES, 1908
Card game was in production until 1935.
$15

HISTORY UP TO DATE, 1901
Card game was in production until 1932.
$15

HOLD THE FORT, 1895
15 × 13; one-piece boxbot and bldup board with parts tray; classic two-player strategy game, 3 pieces versus 50; board shows two battle scenes, U.S. shields, flags, and eagle with White House in the background; cover shows force attacking a hill, tattered flag waving.
$225

HOWDY DOODY'S OWN GAME, 1950s
S&A; 15¼ × 7; four cardboard targets with illust of Clarabell, Flub-A-Dub, Howdy Doody, and Dilly Dally attached to wood and cardboard target stands on wood base, four wood balls, instr on target; © Bob Smith.
$70

THE GOOD OLD GAME OF INNOCENCE ABROAD (New Edition), ≥1901 (© 1888)
18½ × 20, boxbot and buildup are one piece with parts tray, wood box bottom side, instr sheet, two wood dice cups, three wood pawns; repackaged revision of 1888 game is undated, but Parker Bros. "Inc." on box indicates the game is from 1901 or later. Title is parody of Mark Twain book.
$100 for new edition
$225 for original 1888 edition, AMUSING GAME OF INNOCENCE ABROAD

JACK AND THE BEAN STALK, 1895
9½ × 6½; boxbot bd, two wood pawns, spinner; cover illust of bearded giant holding gold cup and knife, and boy; board illust shows castle, farm, country.
$65 Auc. 10/91 $72

THE GAME OF JACK STRAWS, ≥1901
S&A; 4½ × 6; various colored thin wood sticks, shaped as swords, rifle, umbrella, walking stick, etc.; wood handled metal hook used to remove the Jack Straws from the pile; inst sheet is not marked Parker Brothers *Inc.*, though box is; cover shows boy in odd outfit incl strange hat.
$25

JOHNNY GET YOUR GUN, 1928
13½ × 11½; boxbot bd with attached spinner (on wood base) in shape of rifle with wood handle and metal barrel, 16 wood markers, instr in cover; board illust shows 12 animals, most in clothing, incl wolf in glasses reading book "Little Red Riding Hood"; cover shows man with gun bigger than he is, with some animals around him; humorous animal illustrations plus unusual gun spinner add considerable value to this game.
$75

THE JOURNEY TO BETHLEHEM, 1923
12½ × 15½; heavy folded board opens to 24½ × 15 and shows "the location of 145 of the Historic Places Famous in Bible History"; three die-cast Shepherds on camels and three die-cast Wise Men in plain thin cardboard parts box; spinner is six-pointed star; instr sheet; cover shows three Wise Men on camels with one man walking; unusual implements make this a desirable item.
$160

THE AMUSING GAME OF KILKENNY CATS, 1890
$100

KOMICAL KONVERSATION KARDS, 1893
Card game; 6½ × 5; pack of one color question cards, and pack of dif color answer cards; instr sheet; "A kuriously kontrived kaptivating kuriousity." The high price this game fetched at auction is an anomaly.
$30 Auc. 10/91 $110

KRIEGSPIEL JUNIOR, 1915
Gameboard 16 × 22, parts box 5¾ × 4¼; 40 pawns, six bone dice (three thrown per turn), two cardboard dice cups, instr sheet; board, showing cities of Paris, Brussels, Berlin, Vienna, Cologne, and Strassburg, is similar to 1895 board for WATERLOO in terms of path movement, design and rules.
$80

LEAPING LENA, 1920s
S&A; 12¾ × 7¾; one-piece board with attached pegs and easel for standing upright, six rubber rings; target ring toss game.
$65

LINDY, THE NEW FLYING GAME, 1927
#737; Card game; 5½ × 4, divided box bottom; 99 cards (51 mileage cards, 48 event and move cards); (see also "Nucraft Toys", THE NEW LINDY FLYING GAME); cover shows plane flying across ocean, apron shows plane with sunburst background; based on Lindbergh popularity; retail 75¢; similar to TOURING, MILLE BOR-NES, and WINGS. Common, and usually overpriced.
$30

THE MAD MAGAZINE GAME, 1979
Board game with box cover by *Mad* magazine artist Jack Davis. Common, but liable to increase in value more than games from the same period.
$25

The MELVIN PURVIS' "G"-MEN DETECTIVE GAME, 1936
Gameboard lavishly illustrated; three heavy die-cast metal figures. According to correspondence between Purvis and Parker Brothers, Purvis signed a contract in 1935, which was terminated in 1946; his royalty on the 5,600 games sold in 1938 came to $210.
$85

MISTRESS MARY, QUITE CONTRARY, ±1905
17¾ × 10½; boxbot bd, four wood pawns, spinner; board shows four flowers with human heads; based on poem, "Mistress Mary," later titled "Mary, Mary"; cover litho of woman in garden doesn't resemble board litho.
$45 Auc. 10/91 $104

MONOPOLY, 1935 (first edition)
Standard board and black apron parts box; there is no patent number on the gameboard and Parker name appears on the board at the bottom of GO square only, making this edition probably the first Parker MONOPOLY; Charles Darrow © 1933 appears near Jail space; 1935 instr sheet, six wood pawns in different shapes and colors, unmarked money.
$150 Auc. 10/91 $100

MONOPOLY, 1935
With "patent pending" notice in center of board.
$70

MONOPOLY, 1935
Standard size white box; board says © 1935 Parker Bros., with one patent number, Darrow's name © 1933 near Jail space, ten metal tokens incl. rocking horse, lantern, purse; possibly Parker's first large box edition (a later edition than the board with separate parts box).
$55 Auc. 10/91 $89

MONOPOLY, 1935
With two patent numbers.
$25

MONOPOLY, 1936 and later
$10–$15

MONOPOLY, 1935 COMMEMORATIVE EDITION, 1985
10¾ × 10¾ × 3¼ embossed metal box; split and double fold board, "gold-tone finish" tokens include lantern, cannon, rocking horse, iron, top hat, thimble, shoe, open race car, purse, and ship; wood houses; hotels illustrated and marked "Grand Hotel"; 1935 money; deed cards; Chance cards; Community Chest cards. This set is likely to increase in value rapidly.
$55

NUMBER PLEASE, 1961
Based on ABC TV show; the cover pictures host Bud Collier.
$25

ORBIT, 1959
16" × 7¾"; board, two spinners, wood disk.
$45

PANAMA CANAL G., ±1910
21¾ × 14¾; wood boxbot sides, bldup bd with parts tray, four wood dice cups, four wood playing pieces, destination tickets.
$225

PENNY POST, 1892
Gameboard, four metal messenger boys, miniature letter, spinner.
$250

PEPPER, 1906
Card game was in production through 1912.
$15

PETER CODDLES TRIP TO NEW YORK, 1934
Nickel Edition was in production until the mid-1940s.
$15

PICTURE READING GAME, ±1910
Card game; 6½ × 5; 27 heavy cardboard cards (9 × 3) with three bright color images per card; cover shows four children playing game.
$20

PING PONG, 1902
S&A, 12 × 6; two wood rackets (11½" long) with Parker Bros. stamp, two wood net posts 7¾" long, two wood post holders with metal table clamps, net, ball, large instr. sheet with illust of other Parker PING PONG set showing woman playing; box is informational, with no illust.
$20
$125 for long box with illustration of woman and racket

PIT, 1903
Card game; 5¼ × 3¾; 63 cards; the *Boston Herald* on Oct. 14, 1903, said "Pit is the latest game which society has taken to heart . . . . It is an uproarious Board of Trade in miniature—the wheat pit of Chicago in full play. . . ." PIT is the most common proprietary American card game.
$4 card pack edition; $6 box edition; $30 John Held, Jr., cover.

POLLY PICKLES, QUEEN OF THE MOVIES, 1921
19 × 19 board, parts box, four large wood pawns, six wood cubes with letters that spell "M-O-V-I-E-S"; board has caricatures and humorous directives, all in movie theme.
$100 Auc. 10/91 $109

THE GAME OF POPULATIONS, ≥1901
Card game; 6½ × 5; 40 cards (all with same illust) each showing a U.S. city and its population; instr sheet.
$20

THE GAME OF PORTS AND COMMERCE, 1899
Card game; 5½ × 4; 52 cards (13 sets with a photo of a U.S. city in each set and listing three products associated with that city); instr sheet; cover shows a port with ships, large city in background, ocean liner and dock in foreground, and separate image of woman of commerce.
$30

POST OFFICE, 1896
Gameboard shows the details of every building in lower Manhattan; extraordinary and rare, board alone is valued at $500.
nva

PRISONER OF ZENDA, ±1896
Based on book by Anthony Hope.
$600

PUSS IN THE CORNER, 1895
7¾ × 7¾; boxbot bd, 12 wood pawns, spinner with mice illust, instr in cover; board illust shows four cats, incl one crying "No mice for a week"; cover illust, unlike mildly comic rendition of cats on gameboard, is serious drawing of two cats.
$100

QUICK WIT, 1938
Card game; 5½ × 4; 52 cards for game similar to CATEGORIES; cover has signed illustration by cartoonist Gluyas Williams; two identical editions except one cover red on gray, other red on yellow.
$30

QUIT, 1905
Card game; same as BLOCK (see listing).
$20

QUIZ, ≥1920
Card game; 5½ × 4; "The Game of 100 Questions" actually has 101, each on its own card; answer sheet; instr sheet; question about 18th Amendment dates game sometime around or after 1920; cover shows sailing ship with question about what great General it was named after; series A; retail 50¢.
$20

RADIO GAME, 1923
Card game; 7½ × 4¾; 56 cards incl 48 with dif call letters for two stations on each, four "Lis'nin In" cards, four S.O.S. cards; instr booklet; cover shows family listening to early radio with horn speaker.
$75

READY-CLOWN 3-RING CIRCUS GAME, 1952
19¾ × 12¾; folded board opens to 19½ × 19½, four cardboard clowns on wood stands, four cardboard chariots on wood bases, 28 illust cardboard disks (seven each of four colors), four wood barrels, die.
$40

REAL RADIO GAME, 1926
13½ × 9¾; board is map with cities with radio stations; four sheets show broadcasting stations of the U.S., Canada, Cuba, and Mexico;

radio dial card, map pins, large spinner, instr in cover; B&W checkerboard pattern cover is unusual in that it does not show Parker name.
$65

GAME OF RED RIDING HOOD, 1895
9½ × 6½; boxbot bd, two dif size wood pawns, spinner, instr in cover; illust board path; excellent cover illust shows Riding Hood and wolf walking together. VG, one cover crease, some perimeter edge swaths, 1″ apron detached; substitute marker for small pawn.
$350

THE GAME OF RED RIDING HOOD
14 × 11; board opens to 20½ × 10¼; European-style quality painted metal wolf 2″ long and painted metal riding hood nearly 2″ high, wood dice cup, bone die, instr pasted into cover, wood support in box bottom; board illust shows riding hood, wolf, house and workers in forest; cover is plain lettering (no illust) and uninteresting; one of few old games where the high value is based solely on the board graphics and unusual implements.
$150

RICH UNCLE, 1946
14½ × 12½; one-piece stand up heavy board, money cards, dice, Daily Bugle cards, instr sheet; popular game for nostalgia reasons; drawings of cartoon character from MONOPOLY, "Mr. Pennybags." Common.
$45
$30 for 1959 edition

RISK, 1959
Board game that became one of only two territorial war simulation games to be embraced by the general public after WWII (DIPLOMACY being the other). The name "Risk" was suggested by a Parker salesman, the letters R-I-S-K being the combined first initials of his four grandchildren. Collected by players, mainly for the wood pieces.
$25

ROOK, 1906
One of the most popular longest-selling proprietary card games in history; a Geo. Parker favorite that he published under an offshoot company, The Rook Co., when Parker Brothers' decided not to add the game to its line. Very, very common.
$6 ($8 for The Rook Co. edition)

THE GAME SHERLOCK HOLMES, 1904
Card game; 5½ × 4; 56 cards incl illustrated Sherlock Holmes cards; instr sheet; gold lettering on red box; cross-collectible: game is of

much more value to mystery and Holmes collectors than to game collectors; later edition with box illust of silhouette of carriage is more valuable.
$50 red box $65 silhouette box

THE GAME OF SHOPPING, ±1895
Card game; 4 × 5½; numerous cards marked with names and price of articles sold in stores (Toys and Games, Game of Travel, $1.25), 36 cardboard money squares whose values total the value of all articles; instr sheet; cover illust shows two ladies and child at counter of department store; nearly the same as THE GOOD OLD GAME OF CORNER GROCERY.
$40

THE SIEGE OF HAVANA, 1898
Bldup box bot bd with parts drawer, spinner, metal ships, wood pawns, dice, dice cup; excellent illustrations.
$300

SKYSCRAPER, 1937
Four separate small boards, dozens of cards, 150 tokens, and 67 wooden buildings and sections of buildings; billed as "a new Parker game for adults." An excellent example of the quality and quantity of components in games manufactured shortly after the depression (1936–'39), and a good example of Parker's catering to an adult market.
$75

THE GAME OF SNAP, ±1905
Card game; 4¼ × 5½; 27 color cards (9 × 3) incl alligator about to eat black boy fishing, and black native (wearing one sock, one shoe, grass skirt, hat with plume, and ear and nose ring) planting ax into head of white man.
$40
$25 for smaller "Low Priced Edition" with 30 black & white cards (15 pairs).

STAR REPORTER, ≥1937
Same as BOAKE CARTER'S STAR REPORTER (see listing) without Carter.
$50

STOCK EXCHANGE, 1936
7 × 7½ box reads, "Add Stock Exchange to Your Monopoly or Finance Game";30 stock certificates plus six "Advance to Stock Exchange" cards to mix with Community Chest and Chance decks, Stock Exchange paper to place over Free Parking space on your gameboard. Scarce.
$50

STRATOSPHERE, ±1930
15 × 11½, boxbot bd, 4 metal planes, spinner; cross-collectible.
$60

THE SWAMP FOX, ±1960
Board game based on one series of the 1959 *Walt Disney Presents* program, starring Leslie Nielsen (shown on cover) as a general during the American Revolution. Cross-collectible, Disney and TV.
$50

THEY'RE OFF, ±1930
Board game with horse race theme. Common.
$25

THE TINY TIM GAME OF BEAUTIFUL THINGS, 1970
Gameboard, four shopping bags, 36 cards, 1 die; good example of printed litho bd bk and a paste on litho; psychedelic design; character collectible.
$45

TOURING, 1906–1975
One of the most-most common, most popular card games, similar to the LINDY card games and replaced in modern times by MILLE BORNES; originally produced by the Wallie Dorr Company (see listing) in 1906, TOURING was bought by Parker Brothers and kept in the line through 1975; it is interesting to trace the variations in the automobiles and highway system (incl the mileage cards and delay cards) over time; one collector informs us there are at least 15 different TOURING covers; value depends primarily on cover illustration and date of game.

1906: 5¼ × 3¾; 100 cards make a race of 50 miles; instr sheet; distance cards are 1, 3, 5, and 10 miles; obstacle cards are "collision," "puncture," "out of gasoline," and "hauled in"; other cards are "go," "gasoline," "city limits," and "country"; ad card for ROOK; card back is open touring car; cover is the most intricate of all the TOURING covers, showing sports car and bicycle in town and mule pulling touring car in country, with publishing info written on country fence; game is undated, but pat. #836,537 puts it at 1906.
$35

1926: 5¼ × 4; 99 cards=race of 110 miles; instr sheet; distance cards=1, 3, 15, and 30 miles; coated card back is open touring car, cover is covered orange and blue touring car with country and mountain background, red-lined yellow lettering on blue; box marked "improved edition."
$25

1926: cover shows roadster, cycle, and horse pulling car; same contents as other 1926 version; best graphic cover makes this the most valued version.
$30

1937: cover shows car towing trailer.
$20

1937: cover shows car in front of houses; trip of 240 miles; mileage cards=5, 15, 25, and 45.
$15

1947: cover shows roadmap in background; same as later 1937.
$10

1954; cover shows "45" speed; same as later 1937.
$5

1958; cover shows map drawn in letters of title; trip=590 miles; mileage cards=25, 35, 50, and 75; delay cards include "broken spring," "missed curve," "burning oil," "brake adjustment," "stop to refuel"; other cards include "wrecker"; "city limits" and "country" cards of earlier versions are replaced by "populated area" and "freeway."
$5.

THE NEW GAME TOX, 1894
8½ × 8½; boxbot bd, 25 numbered markers; game is based on drawing and placing numbers and requires no dice or spinner; illust around perimeter of board are Brownies that are probably copies of Palmer Cox style; title of game, TOX, suggests play on

Cox name, possibly because his name could not be used; cover illust is mountain lake scene; title and illustrations have nothing to do with game.
$150 Auc. 10/91 $154

THE TROLLEY CAME OFF, ±1900
Card game.
$75

TWENTIETH CENTURY LIMITED, 1904
Board game was in production through 1914; cross-collectible, trains.
$150

THE UNITED STATES AIR MAIL GAME, 1930s, (© 1929)
18 × 14¾; updated version (graphically) of FLYING THE UNITED STATES AIR MAIL (see listing), with identical contents; cover shows U.S. air mail plane, single prop, with over-the-cockpit wing, two pilots, and U.S. mail truck.
$75 Auc. 10/91 $87

THE GAME OF UNITED STATES HISTORY, 1903
Card game; 5½ × 4; box shows U.S. HISTORY title, while title of instr booklet is OUR NATIONAL LIFE and is from the United States Playing Card Co.; 56 cards (eight in each of seven categories); cover illust shows Indians watching men row to shore from distant sailing ship.
$25

WATERLOO, 1895
21 × 14, boxbot and buildup are one piece with parts drawer (pat. 1894), 40 wood pawns of 2 sizes, 2 wood dice cups, 6 bone dice, instr pasted in cover, picture Napoleon, Wellington, Marshall Ney, and Blucher; gameboard has no title but shows cities of Brussels, Namur, Versailles, and Paris in the four corners, plus Charleroi, Quatre Bras, and Ligny; brief history explains the battle of June 18, 1815, near Brussels; cover shows battle scene, Paris 1815, and "On with the dance, in Brussels".
$550 Auc. 11/91 (soiling, aprons and 2 pawns missing) $500

WE, THE MAGNETIC FLYING GAME, 1928
S&A, 16½ × 8¼; six 6½" square one-piece boards representing landing fields, 16 metal planes, four poles with string and magnets, 15 cardboard disks, instr sheet; fields include Roosevelt (New York), Bolling (Washington, D.C.), Callender (New Orleans), Municipal (Oakland), Woodward (Salt Lake City) and Chicago Municipal Airport; fish pond style game; title is from book by Charles Lindbergh published by G.P. Putnam's Sons in 1927.
$80 Auc. 10/91 $125

WHO?, ±1900
Card game; 6½ × 5; 60 numbered cards.
$20

WIDE WORLD, AND A JOURNEY ROUND IT, 1896
23¾ × 16¾; one-piece bldup and boxbot bd with parts tray, four large turned wood pawns, four wood dice cups, 55 cardboard disks, four bone dice, instr in cover; path game shows photographs of cities of the world; cover shows ship, windmills, and Sphinx, plus photographs of Paris, London, and the Statue of Liberty; one of the earliest uses of photographs in a board game.
$600

WINGS, THE AIR MAIL GAME, 1928
#739; Card game; 5½ × 4; 99 cards with two dif. cardback colors; cover and aprons show biplanes; concept is similar to LINDY, THE NEW FLYING GAME and TOURING; game was in production through 1939.
$30

THE WORLD'S FAIR GAME, 1892
21 × 14; cover shows detailed illustrations of the grounds of the Chicago exposition.
$1200 Auc. 11/91 $1400

WORLD WIDE TRAVEL GAME, 1956
"This Week Magazine," Sunday newspaper supplement, Dec. 30,1956.
$10 (detatched from or still part of the magazine)

YACHT RACE, 1961
Large gameboard, six 2" high plastic sailboats on metal stands; printed bldup of Long Island Sound to Cape Cod and Santa Monica shore; original game had heavy die-cast metal sailboats; possibly the most substantial post-war Parker Brothers game in terms of components.
$85 with metal ships
$55 with plastic ships

YOUNG PEOPLE'S GEOGRAPHICAL GAME, ±1900
Card game; 4¾ × 6½; cover illust of Boston Harbor and the Golden Gate.
$20

R.H. Pease
516 Broadway, Albany, NY
≤1845–1850s

Early manufacturer of card games (all scarce or rare), such as BIOGRAPHICAL AMUSEMENTS (1845, "A game on the distinguished men of America"), THE COMIC GAME OF THE MULTIPLICATION TABLE, THE MODERN GAME OF DOMINOES ("To match words and make nouns of two words, instead of Dots, as in the old Game."), HISTORICAL AMUSEMENTS (±1845, "A game on the Kings, Queens, and Distinguished Individuals of England."), THE ROUND GAME OF THE JEW, THE MERRY GAME OF ODD FIGURES, PETER PUZZLEWIG'S MIRTHFUL GAME OF HAPPY HITS AT USEFUL KNOWLEDGE (with 48 engraved cards), THE POOR OLD SOLDIER AND HIS DOG ("A Merry Round Game. By the Author of the Golden Egg."), PROF. PUNCH'S POPULAR GAME OF WHAT D'YE BUY?, and GAME OF TRADES, OR KNOWLEDGE IS POWER. (Auc. 6/92 $1000).

THE GOLDEN EGG, ō1845,
Card game; 21 cards, some with beautifully colored illustrations, others with words only; instr sheet. "A merry round game (with) full colored cards."
$275 Auc. 10/91 $109 (incomplete, cards worn, no box)

Elizabeth Magie Phillips (See **The Adgame Co.**)

H.J. Phillips Co. Inc.
354 Fourth Ave., New York, NY
1920s

HOME DIAMOND, 1913
nva

KEEPING UP WITH THE JONESES, 1921
This standard size board game was packaged in an envelope; the wonderful illustrations are by the artist of the comic strip of the same name as the game, A.R. "Pop" Momand.
$85

QUIZ OF THE WIZ, 1921,
Card game; 5¾" × 3; numerous general interest question and
answer cards (history, arts, science, geography), instr sheet; the
more common version has instr and cover with a cartoon illust by
Pulitzer prize winning cartoonist J.N. Ding (Darling), showing young
man saying to older scientist, "Oh! Mr. Edison play the game."
$45 for version with Ding illustration
$20 for plain version

Piroxloid Products
New York, NY
1920s

THE ANCIENT GAME OF THE MANDARINS, 1923
9 × 5½" × 3; Mah Jongg box contains four tiers of polished wood
tiles, one tier of implements including: four bone disks (East, South,
North, and West), one celluloid disk holder ("Chwang Tsz"), two dice,
many celluloid counters; detailed instr booklet with many illust.
$75

BIG SIX, CHRISTY MATHEWSON INDOOR BASEBALL GAME, 1922
16¾" × 22¾"; oversized baseball game showing Mathewson on the
cover.
$950

Playjoy (Logo for **Stoll & Einson;** see listing)

Pla-Mor (See **Arrco Playing Card Co.)**

Jim Prentice (See **Electric Game Co.)**

Theodore Presser
1712 Chestnut St., Philadelphia, PA (1880s)
1908 Chestnut St., Philadelphia, PA (1890s)
Bryn Mawr, PA (±1900)

Presser specialized in music games.

ALLEGRANDO, 1884
Card game; 40 cards show staff with cleff, sharps and flat, time
signature, and notes; game by W.L Hofer teaches names and values
of notes and rests, keys, time, etc.; card back shows attractive
silhouette of pianist and piano with candelabra.
$35

ELEMENTAIRE MUSICAL GAME, 1896
Game by M.S. Morris.
$35

THE GREAT COMPOSERS, ≥1901
Card game; 68 cards (17 sets of 4), all with photographs, including
photos of 17 great composers; game is undated but one card lists
death of Verdi as 1901.
$40

J. Pressman & Co.
Brooklyn, New York
1922–1947
  Pressman Toy Corp.
  200 Fifth Ave., New York, NY
  Factory: New Brunswick, NJ
  1947–Present

The company was founded in 1922 by Jack Pressman, who later
went into partnership with Max Eibetz; Eibetz ran the factory while
Pressman handled sales. One of their early addresses was 346
Caroll Street in Brooklyn. After Jack Pressman married in 1942, he
wanted to break up the partnership with Eibetz, but Eibetz refused
to either sell his half of the business or buy Pressman's. In 1947
the partnership split, with each taking a part of the business, and
Pressman changed the company name to Pressman Toy Company.
Bill Pressman, Jack's brother, once the sales manager for Pressman,
eventually left the company to work for Hassenfeld Brothers (Hasbro).

In 1947 the factory moved from Brooklyn to the Marcal Building in Patterson, New Jersey, then back to Brooklyn, in Bush
Terminal. Pressman's wife Lynn began to oversee the company's
operation around 1953 when Jack Pressman became ill; she took
over as President of the company after the death of her husband
in 1959. Sometime later the factory was moved to its current
location in New Brunswick, New Jersey.
  The office was located at 1107 Broadway in New York City until
it moved in 1969 to its present location in the Toy Building. The
1967 Pressman catalog indicates that the company was going to
move later that year to 2 Penn Plaza, but that move never took
place. That same catalog celebrates the 50th anniversary of the
company, indicating it was founded in 1917, but this is apparently
an error.
  Edward Pressman, the elder of the two sons, became President
in 1968 or '69, and Lynn Pressman became chairman of the board.
Edward Pressman's love, however, was the film industry, not the
toy industry. Though he is still a Vice President of the company,
after 1976 he devoted most of his time to film production and is
now a highly successful producer. His younger brother James took
over the presidency of the company in 1977.
  A 1974 catalog contains a letter by Lynn Pressman stating that
the company name would be changed from Pressman Toy to "The
Pressman Corporation," because of the company's expansion program, which would include "the manufacturing of other products
such as Adult Games." This name change never took place.
  Pressman allegedly was the first company to introduce Chinese
Checkers into the U.S. Some sources say this was in 1928. The
company produced WORDY in 1938 which was almost identical to
SCRABBLE, sold by Production & Marketing Co. eleven years later,
except that the point values for letters were indicated by the color
of the tiles. Lynn Pressman insists she "knocked-off SCRABBLE," but
the game wasn't called that until 1948, which suggests that WORDY
was based on one of the SCRABBLE prototypes, AUTO-WORDS
and CRISS-CROSS WORDS, dating back to inventor Alfred Butts's
work in the early 1930s.
  Pressman's early boxes were of very thin cardboard construction, making them less desirable to collectors. Because of the
weaker boxes, it is harder to find J. Pressman games in undam-
aged condition; however, warehouse finds must have been uncovered recently as multiple games from a 6½" square-box series
manufactured before or during World War II have surfaced in mint
condition.
  An unusual exception to the early flimsy packaging is a large
wooden game with metal motorcycles, the metal Chinese Checkers
boards (see listings), and some of the non-game items.
  Besides games, the company once produced toys, playsets,
bubble-making sets, sewing sets, and educational items. It was one
of the first companies to produce children's barber sets, the first
beauty kit in a hat box, and the first dentist set. Lynn Pressman was
the first to package a doctor's kit in a doctor's black bag (she had
a particular interest in that product allegedly because both Pressman boys had asthma). She was also one of the first to use an artist
from the fashion world to design boxes, one of the first to use ideas
from noted inventor Marvin Glass, one of the first to use television
to promote a game, even one of the first to hold a major buyers'
party at toy fair; at one time she may have been the only women
president of a game company.
  Some of Pressman's bubble sets and tiddley wink games have
a hidden value: the small glass bowls were made by the Akro Agate
Co. (see listing), a company noted for its glass marbles, and they
are sought after by marble collectors.
  The company is noted also for generic classics like checkers and
chess, children's games such as BINGO, PICK-UP-STICKS, TIDDLY
WINKS, and TIC TAC TOE, and copy-cat games, such as TRI-OMI-
NOES (which is the same as CONTACT by Volume Sprayer Mfg. Co.,
1939). Pressman is also known for purchasing other companys'
famous games, such as WA-HOO (Wa Hoo Sales Co., 1953),
BLOCKHEAD (Saalfield Publishing, 1954), CONCENTRATION (Milton Bradley, 1959), LIE DETECTOR (Mattel, 1961; revised 1988),
FAMILY FEUD (Milton Bradley), JEOPARDY (Milton Bradley), MAS-
TERMIND (Invicta, 1972), and OTHELLO (Gabriel, 1976). The
company now has a wide line of games for children and adults,
including VCR games and deluxe family board games, and of late
has been one of the most profitable companies in the sagging toy
business. Jim Pressman still heads up the company, making it the
oldest family-owned game company in the U.S.

J. Pressman & Co.

Many of the games are valued under $25, including BANG BIRD, BASEBALL (#3333, 11½″ × 9″; folded board with attached spinner), CHINESE CHECKERS (three-hole base per player), CHINESE TILES (144 white gumwood tiles, 4 lacquered wood racks with attached money holders, simulated leather suitcase), DUCK PINS (cover illust. shows duck bowling at 2 Brownie-like characters), HOP CHING (wood frame board, 60 marbles, ten-hole base per player), INDIA (cover shows work elephant in jungle), JUMBO TIDDLEDY WINKS (glass cup, cover shows elephant), PARLOR CROQUET (4 mallets), RING TOSS (#7216 with 2 beaded rattan rope rings), SKEE CUPS, TEN PINS, TRICKY STICKS (± 1923, #6 has 17 wood sticks, #41 has 41 sticks), and WHIRLING TEN-PINS (± 1940, boxbot board with attached wood post holder, post with metal swivel and ball, 10 wood pins 2″ high).

BOMB THE NAVY, ± 1940
#1501, 6½″ × 6½″, 3 cardboard ships, 3 wood bases, wood cannon, 3 wood ammunition pellets; cover illust. of battleship.
$30

ELECTRIC SPEED CLASSIC, ca. 1930
12″ × 20″ all-wood board with 10″-diameter wheel to which eight 2″-long lead motorcycles are attached. Spinning wheel causes row of eight lights to go on and off; when wheel stops, the light remaining on indicates race winner. Finest known example of a Pressman game. Cross-collectible for motor-cycle enthusiasts. Scarce.
$650

FLASH, ± 1940
#6765, 14¼″ × 14¼″, wood box bottom, two-piece wood and metal top, 8 wood pins. A smaller version with only 4 wood pins is worth half.
$30

FOTO-FINISH HORSE RACE, ±1940
#1021, 19″ × 12½″, bldup board with attached spinner, 5 plastic horses, instr.; cover is collage of horse race photos.
$45

HOLD THAT TIGER
#65, 12″ × 12″, wood board, cover shows large tiger, background elephant stalked by two stick-figure black natives—one of Pressman's best covers.
$85

MODERN GAME ASSORTMENT, ±1930
2 wood-framed double-sided boards—checkers, backgammon, Chinese checkers, Michigan pool—8¼″ high cylindrical containers with 60 marbles, 30 wood checkers and two dice; the value is in the marbles.
$40

TIDDLEDY WINKS
#3072, 13¾″ × 11″, bld-up board with implement tray, 4 large and 8 small plastic discs, glass cup (probably Akro Agate), 4 felt pads, ±22 wood pins 2″ high, instr., cover illust. shows stylized drawing of a drum major.
$20 to game collector, $40 and up to Akro collector if glass cup is Akro.

WHIPPET RACE, ±1940
#3722, 13¾″ × 11″, board, 6 wood dogs, 2 wood hurdles, 2 dice, money; cover and board show greyhounds chasing rabbit. Cross-collectible for (and much more valuable to) dog race collectors.
$35

WORDY, 1938
#2251, 17″ × 17″, one-piece board, 107 color-coded letter tiles, 4 cardboard racks, instr. sheet. Same as SCRABBLE, with color of tile indicating point value; game allegedly copied from pre-SCRABBLE prototype. Large size and playability seem to have resulted in excess wear; difficult to find in excellent condition.
$45

YACHT RACE, ±1940
#930, 19″ × 12½″, bld-up board with attached spinner, 4 plastic horses, instr., cover illust. shows three yachts.
$25

Pressman Toy Corp

Because of licensing and sturdier packaging, many of the later Pressman games are more valuable than the earlier ones.

ACTION BASEBALL, ≤1967
S&A; 19½ × 15; wood-framed metal board 14x19 with attached spring action ball pitcher and bat, bell behind home plate; the generic form of the game that later used the names of Mickey Mantle, Roger Maris, and Tom Seaver.
$25 generic
$75 for Mickey Mantle
$85 for Roger Maris
$100 for Tom Seaver

BIG LEAGUE ACTION BASEBALL, ≤1967: (See ACTION BASEBALL)

FLYING SAUCERS, ±1950
S&A; 14 × 14; toss game; 13½″-diameter metal wheel is spun while wood pieces with magnets are thrown at it.
$35

GROUCHO'S TV QUIZ, ±1954
Based on Groucho Marx's television quiz shows.
$110

HOME GAME, ± 1950
17″ × 13″ box, board game, 4 one-piece boards, plastic buildings, 2 dice, pack of cards, money, instr. booklet.
$50

THE LONE RANGER AND TONTO SPIN GAME, ≤1967
Action game #1119, 15½ × 10; bldup bd 10x15 with top.
$25

MAGNETIC FLYING SAUCERS, ±1950
#2291, 14″ × 14″. S&A. 13½″-diameter rotating metal wheel on wooden stand; 4 wood discs with magnets attached. Discs are thrown at board for score. Cross-collectible for space collectors.
$35

RAT PATROL SPIN GAME, ≤1967
Action game #1116, 15½ × 10; bldup bd 10x15 with top; war illustrations on board and box cover, jeep on cover; based on TV show of 1966.
$35

SUPERMAN SPIN GAME, ≤1967
Action game #1121, 15½ × 10; bldup bd 10x15 with top.
$65

THE TEMPLE OF FU MANCHU GAME, 1967
S&A, 21X13; boxbot bd with 3-D plastic pieces, chopsticks.
$30

THE TIME TUNNEL SPIN GAME, ≤1967
Action game #1115, 15½ × 10; bldup bd 10x15 with top; based on TV show of 1966.
$100

TOURNAMENT LABYRINTH, 1980s
S&A; all-wood movable maze game consisting of a platform within a box, and two knobs used to control the horizontal and vertical tilt of a maze platform; based on the game invented by a young Swede in the early '40s, manufactured in 1946 by Brio, a Scandinavian company with a subsidiary in Wisconsin, and introduced to U.S. markets around 1950 by FAO Schwarz and Abercrombie & Fitch ("Brio" stands for "Brothers Ivarsson of Osby," and was established in 1884 in Osby, Sweden). According to Brio, over three million LABYRINTH games were sold annually worldwide—before the Pressman look-alike, and before Brio changed to plastic. Brio once stated that the game "has been found useful in rehabilitating shell-shocked war veterans." The Pressman game is collected for its play value only.
$15

W.S. Reed Toy Co.
Leominster, MA
games: 1880s–≥1919

W.S. Reed was founded in 1875 and renamed the Whitney Reed Chair Co. in 1898, after which it still made toys.

GAME OF POLITICS, OR THE RACE FOR THE PRESIDENCY, 1887
Gameboard 18½" × 18½" shows drawings of the presidents through Harrison, plus electoral votes allowed the 42 states; game by Jeanie P. Clarke was dated also 1888 and 1889; some boards were also marked "Forbes," which may have been the name of the lithographer.
$175 Auc. 6/92 $300

THE WORLD EDUCATOR, 1888 and 1919
15¾" × 7; wood box with wooden roller (acts as spinner) attached inside; question and answer cards 13½" × 6". This was one of the earliest games ever advertised, and a good example of the combining of education and play. This game is not uncommon, and is often seen priced way above its expected value (possibly because it is often sold by "toy people" who put high value on the Reed name).
$125 for the original
$55 for later editions.

The Regensteiner Corp.
310 S. Racine Ave., Chicago, IL
1920s

KUIT-KUTS, 1922
Game of interchangeable faces and bodies was designed by noted cartoonist Charles Lederer.
$40

MAR-JUCK, 1923,
15½" × 6¾"; Mah Jongg game with 144 cardboard tiles, four long metal racks, 2 bone dice, 116 cardboard disks, four counter trays, 12-pg instr book; good box illust shows Chinese man in full garb with hat, smoking long pipe, at table with game; box copy reads "Mar Juck, the correct name for the great Chinese game . . . Chinese for 'Sparrow' . . . also known as Mah Juck, Ma Jong, Mah Cheuk, Mah Diao, and Mah Chang."
$30

Reiss Games
Orange, CA, and New York, NY

Reiss, a company known for its hand-held dexterity puzzles, is now a subsidiary of National Paragon.

MARY HARTMAN MARY HARTMAN, ≥1976
Gameboard, action cards, episode cards, 11 character pieces consisting of photos of eight characters including Dabney Coleman; based on the 1976–77 TV parody created by Norman Lear; likely to show a greater-than-average increase in value over time.
$35

Remco
Harrison, NJ
games: ±1960–1970s

Popular toy company in the 1960s made a few games that are now collectible, including HAWAII FIVE-O and MOD SQUAD (both 1968).

Replogle Globes Inc.
1901 N. Narrangansett Ave., Chicago 12, IL

GLOBAL AIR RACE, 1952
13 × 9¾" × 9¾"; metal globe 12" high, 8" diam., with spinner base, four metal magnetic planes, airport finder device with miles traveled and gas used, money, and cardboard disks; often found without box.
$85
$55 without box
$35 globe only

HOLIDAY, 1958
11½" × 10; globe, eight 2-fold boards 18 × 9½" showing path with city locations around the world, 6" × 6" spinner, four passports, four kinds of currency, 30 adventure cards, four tokens, currency converter, distance and travel cost computer.
$65

Revell
Venice, CA
1950s–1960s

Revell was a toy company famous for model cars, planes, and ships; the company used primarily plastic products and made few games.

THE GAME OF YERTLE, 1960
A balancing game with 21 plastic turtle yertles, tray, post, and bldup with attached spinner; box illustrated by Dr. Seuss.
$75

(Oglesby/Stock collection)

Rex Manufacturing Co.
Chicago, IL
1930s

GREYHOUND RACING GAME, 1938
#620; 9½″ × 6¼″; die-cut board glued to bottom has five metal dogs fixed into racing slots; built-in spinner; cover shows five dogs racing after mechanical rabbit.
$25

KENTUCKY DERBY, ±1938
Same style game as above with horserace theme; later games changed from metal to plastic horses; box showed 1930s date for decades. Common.
$25 for metal horse edition
$10 for plastic horse edition

Frank H. Richards
Troy, N.Y.
±1885

TRIANGULAR DOMINOS, 1885,
3½″ × 2¼″; metal box with hinged lid; 36 cardboard triangles with domino pips drawn along one or more sides; forerunner of TRIOMI-NOES.
$60

Rook Card Co.
Salem, MA
1910s, 1930s

Supposedly, when Geo. S. Parker wanted to publish the game of ROOK, one of his favorites, Parker Brothers was against putting it in the regular line, so George Parker established the Rook Card Co., technically a division of Parker Brothers, and produced the game.

MAKE A MILLION, 1934
Card game; 55 cards incl tiger, bull, bear, money cards, and number cards; instr booklet.
$15

ROOK, 1906
One of the most popular old card games in the U.S.; patented 1910; very common.
$8

Rosebud Art Co., Inc.
New York, NY
1920s–1940s

Rosebud was a significant company during the 1930s, producing a number of games with excellent graphics, and procuring such licenses as King Features' "Popeye."

BAG OF FUN, 1932
Stunt booklet and cloth bag of numbers.
$20

BIG APPLE, 1938
#85; this is not the game of New York City (called "The Big Apple" decades later), but the game whose name is taken from the dance craze of the mid-1930s; nothing about the game reflects the dance, however.
$50

BINGO, ±1925
#32; 6½″ × 10; stylized cover.
$25

JUNGLE HUNT, ±1940
S&A; #175; 15¼″ × 12¾″; ring-toss game with bldup bd, metal rings, 48 animal cards, and 4 cage cards.
$35

KING HIGH, ±1925
#3; 13 × 13; die-cut bldup bd with four wood corner ramps for marble; box and board have same illust of King in center, plus Prince, General, Captain, and Kitchen Cop in each corner.
$45

KITTY KAT CUP BALL, ±1935
$80

LIFE OF THE PARTY, ±1940
Stunt game with cardboard donkey spinner; the game came in two sizes.
$25 for small size with stunts shown on board
$35 for large size with booklet of stunts and large cardboard donkey spinner.

THE MARATHON GAME, ±1930
13½″ × 8; blodup bd with attached spinner; simple luck track game; good cover illust of runners.
$50

POPEYE PIPE TOSS GAME, 1935
#17; S&A; two sizes: 4½″ × 9½″, with an 8¼″ cardboard Popeye that fits into stand affixed to boxbot, and 5 × 10¾″, with a 10″ cardboard Popeye; 3 dif size cardboard rings, instr in boxbot; larger version has 3¾″ wood pipe that fits into Popeye's mouth; © King Features Syndicate, Inc.; cover illust of pipe-smoking Popeye face. Both very common.
$30 for small version
$45 for large version with wood pipe

ROLAWHEEL, 1926
#36
$35

Royal Toy
Worcester, MA
1930s

ALEE-00P, 1937
S&A; cannister contains angular wood pieces that can be flipped a distance when hit; title is based on comic strip character; subtitle is Oscar' and his Oops"; © Stephen Slesinger; exact same game as FLIP JACK by Russell.
$25

Ruckelshaus Game Corp.
Newark, NJ
1939

Nothing is known about this company, nor have any games been located other than the one listed below. But the exceptional quality of that one game leads us to hope that other games will turn up.

THE BLACK FALCON OF THE FLYING G-MEN, 1939
Superb cover illustration of game based on film serial; cross-collectible in areas of mystery, adventure, and G-Men.
$300

Russell Mfg. Co.
Leicester, MA
≤1922–1950s

Russell is known mostly for its card games, along with some skill and action items. The earlier Russell games seem to have more "character" than the later ones. Some unmarked games can be ascertained as Russell because of striped apron box wrap. Games that can be found for $25 or under include AUTHORS (1920s, with authors' photos; cover illustration by Phillips), CROSS-NUMBER (1939), CROSSWORD LETTER GAME (1938), FLIP JACK (1930s S&A game in a cannister; exactly the same game as ALEE OOP by Royal Toy), and MICKEY MOUSE CANASTA JUNIOR (1947).

BASKET BALL, 1929
#217; S&A; 10 11/2 × 10½″; one of four "door-knob games" in which balls are thrown at die-cut boxbot bd designed to hang over doorknob; illust of black player; other games in series include AIRPLANE SHOT, CIRCUS SHOT, CHAMPION SHOT.
$85

(Fink collection)

GAME OF DOCTOR QUACK; ±1922
Card game; 5 × 6½″; 32 cards with five phrases on each; instr sheet has story with words left out; this parlor amusement is non-competitive; Russell name does not appear anywhere, but signed Phillips illustration and apron wrap indicate Russell.
$40

GOOF RACE AND TEN PINS, ±1930
S&A; stand-up cardboard characters, ten pins, wood balls.
$35

HOWDY DOODY GAME, 1954
Card game.
$30

LIBRARY OF GAMES, 1939
Set of six card games; 5¾" long rack box consisting of six miniature "matchbook-style" games each 1¾" × 2¾"; games are OLD MAID, ANIMAL RUMMY, CROSSWORD, AUTHORS, SLAP JACK, and DR. QUACK; the later three are dated 1935, ANIMAL RUMMY is 1939; instr sheets for all except instr card for OLD MAID.
$25

MICKEY MOUSE LIBRARY OF GAMES, 1946
Set of six card games; 5¾"-long rack box consisting of six miniature "matchbook-style" games each 1¾" × 2¾"; instr sheets in each; games are DONALD DUCK, PINOCCHIO, BAMBI, THE THREE LIT-TLE PIGS, SNOW WHITE AND THE SEVEN DWARFS and MICKEY MOUSE (with cards depicting Mickey, Minnie, Pluto, Big Bad Wolf, Three Little Pigs, Ferdinand the Bull, and Clara Cluck).
$45

OLD MAID FUN FULL THRIFT GAME, ±1940
Card game.
$30

PAN-CAKE TIDDLY WINKS, 1920s
S&A, #211; 11¾" × 9; bldup board, 20 celluloid disks (four tiddles and 16 winks); cover shows black "Mammy" character holding pancake stack, board shows three blacks.
$90

TORTOISE AND THE HARE, 1922
6 × 10; gameboard of thin cardboard, two wood pawns; instr in the center of the board call for dice, but the instructions have teetotum (spinner) numbers surrounding them; TORTOISE AND THE HARE, one of the first Russell games, is one of the few board games made by the company and is also one of the company's best games; the illustrations are drawn by Phillips, an artist whose talents graced other Russell games. .
$50

THE COMICAL GAME OF WHIP, ±1920
#503; card game; 6½" × 5; 32 cards (8 × 4) incl eight well-drawn and detailed cartoon illustrations.
$35

Saalfield Publishing Co.
Akron, OH
games: ≤1911–1950s

Arthur J. Saalfield founded a publishing firm in 1900 that a decade later was specializing in children's books, then die-cut puzzles, playsets, and games. The company went bankrupt in 1974. Some of the company's larger board games, cloth games, and licensed products are quite desirable.

ANIMAL GAME, 1925
#601; board game based on the work of Thornton W. Burgess and illustrated by Harrison Cady; retail price $1.00; cross-collectible, illustrators/Cady.
$115

BILLY WHISKERS, ±1924
$75

BLOCKHEAD, 1954
First manufactured by Saalfield Publishing, BLOCKHEAD (now sold by Pressman) has the distinction of being one of the few games unchanged after thirty years and one of even fewer games still made entirely of wood.
$15

FIRE FIGHTERS!, 1957
9¾" × 10¾"; bldup bd, punch out pieces; children's game.
$25

THE GREATEST SHOW ON EARTH, 1924
Board game.
nva

HOOT, ±1930
Card game based on the work of Thornton W. Burgess and illus-trated by Harrison Cady; cross-collectible, illustrators/Cady.
$65

JOLLY PIRATES, 1938
10½" × 15 book of heavy cardboard pages; center pages open into board, other pages have playing pieces to cut out.
$35

WASHINGTON'S BIRTHDAY PARTY, 1911
Cloth game, pin-the-tail variant; object is to pin the cloth hatchets close to the cut on the cherry tree. One of the earliest Saalfield games.
$95

Saxon Toy Corp.
1127 Atlantic Ave
Brooklyn 16, NY
1940s

The company produced a series of ELECTRIC QUESTIONER style question and answer games with metal boards and buzzer and light; games include QUIZ-LITE (question and answer game), ROLL-LITE (combination roulette and PUT AND TAKE game), STRIKE-LITE (baseball game), and TACKLE-LITE (football game).

TRAVEL-LITE, 1946
18¼″ × 12; cardboard bldup bd 12 × 9 plus metal bldup bd 9 × 11, four celluloid airplanes, instr sheet; two dials and attached metal spinner on the metal board indicate moves; excellent litho on metal shows scenes of plane, parachutist, and city skyscrapers; cover litho shows youth playing game.
$75

John Scarne Games, Inc.
Fairview, NJ.
±1935–1970s

Scarne was a game inventor and author of books on strategy and card games (playing cards) and gambling games, possibly trying to set himself up as the new "Hoyle." In the board game area he is probably best known for TEEKO, a game he tried to establish nationally with tournaments and clubs in the "GO" or "PENTE" tradition, and for which he wrote a book devoted to the strategies of the game. Scarne's games include FOLLOW THE ARROW (≤1947), and KNOCKOUT (1935–37), a game that featured world heavyweight champion James J Braddock (but it is not known if the game was actually comercially produced). The game that bears the inventor's name, SCARNE (≥1939), was on the market for two years.

CHALLENGE,1947 or '49
Solitaire game that touts inventor Scarne as the "world's foremost game authority."
$25

TEEKO, ±1948, 1952.
Strategy board game with large, checker-like "lucite" pieces; the title comes from: T from Tic-tac-toe, E from Chess, E from Checkers, K from Checkers, O from Bingo.
$30

Schacht Rubber Mfg. Co.
Huntington, IN
1920s

DAISY CLOWN RING GAME, 1927
$15

DAISY HORSESHOE GAME, 1927
$15

W.H. Schaper Mfg. Co.
1800 Olson Highway
Minneapolis 11, MN
1949–present

Schaper is known primarily for his COOTIE game, which he allegedly invented in 1949; however, evidence indicates that virtually the same game existed long before then Most Schaper products used many plastic parts. Schaper games popular through the 1950s having only minor value as collectibles include DUNCE, LI'L STINKER, MILL, PICKIN', PUT AND TAKE, TUMBLE BUG, SCARE CROW, SHAKE, SKUNK, SNAP-EZE, SPARETIME BOWLING, SQUARES, T-OFF, and TIDDLE-TAC-TOE.

COOTIE, 1949
$25 (original version)

I'M GEORGE GOBEL, AND HERE'S THE GAME, 1955
The value is in the name, not the game.
$40

MOON BLAST OFF
$30

STADIUM CHECKERS, ±1954
Schaper's most popular classic, this game is worth much more to players than collectors.
$12

Joseph Schneider

Manufacturer of bagatelle (pin ball) games, many of which bore only his initials, "JS." The value of any Schneider game depends primarily on the illustrations of the painted metal, but most of the games are worth about $40.

Doremus Schoen & Co.
64 Grand St., New York, NY
1920s

BANG BIRD, 1921
14½″ × 11½″; target game with three celluloid birds with something in them to make them rattle, two telegraph poles, black net, gun.
$30

TUMBLIN FIVE ACROBATS, ±1925
S&A puzzle game; boxbot felt board with holes, five jumping beans; normally a solitaire puzzle, this item includes rules for scoring a competitive game.
$20

O. Schoenhut
2001 E. Hagert St., Philadelphia, PA
2046 East Castor Ave., Phialdelphia 34, PA

(Otto F.) Schoenhut, a major name in toys and dolls, made few games, most of them traditional items.

4-5-6 PICK UP STICKS, 1936; revived 1947
$15

TIDDLE TENNIS, 1938
TIDDLY WINKS played on an 18 × 10 felt tennis board with cardboard net, rackets, and bag of tiddle tennis balls.
$25

WA-HOO PICK 'EM UP STICKS, ±1936
S&A; 8 × 2¾" slipcase; 41 painted-tip wood sticks, score sheets, instr; the five types of sticks are given Indian names; unmarked game is probably Schoenhut because of resemblance to 4-5-6 PICK UP STICKS game; cover shows two Indians holding the sticks.
$25

Geo. E. Schweig & Son
Philadelphia, PA
1930s

BANNER LYE CHECKERBOARD, ±1930
Advertising premium for Banner Lye.
$20

WHAT WOULD YOU DO?, 1933
Card game; 3½" × 2¾"; parlor pastime divides cards into question cards and answer cards; called "The funniest game ever written," it is not really a game (no win or lose) and would not pass the humor test of time.
$15

E.G. Selchow & Co.
41 John Street, New York, NY
1867–1880
   Selchow & Righter
   New York, NY
   Bay Shore (Long Island), NY
   1880–1986

Elisha G. Selchow was assigned the rights to Albert Swift's toy and game publishing business in 1867, then formed a partnership with John Righter (the manager of Swift's business) in 1870 under the name "E.G. Selchow & Co." Most Selchow & Righter promotional material indicates the company was founded in 1867, though an 1877 catalog reads "Established in 1864." The 1864 date may have referred to when Swift first opened his shop, which we know to be shortly after the Civil War. There is still some question as to what happened between 1864 and 1867, when Selchow may have just *started* to assume rights to Swift's business, and 1870 when he "officially" took over the business and brought John Righter in as a partner.

Except for maybe PIGS IN CLOVER (ca. 1870) and CORN AND BEANS (1875), E.G. Selchow games are hard to find. Selchow's greatest contribution to game playing in the United States was

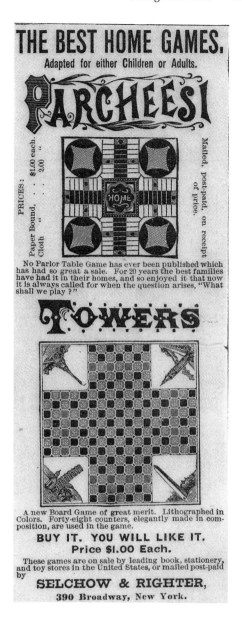

PARCHEESI, taken from the national game of India, PACHISI. Bayard Taylor, an American correspondent for the New York *Tribune* in 1844 (he died in 1878) mentioned PARCHEESI in his book, *India, China and Japan* . One of the earliest trade-marked games in the U.S. (1874), PARCHEESI was first published around 1870. It is interesting to note that although the PARCHEESI name with that spelling was trademarked giving E.G. Selchow & Co. sole ownership, another New York company, H.B. Chaffee, also sold an early (±1880) PARCHEESI. This becomes even more significant when one realizes that H.B. Chaffee was in partnership with Fred M. Selchow (see **Chaffee & Selchow**) between 1897 and 1899; in 1897 and 1898 Fred Selchow and Elisha Selchow lived at the same address (17 W. 124th St., NYC); their exact familial relationship is not yet known. Elisha moved to Port Chester in 1899.

Selchow & Righter were initially "jobbers"—they sold games for other companies. One hundred forty nine Milton Bradley games and puzzles were listed in the E.G. Selchow 1877 catalog. Forty-five McLoughlin games and blocks were listed as well, including the games of JOHN GILPIN, LIFE'S MISHAPS, and PILGRIM'S PROGRESS. The company also offered AUTHORS, BEZIQUE, CITADELLE (a skill and action game), SIEGE, and four versions of

PARCHEESI, THE GAME OF INDIA. E.G. Selchow & Co. also sold Crandall's blocks, embossed dominoes, planchettes (the heart-shaped pieces that "float" on top of Ouija boards or on paper), McLoughlin books and dolls, Eclipse Comic Playing Cards, iron and tin savings banks, Indian clubs, kaleidoscopes, boxing gloves, calliopes, thermometers and barometers, lamps, pocket stoves, tricks, "castenetts" [*sic*], artificial ivy and autumnal vines, and a toy mouse.

In 1877 Selchow purchased the entire stock and copyrights of Adams & Co., Boston. In 1880 the company name was changed to Selchow & Righter, and in 1910 the company incorporated. In 1923, years after both E.G. Selchow and John Righter had died, Miss Harriet T. Righter became president, and in 1927 the company stopped jobbing games and began to manufacture its own. The Selchow & Righter company never seemed to fare as well (in terms of national recognition at least) as the big three, McLoughlin, Bradley, and Parker, but it has its own success story. The company started almost two decades before Geo. S. Parker Co. and remained a family-owned company long after Parker had been bought out, and after the giant Milton Bradley sold out as well. The company's association with SCRABBLE when making the gameboards for the Production and Marketing Company after 1948, and the eventual purchase of the rights to SCRABBLE, changed Selchow & Righter's direction; by the 1970s its products were primarily word games, many of them SCRABBLE derivatives. In the 1980s the company was once again the big winner following the phenomenal success of TRIVIAL PURSUIT, to which they had obtained the rights.

In the wake of this success, in 1986 Richard Selchow stunned the industry with the sale of his 119-year-old company to Coleco, a firm that a short time later filed for bankruptcy and was eventually bought by Hasbro. The PARCHEESI and SCRABBLE names still adorn new game boxes, but the Selchow & Righter name is now relegated to history.

E.G. Selchow

CORN & BEANS, 1875
5½ × 3¾; subtitled "The Funniest Game Out," this game actually contained kernels of corn and beans, along with wood dowels, teetotum, and pawns; "The dish of corn and beans is food for the body, but the game of "Corn & Beans" is food for the mind. It is a source of infinite delight to the little folks, and . . . impresses upon their minds, to carry with them through life, valuable historical facts . . . which they could learn in no other way, except by hours of wearisome study."
$85 ($55 for the later S&R version, which bears the same 1875 date)

PARCHEESI, 1974 (pat. date)
nva

SLICED OBJECTS
Puzzle/puzzle game; 9″ × 8″. (See S&R description for SLICED ANIMALS.)
$110

VIGNETTE AUTHORS, 1874
$60

Selchow & Righter

ASSEMBLY LINE, 1953
This game has more plastic pieces (parts of automobiles) than almost any other game, and is sought after by auto enthusiasts, collectors of pre-1960 games, and people who still remember playing it in their youth.
$60

BLAST OFF, 1953
18¼ × 15¼; bldup bd with plexiglas attached spinner, six cardboard "planets" with pegs, four plastic/celluloid rocket ships, 20 cargo cards.
$45

BUSTER BROWN AT THE CIRCUS, ±1906
Card game; 5¾ × 7¾; 40 color cards with wonderful illustrations, including one of the Yellow Kid (first U.S. comic strip character) and a black, "Topsy."
$140 Auc. 6/92 $325

CABBY, 1938
Litho board and parts box, six metal cabs with post, six metal police cars, 28 celluloid rings (as passengers that fit on cab posts), six dice cups, six dice; bd bk litho. "The game with rules made to be broken" is frequently requested by players and those who remember it from their youth.
$65 for 1938 edition, "low gloss" board
$50 for 1940s edition, "high gloss" board

CARGOES, 1934
#42; 16¼ × 9½; two-fold board, 66 cards, die, four metal ships; typo on instr say "66," leaving out the word "cards"; the gameboard is illustrated by William Longyear. The game was in production 1934–1963.
$60 for earliest full box version
$45 for board plus parts box
$30 for post–WWII editions

CHAMPS, THE LAND OF BRAWNO, 1940
The game, which has an unusual cover silhouette illustration, was in production 1940–1942.
$50

CHINAMAN PARTY, 1896
Large cloth pin-the-tail variant requires players to pin the queue on the Chinaman; according to Katharine Morrison McClinton, this game may have been invented by Jesse Crandall.
$130

DECOY, 1940
One-piece wooden gameboard with wood pieces shaped like ducks; strategy game. The wood board is somewhat rare; cardboard (bldup bd) versions are easier to find.
$75 wood board
$30 cardboard

DICK TRACY THE MASTER DETECTIVE GAME, 1961
$50

DONKEY PARTY, 1887
Cloth pin-the-tail game.
$25

ED WYNN, THE FIRE CHIEF, 1930s
$55

FLYING ACES, 1940s
$50

FOXY GRANDPA HAT PARTY, ±1906
Linen paper board, pin-the-tail variant. Early and fine example of a licensed game.
$90

HAVE-U IT?, 1926
Based on Ciara Bow, the "It" girl, from the film *IT*, the 1927 Elinor Glyn story.
$35

HUGGIN THE RAIL, 1948
Auto race game with innovative move determinator: plastic device with small colored balls inside that mix up when shaken and then line up to determine sequence of play.
$35

JAMBOREE, ±1937
#43; embossed blue on silver cover with simple Art Deco design; gameboard by William Longyear is path game showing Miami, Havana, Atlantic City, the Alps, and Paris; four each of trains, boats, cars, and planes; eight embossed tokens, 38 cards, $65,000 in money, two special dice, dice cup, eight instruction cards; unusual in that two to sixteen people can play; subtitled "The Sky's the Limit"; retail $1.00.
$70

KATZY PARTY, 1900s
Illustrated envelope 9 × 7; 30 × 13 linen paper board is pin-the-tail variant; object is to pin one of 28 cats along a fence; excellent orange, yellow, and black and white scene of houses with back fence and howling cats.
$120

KOMIKAL KONVERSATION KARDS, 1893
The game was in production 1893–1901.
$30

LITTLE COLONEL, ±1936
15 × 9½; eight heavy cardboard figures up to 5½ tall on metal stands includes four black characters; four pawns, dice cup, two dice; gameboard shows all the houses from the book on which the game is based.
$85

MEET THE PRESIDENTS, 1953
$25

MR. REE, 1937
The game was in production from 1937 to 1957; a new edition came out in 1957 (with plastic characters) and lasted until 1966. Early versions came with board and parts box or completely boxed and had anywhere from 90 heavy stock cards to 104 cards, eight cardboard tubes, four weapons (some metal, some merely illustrations on cardboard), and an instr book. The second most desirable version is a rare one with eight plaster heads that fit into the cardboard tubes; the best (and more rare) version has a resin substance in each plaster-headed tube with something loosely trapped inside, so that if any tube is lifted and shaken, it has weight and rattles whether or not the searched-for weapons are inside. Original boards were by S&R artist William Longyear, and all lettering was by hand.
$110 for versions with plaster heads and resin in the tubes
$85 for versions with just plaster heads
$50 for versions with just metal weapons
$25 for all other early editions
$15 for new (post 1957) editions

MR. DOODLES DOG, ±1940
Gameboard, four metal bones, metal dog, four wood pawns, large spinner; most of the game's value is a result of its creator being Howard Garis (of UNCLE WIGGILY fame).
$50

NUMBLE, 1968
Selchow and Righter tried to capitalize on the success of SCRABBLE with a similar game using numbers instead of letters; as might be expected with any "math" game, it was not very successful. The game is sought more by players than collectors.
$20

PARCHEESI, 1967
Because this game has been so popular for so long, and has changed so little, mosts sets (even the earliest ones) do not command more than $15 or $20. However, the centennial edition, limited and each set numbered, had sterling silver caps on plastic pieces, and dice

cups that read "1867–1967." This item should increase in value greatly over time.
$55

PETER PAN, 1927
One of S&R's most interesting and beautiful games; box with small holes has marble and bell inside used for determining movement of the four metal people tokens on the board—the box is lifted and shaken and when the marble hits the bell (signifying Tinkerbell talking), the box is put down and the number of moves is shown by which hole the marble can be seen through.
$140

THE NEW GAME PIGGIES, 1894,
S&A; 12½ × 12½, heavy wood board with metal railings in wood posts; 12 numbered wood pigs painted white with pink eyes, nose, and mouth, with metal feet, ears, & tail; four poles (called "whips") with string and ring attached; instr pasted in cover; FISH POND style guessing game, © C. Begerow; instr read "Put the pigs in the pen promiscuously . . . "; cover shows six pigs walking arm in arm; the only company marking is "S & R, New York."
$350 Auc. 11/91 $550

PIGS IN CLOVER, ±1880
S&A; 6"-diameter wood base with cardboard dividers, three wood marbles, wood center pen, no company markings except for PAR-CHEESI ad inside front cover; this is the first popular dexterity puzzle in the U.S. and was invented by Crandall, famous maker of blocks.
$110

RADIO RAMBLE, 1927
11 × 12¾; U.S. map board showing call letters for some stations, four cardboard announcers on wood stands, heavy board double dial spinner, partial bldup with instr.
$60

RAINY DAY GOLF, ±1920
Separate gameboard 21½ × 14 and parts box, four metal golf balls, special die.
$100

SCRABBLE, 1953
The country's number one word and tile game, is the only trade-marked game listed in the 1983 second revised edition of *Hoyles Rules of Games* . Because the game is so common and has changed very little since it was first produced, it is of minimal value to collectors. Unusual SCRABBLE sets and deluxe versions are valued at over twice the standard set; the rare vinyl board sewn into cloth and sets with plastic scoring racks and ivoroid tiles are worth $50 and $25, respectively; an April, 1954, advertisement in *New York* magazine featuring a cartoon by Dedini is worth $15.
$12

SLICED ANIMALS, ±1900
Puzzle/puzzle game; 9 × 10; 71 cardboard stips fit together to make 16 animals, with the letters of the animal's name at the bottom of the image; unusual in that the instructions include rules for a game similar to GO FISH.
$90

SLICED BIRDS, ±1900
See description for SLICED ANIMALS.
$90

SNAKE EYES
Card game; cover shows two blacks peering over title with dice roll beneath. This game was in production through 1957; there are different size versions available, including a Junior Edition with the character illustrations on a bldup board.
$60 #27; 1941; 11 × 7½ × 2¼; somewhat common.
$70 #77; 1937
$65 #206; 1941; 14 × 12½ Junior Edition

STRAIGHT ARROW, 1950
Based on the radio program.
$45

SWEEP, 1929
10¾ × 6½; boxbot bd. This is one cover (and a good one!) where a witch and man-in-the-moon did not signify a fortune telling game. The game was in production from 1929 through 1937.
$40

TRIVIAL PURSUIT, 1985
Board and card game; since millions of sets of this popular game were sold, it is unlikely to become highly collectible in the near future. What does have potential value, however, are the promotional items, including a calligraphed invitation to play the game aboard the liner *QE2* , dated Jan. 12, 1985; a record album cover; and a gameboard on mirrored glass.
nva

WOOD ANAGRAMS, ±1920
Letter tile game; 8¼ × 5½; wraparound litho shows elves cutting trees in forest—one of the best ANAGRAMS covers ever seen.
$60

Simon & Schuster
386 Fourth Ave., New York, NY
games: 1930s

The famous book publishing firm produced two games based on the party books of Jerome S. Meyer. The games are more fun to play than they are valuable to collect.

MENTAL WHOOPEE, 1936
Party games on paper.
$15

SNAP JUDGMENT, 1933
6¼″ × 9¼″ box with eight sheets that unfold to 17¼″ × 26¼″ ! Answer card, letter-writing-quality note pad, instr on box bot. Game sheets have photos to identify, including world buildings, famous men and women, child photos of stars, puzzle piece photos of

famous people, famous teams, etc. Tongue in cheek introduction on box shows photo of the Smith Brothers as "Simon" and "Schuster," and is signed "Essandess" for "S" and "S".
$50

J.H. Singer
±1880–1899 (possibly also 1901)
games: ±1890–≥1900
J.C. Singer
1898–1900
New York, NY

Jasper H. Singer, born 1846, was listed as early as 1880 in the New York City directories as being in the paper business. His name disappears from the directories in 1900, then reappears for one year, 1901 (but no games have been located with that date). His wife, Jane C. Singer, born 1852, headed the company for two years, 1899 and 1900, though there is a J.C. Singer game from 1898. In 1900 the Singers lived with two sons and three servants in the Hotel Cambridge in New York City.

All J.H. and J.C. Singer games look similar and are marked similarly except for the middle initial; J.C. Singer games may be worth slightly more because of their comparative rarity. Some Singer games were marked only "JHS NY." NELLIE BLY and the illustrations on SHOP BOY suggest a tie-in with McLoughlin. Most games were card games or tiny (4″ × 4″) board games, with instructions on the cover obscuring much of the illustration, but the larger Singer board games have excellent lithography and are highly prized.

J.C. Singer

HEL-LO TELEPHONE GAME, 1898
Cards and wooden toy telephone; this could be the first game marked J.C. Singer.
$80

T.G.O. KLONDYKE, 1899/1900
12½″ × 9¼″; one-piece board, large spinner with movement notations, wood markers, instr on board; superb period piece.
$250

LONDON BRIDGE, 1899/1900
S&A, 14¾″ × 4; die-cut board with archways fits upright between two wood stands; instr on cover; marble roll game.
$75

(Krim collection)

THE GAME OF MARRIAGE, 1899/1900
$70

J.H. Singer

AUTHORS, ±1890
$25

THE GAME OF BOPEEP, 1890
One-piece gameboard.
$150

DR. BUSBY, ±1890
$30

GAME OF COCKED HAT, 1892
S&A.
$250

CUCKOO, A SOCIETY GAME, 1891
5 × 6½; six gameboards, each 4½″ square, each with different 9-square color pattern; wood dice cup, special die with colored sides, wood markers; the game says neither "published by" nor "manufactured by," but "Invented by" J.H. Singer.
$75

THE DOG SHOW, 1890s
7¼″ × 7¼″; one-piece board with attached spinner, four wood tokens, 1″ square cardboard pieces for bull dogs, fox hounds, pointers, pugs, and spaniels; cover shows four dogs, instr on cover.
$70

FIVE LITTLE PIGS, 1890s
Card game; 4 × 5¼″; 40 cards (eight each of five types); box marked only "JHS NY."
$40

THE 400 GAME, ±1890
Board game; the illustration of the party scene on the cover is one of Singer's best.
$125

GO BANG, ≤1898
5¼″ × 5½″; one-piece bd, wood markers, spinner, instr on cover.
$35

THE GAME OF GOLF, ≤1898
7¼″ × 14¼″; one-piece board, spinner, wood markers, instr sheet.
$115

GAME OF GOOSEY GANDER, OR WHO FINDS THE GOLDEN EGG, 1890
$900 Auc. 6/92 $1150

A MERRY GAME OF POSTING, ±1890
Heavy gameboard, large block spinner, four pawns, wood markers.
$300

NELLIE BLY, ≤1898
7¼″ × 14¼″; one-piece board, spinner, wood markers, instr sheet.
$90

OLD MAID, 1890s
$20

PETER CODLE [sic] AND HIS TRIP TO NEW YORK, ±1890
Card game; cover shows man carrying pumpkin.
$30\

GAME OF SAILOR BOY, 1889
$500 Auc. 6/92 $525

THE SHOP BOY, 1890s
5¼″ × 5¼″; one-piece board, two wood markers, 4-number spinner, instr in cover; board is MESSENGER BOY theme, with checkerboard path leading to center space, "success"; cover illust of boys carrying packages, one boy dropping them during fight, is similar to McLoughlin cover of 1891 THE ERRAND BOY.
$70 Auc. 10/91 $94

GAME OF SHOVEL BOARD
$550 Auc. 6/92 $425

SNAKE GAME, 1890s
7½″ × 7½″; boxbot bd, four wood markers, teetotum; cover shows snake in grass; board path is body of snake.
$80

TOBOGGAN SLIDE, 1890s
5¼″ × 5¼″; one-piece board, two wood markers, 4-number spinner; board is simple path showing children on three toboggans, church and house; cover shows girl pulling toboggan; instr on cover.
$85 Auc. 10/91 $73

WHERE DO YOU LIVE, 1890s
Card game marked only J.H.S. N.Y.
$50

GAME OF YACHTING, ≤1898
5¼″ × 5½″; one-piece bd, wood markers, spinner, instr on cover.
$45

The Skip-Bo Company
Brownfield, TX
1967–1980

Hazel Bowman copyrighted the original SKIP-BO card game in 1967, then sold it to International Games in 1980. It is the second largest-selling game in International Games' line today, but the original is hard to find. The International Games version was made different in design from the original SKIP-BO in order to protect the game from competitive "knock-offs."

SKIP-BO, 1967
Card game in a velveteen red box.
$20

Smith, Kline & French
1920

CHASING VILLA, 1920
Gameboard 18 × 18 and parts box 4 × 3; cardboard pieces on wood stands, instr sheet; interesting theme and excellent graphics.
$110

REDSKIN & COWBOY
$150 Auc. 6/92 $170

Snow Brothers
Worcester, MA
1870–1872

The two Snow brothers, Ezra (E.H.) and Edward, began a game legacy that encompassed at least six companies. The descendant companies of Snow Brothers are listed here (the number in parentheses following each company indicates the number of games known to have been produced by them):
West & Lee (Presbury West and George Lee), 1873–1875
Wm. R. Gould, 1875 (17)
Noyes and Snow (with Henry Noyes), 1876 (5)
Noyes, Snow and Co., 1876–1879 (25)
Snow, Woodman Co. (with Russell Woodman), 1879 (3)
E.H. Snow (Ezra Snow), 1882 and/or 1883

E.H. Snow
Worcester, MA
1882–1883

THE LION & THE EAGLE, OR THE DAYS OF '76, 1883
Card; 8¼″ × 5¾″; 52 cards, instruction sheet.
$80

Snyder Bros.
100, 102, 104 West Water St., Elmira, NY

The company, which listed itself as "printers," apparently made only one game, but a popular one.

TROLLEY, 1904
Card game; 4½″ × 2¾″; series of Trolley Car, Motorman, Conductor, Fare, Passenger, and Transfer cards, each series with its own illust; instr sheet; retail 40¢. There must have been a "warehouse find" since the game is common and easily found in excellent to mint condition.
$40

Sports Illustrated Games
Box 619, Radio City Station, New York, NY 10020
1960s and 1970s

BOWL BOUND
became COLLEGE FOOTBALL
$45

COLLEGE FOOTBALL
originally called BOWL BOUND
$30

HANDICAP GOLF
$55

Standard Toycraft Inc.
Brooklyn 6, NY
1940s/'50s–1960s

BEVERLY HILLBILLIES, 1963
Based on the TV show from 1962 to 1971
$35

PETTICOAT JUNCTION, ±1964
Based on the TV show from 1963 to 1970.
$55

LITTLE LEAGUE BASEBALL GAME, ±1950
#752; gameboard with attached spinner and event charts, instr on illust bldup, four plastic disks; approved by the Little League Association; retail $1.59; cover photo of pitcher, catcher, and umpire, with youth swinging bat.
$45

THE MY FAIR LADY GAME, ±1962
Based on the play, not the 1964 movie, making it one of very few games to be based on theater. Uncommon.
$40

Stirn & Lyon
New York
1870s/1880s

Makers of wood toys, doll houses, and very few games.

COWS IN CORN, 1889
S&A; wood box with paste-on litho on sliding top; cardboard bldup sections form pen and platforms for marble dexterity game.
$110

RINALDO, ±1880
S&A; 11½″ × 10½″ heavy wood box comes apart to make moving target game; illustrated box bottom is target showing polar bears being attacked by hunters and dogs, and marching military with U.S. flag; 10″ diameter litho on wood revolving target has illust of officers and flags from dif countries on one side and animals and their hunters on other side; two 2½″ diameter holes provide area through which dart must pass for the highest score; eight wood pieces fit together to form the stand for target and metal blowgun shooter, plus mechanism for pulling string which causes target to revolve; litho on wood box shows two illustrations of adults playing and of children with game setup; illustrated instr inside cover are for games of "The Chase," "National Standards," and "Junior Creedmore"; exceptional and rare early litho on wood mechanical toy

game is similar in style to Bliss and is illustrated in 1880s Bradley catalog.
$800

Stoll & Edwards Co. Inc.
65–67 Madison Ave.; 425 4th Ave. (≤1929), New York, NY
≤1921–≥1929
Stoll & Einson
Long Island City, NY
1934–1935

The connection between the two companies is evidenced primarily by the name Stoll in both companies and by the game of TREASURE ISLAND, virtually the same game issued by the two companies 11 years apart. Stoll and Edwards was still listed in the city directories in 1934/35, though no games have been located bearing their name after the Stock Market crash of 1929. The assumption is that Stoll was the same man in both companies, and it took a few years of recovery to get back into business. Stoll and Edwards often used an "S&E" logo. They published a number of games based on children's books and stories; BLACK BEAUTY, even included the book with the game.Einson-Freeman (see listing) operated during the same period, in the same city, and with an illustrated book logo very similar to Stoll & Einson's Playjoy logo, suggesting yet another connection.

Stoll & Edwards

Some of the games that can be found for around $25 or less include CHILDREN'S LIBRARY OF CARD GAMES (1922, published in conjunction with Noble & Noble), COO COO (1925, punch board parlor game published with Herbert Specialty Mfg. Co., Chicago), COO COO-NUNDRUMS (16 × 16 gameboard, retailed for $1), COO COO BOO, and GAME OF SNAP.

GAME OF ALICE IN WONDERLAND, 1923
8½ × 16½; board game.
$85

BLACK BEAUTY, 1921
One-piece gameboard, four Bakelite markers, spinner, hardcover copy of Anna Sewell's 1877 book.
$65

CINDERELLA, 1923
8½ × 16½; gameboard, punch-out heart-shaped cards, spinner, wooden pawns; gameboard © Noble & Noble.
$45

DEFENDERS OF THE FLAG, 1922
Card game was also made by Noble & Noble; cross-collectible, military.
$45

GAME OF MOTHER GOOSE, 1921
9½ × 12¼; heavy one-piece board, four markers, spinner, illustrated parts envelope; excellent box cover illust by Doris Holt.
$50

GAME OF PEGPIN, 1929
Heavy one-piece board; pegs.
$25

PONY EXPRESS, 1926
13 × 13; one-piece board.
$55

SCOUTING, 1926
One-piece board, four cardboard scouts and wood bases, spinner, instr in cover; not a Boy Scout theme but "The Great Pioneering Game For Boys"; cover shows Indian Scout and silhouettes of Indians.
$55

THE THREE BEARS, 1922
Card game also published by Noble & Noble; cross-collectible, bears.
$35

THE GAME OF TING-A-LING, 1920
$45

THE ADVENTURES OF TOM SAWYER AND HUCK FINN, 1925
Large board game. (See listing under Stoll & Einson.)
$85

TREASURE ISLAND, 1923
Exact same board game (except for different coloring) as 1934 Stoll & Einson game of the same title; based on the 1883 Robert Louis Stevenson book .
$45

Stoll & Einson

THE ADVENTURES OF TOM SAWYER AND HUCK FINN, 1934
#2213; 10¼" × 20; thick folded board, four wood pawns, three special dice with number 1–4 and star and moon symbols, 15 numbered cards 3" × 3" with illust and captions, such as "Tom Sawyer beguiles the boys into whitewashing the fence," inst sheet pasted in cover; path board illust same as cards, board marked "By permission of the estate of Samuel L. Clemens and the Mark Twain Co."; cover shows two boys, one sitting on fence and the other with straw hat and fishing line.
$75

CINDERELLA, 1934
Similar to Stoll and Edwards game of the same name.
$30

DOG SWEEPSTAKES, 1935
S&A; seven cardboard dogs race on strings; great bulldog cover.
$75

PIRATES RAID, 1934
11½ × 19¾; heavy board opens to 22 × 18, black marbling bd back, eight cardboard ships on wood bases, instr sheet; two-player strategy game with each having dif battle strengths on board that is map of Spanish Main and West Indies.
$80

TREASURE ISLAND, 1934
Exact same game (with different coloring) as the 1923 Stoll and Edwards game of the same title.
$45

T.H. Stough Co.
Jeannette, PA
1920s
See **Archer Toy Co.**

STO-AUTO RACE, ±1920
$25

STO-QUOIT, ±1920
$15

Stox, Inc.
111 West Monroe St.,
Chicago, IL
tel. Randolph 5456

THE GAME OF STOCK EXCHANGE, ±1940
18½" × 18½", three-fold board with uneven sections opens to 29 × 17, three large special dice (two show 12 stocks, one indicates "up" or "down"), 24 celluloid markers showing "long" and "short"; stocks incl Areo, Dupont, Erie, Fisk, Ward, Alton, Nash, and Sears; game also came as board and separate parts box; retail $3; cover reads, "The Preferred Game" and "Incorporated under the laws of probability and chance."
$65

Strauss Mfg. Co.,
395 Broadway, New York, NY

KINDERGARTEN LOTTO, 1904
BINGO style puzzle game; four illustrated puzzle trays, 24 pieces; excellent "European style" litho illustrations, esp. cover of adult and children playing.
$80

Supply Sales Corp.
Geneva, NY
1920s

Games include DOUBLE CROSS, MALTA, ROLL-O BASEBALL, ROLL-O FOOTBALL, ROLL-O GOLF, ROLL-O MOTOR SPEDWAY, and THE TRAVELING SALESMAN (all ≤1923).

LA HAZA, 1923
4½" × 4½"; four one-piece pressed board gameboards, two dice, numerous disks, instr sheet; bingo style game; © George Hawley.
$20

Talicor (See **The Ungame Company**)

Peter G. Thompson
Cincinnati, OH
1880s

Makers of educational card games. The company was bought out by McLoughlin Bros.

HISTORICAL CARDS, 1884
Card game; 5½" × 4½" × 1½"; 200 cards with one or more persons (and some places, objects, or events) listed on each card, with facts about each listing; instr sheet; © Freeman & Riddle, Columbus, Ohio; cover is black and white, with lettering and geometric and flower design; same style as GEOGRAPHICAL CARDS.
$30

GEOGRAPHICAL CARDS, 1883
Card game; 5½" × 4½" × 1½"; 200 cards with one or more places listed per card, with facts about each listing; instr sheet; © Freeman & Riddle, Columbus, Ohio; cover is black and white, with lettering and geometric and flower design; same style as HISTORICAL CARDS.
$30

GAME OF MYTHOLOGY, 1884
$45

VERBORUM, 1883
Card game; 54 cards each with a letter or number, all with a winter scene of kids with sleds and ice skating; slipcase-style box; subtitle "Word Building."
$30

THE GAME OF WANG, 1883
nva

3M
3M Center, St. Paul, MN 55101
1970s
"3M" stands for "Minnesota Mining and Manufacturing." The company, which made mostly strategy games, was bought out by Avalon Hill. 3M games are collected for their play value more than anything else. 3M games that can be found for around $25 or under include BID AND BLUFF, BIG LEAGUE BASEBALL, FOIL GAME, SPEED CIRCUIT, and THINKING MAN'S FOOTBALL.
3M games that have been offered to collectors by the Avalon Hill Company include (with AH prices noted) CONTIGO (1974, deluxe edition; $50), HIGH BID GAMETTE (1970, $75), IMAGE (1972, $35), MONAD (1969 "perfume box" ed. or small bookshelf gamette; $75), PLOY (1970, $50), and VENTURE (1969, $50); however, these games can probably be found for considerably less.

ACQUIRE, 1962
Excellent game for four or more, based on buying and selling property. Collectors should note that the first, limited-edition, test-market version of ACQUIRE had a folding board and a larger box than the final version manufactured in 1963.
$50 first limited edition
$20 all others

DIPLOMACY
One of the only two territorial war strategy games to become popular with at least a portion of the general public (Parker Brother's RISK is the other). It was copyrighted in 1959 by Games Research Inc., then sold to 3M. According to the May, 1973, issue of *Games & Puzzles* magazine, it was Dr. Henry Kissinger's favorite game.
$20

FACTS IN FIVE, 1967
Classic game of categories.
$25

OH-WAH-REE, 1962
Classic game of MANCALA or WARI.
$20

SLEUTH, 1971
A revision, sans gameboard, of a 1967 game developed by Sid Sackson for Ideal Toy Corp. called THE CASE OF THE ELUSIVE ASSASSIN, an Ellery Queen mystery game.
$20

TWIXT, 1963
This classic two-player strategy game is based on the knight's move in chess, and requires a player to build a wall from one side of the board to the other before an opponent connects the other two sides; invented by Alexander Randolph.
$25

Today's Kids (See **Wolverine**)

Toycrafters (See **Valley Novelty Works**)

Toy Creations Inc.
340 Claremont Ave., Jersey City, NJ
200 Fifth Ave., New York, NY
late 1930s–1940s

Toy Creations was very active during the 1940s, producing a number of patriotic games (they were able to pick up a Kate Smith license) and skill and action items. Games that are still available for under $25 include KLIX DICE (1939), PILE 'EM HIGH (1940s), and POT 'O GOLD (1940).

BOMBS AWAY, ±1944
One-piece pressed wood gameboard 18 × 18, parts box 4" × 4" containing bombsight and bombs.
$50

DEMOCRACY, 1940
Gameboard with spinning dial, eight charts, 48 cards, six wood pawns; red, white, and blue cover has no illust.
$25

EAGLE BOMBSIGHT, 1940s
$40

KATE SMITH'S OWN GAME AMERICA, 1940s
#125; 16½" × 9; 144 cardboard tiles incl state maps, capital cities, products and industries, favorite sons, and American flags, which "are symbols of freedom, and accordingly, may be used freely in place of any other needed tiles"; four cardboard 2-piece racks, cardboard markers; when implements are laid out correctly in the box, the entire image resembles the American flag; red, white, and blue cover shows Kate Smith at CBS microphone, drawings of the White House and Capitol; Kate Smith's royalties on the game were to be donated to her favorite charity.
$65

OFFICIAL BASKETBALL, 1940
$30

OFFICIAL HOCKEY, ±1940
#152
$30

SPOT-A-PLANE, 1942
$50

The Toy Tinkers
Evanston, IL
games: 1914–≥1935

The Toy Tinkers are known mostly for TINKERTOYS, the wooden dowel and disk building set patented in 1914. Though most of their items were building or playset related, the company did make a number of games. Child Guidance acquired TINKERTOYS, and Hasbro took them over from Child Guidance in 1985.

JUMPY TINKER, 1920s
S&A; 10½″ × 5½″; two 5½″-long wood springboard catapults, five mini clothespins (called pickets) for connecting box top and bottom, five cardboard rings, instr on bottom of box.
$30

PEEZA, 1935
S&A; 5¼″ × 7; 50 1″ diam. red wood disks, seven round-edged disks color coded for dif. players, seven balls, one cone shaped foundation block, one shaker, instr. sheet; high quality wood tower building game.
$45

TINKERPINS, 1916
S&A; 31½ × 2¾ paper mailer-wrapped box; intricate construction of two long, connecting thin "alleys" creates a cross between bowling and shuffleboard, where player sends rolling device along first section of alley into opponent's area in an attempt to knock over pins without the rolling device reaching the grooves at the alley's end; after opponent's pins are knocked down, first player's pins pop up for opponent's shot.
$90

TINKER TOSS, 1920s
S&A; 24 × 1¾″ × 1½″; two 24″ long wood foils (sticks), two wood balls attached together by a short string; the object was to toss the balls from one player's foil to the other's.
$40

Traffic Game Co.
Allentown, PA
±1952

This one-game company produced the now-classic game of PARK & SHOP, then sold it to Milton Bradley in 1953.

PARK & SHOP, ≤1952
Gameboard and 6″ × 5″ parts box; six metal cards, six metal men, die, shopping cards, pedestrian cards, motorist cards, and parking ticket cards. This was the first game to be devised around a shopping center; the board back litho explains the origin of the game at the Allentown, PA, $100,000,000 Retail Center; the game was sponsored by local newspapers. Scarce.
$70

Transogram
New York, NY
Brooklyn, NY
1915–1969
games: 1931–≥1970

Transogram is one of the major game companies of the 1900s, producing a variety of products from the post-depression era through the period of early television. The company first manufactured tissue embroidery patterns which could be applied to cloth using a hot iron. Charles S. Raizen took a summer job at the company and devised a way to transfer images using friction—a stick rubbed across the back of the image that would transfer it onto another piece of paper—hence the company's first name, the Friction Transfer Pattern Company. The company was more successful selling the item as a toy (with "fun" images) rather than as embroidery patterns, and by the end of 1915 the transfers were being used in Sunday newspapers and had been awarded a Gold Medal at the Panama Pacific Exposition. Raizen then bought out his boss and took over as president of the company in 1917, at which time he changed the name to Transogram.

Raizen established one of the first toy and game designers' think tanks, the Toy Research Institute, and tested his toys with the help of a child psychologist; starting in the 1920s Transogram toys were marked "Kid-Tested." Raizen started obtaining licenses, such as for a Little Orphan Annie clothes pin set for which "Annie" creator Harold Gray designed the packaging. Al Capp, who was later to become the creator of "Lil Abner," was also a graphics designer for Transogram. Throughout the 1920s the company made toys and playsets, and activity items; then in 1929 the company produced ORJE, THE MYSTIC PROPHET, the first item to resemble a game (it was actually a solitaire fortune telling pastime).

RIDING COWBOY & KNUCKLE DOWN was one of the first Transogram games, developed in 1931. The company's game line grew tremendously throughout the '30s, bolstered by the success of BIG BUSINESS in 1935, about the same time Parker Brothers' MONOPOLY started to take hold. Transogram expanded its interest during the 1940s (into such areas as children's toy furniture), and between 1940 and 1955 the number of games manufactured was minimal, especially compared to its heyday in the 1930s.

When Transogram entered the arena of television games, beginning with DRAGNET in 1955, the company once again became a major force in the American game industry. Next to Bradley, Parker, and Selchow & Righter, it was one of the top game companies (along with Ideal and Lowell) throughout the late 1950s and early '60s. In 1962 the company changed from being privately owned to being a public company listed on the New York Stock Exchange. Around that time, a national contest resulted in the use of a new logo, featuring an amorphous-shaped character dubbed "Transy."

During this period, Raizen was the president of the Toy Manufacturers of America (he was elected posthumously to its Hall of Fame in 1986). He died in 1967 and the company was sold two years later and eventually foundered.

Transogram games from the 1930s often used thinner cardboard than other companies, and the games sometimes appear less substantial. Also, the illustrations often lacked sophistication, though that may have been part of the company's attempt at aiming its products almost exclusively at children. In spite of its proliferation of games during the 1930s and its importance in the industry, Transogram did not produce the kind of quality games that are highly sought after by pre-war collectors; there are some notable exceptions, however. Some of the television games, though, in spite of being usually ordinary in terms of gameboard and implements, are highly prized because of their licensed chacracters, themes, and covers. TV and other games that can still be bought for around $25 or less include LUCKY BINGO (1936), MICHIGAN KITTY (1938), PLAY YOUR HUNCH (1960), PUT AND TAKE (1939), TIC TAC DOUGH, and TRUTH OR CONSEQUENCES.

Most early Transogram games were dated with roman numerals.

ADVENTURES OF POPEYE GAME, 1957
Four cardboard Popeye figures in wood stands, 32 wood markers, shaker box with Popeye illust, 24 cardboard discs, 16 cards, spinner, instr sheet; cards and board include black character Hygmy Pygmy; board illust shows Popeye on island with empty

spinach cans, Bluto flying after Popeye's punch, Olive Oyl tied to post, and Wimpy with plate of burgers.
$60

BEN CASEY M.D., 1961
Gameboard, printed die-cut bldup with four cardboard Casey figures, plastic stands, 66 cards, die, instr sheet; cover shows picture of Vincent Edwards and illust of hospital room operation; based on the ABC TV show.
$30

BETSY ROSS AND THE FLAG, 1950s
$30

BIG BUSINESS, 1936, 1937
$25 (later editions are worth less)

BUCKING BRONCHO, 1930s
S&A; 9¾″ × 9¾″ × 2¼″; boxbot bd with attached posts, wood pins, spinning top; good cowboy illustration.
$50

CALLING SUPERMAN, 1954
17½″ × 9, bldup bd with 2 attached spinners, cardboard Superman playing piece on wood base, deck of headline cards, plastic pawns.
$110

DOG RACE, 1937
#1213, 14¾″ × 10¾″; thin cardboard board 21½″ × 12¼″; six wood dogs, four hurdle post stands, two hurdle posts, three wood dice, money; the track game is a standard race game; however, "the game playing money in this game may be used to buy and sell the dogs if you so desire."
$30

DRAGNET, 1955
Based on the TV show. Common.
$60

HAPPY LANDING, 1938
S&A; two sizes: 12 × 12; 10¾″ × 10¾″; bldup bd with metal cup attached in center; tiddley wink variant has four wood pieces for snapping wood markers; good graphics shows airplanes and landing field.
$45 (either size)

HASHIMOTO-SAN, 1963
Based on the *Hector Heathcote* TV cartoon show (1963–64).
$80

HECTOR HEATHCOTE, 1963
Based on the TV cartoon show (1963–64).
$85

HUNGRY WILLIE, 1930s
S&A; #700G; 14 × 8; tossing game, requiring tossing small playing pieces into the die-cut mouth of Hungry Willie. The brightly colored cartoon cover illustration is one of Transogram's best.
$70

JACKIE GLEASON'S AND AW-A-A-A-Y WE GO, 1956
$125

JOHNNY RINGO, 1959/60
Based on the TV western starring Don Durant, 1959–1960. Scarce.
$125

THE KENNEDYS, 1962
Gameboard, 72 turn-of-event cards, 36 category cards, 36 misc. cards, money, two dice, six pawns; cover illust shows six Kennedy faces carved into mountain, as in Mt. Rushmore; box marked "Transco Adult Games, a Division of Transogram"; © Harrison & Winter; this game is somewhat common, so value is not relatively high; however, the value may increase more rapidly than similar items over the next decade.
$65

KROKAY, 1955
#3407; S&A; 23 × 5½″ × 3; four 22″ long wood mallets with 5″ long heads, four wood balls, two posts, nine metal wickets, instr sheet.
$30

MOVIE MILLIONS, 1938
14½″ × 12¾″; one-piece board, photo cards of actors, directors and critics, wood pawns, money; stars include Olivia de Havilland, Anne Sothern, Betty Grable, Humphrey Bogart, Bing Crosby, William Boyd, and many others.
$100

MY FAVORITE MARTIAN, 1963
Board game shows Ray Walston and Bill Bixby; based on the 1963–66 TV show.
$60

PERRY MASON MISSING SUSPECT GAME, 1959
$45

PHILIP MARLOWE, 1960
$40

RIDE 'EM COWBOY & KNUCKLE DOWN, 1931
S&A; marble game with two die-cut setups for marble roll; © Edward McCandlish. This is one of the best examples of the high quality illustrations Transogram sometimes used.
$70

ROUTE 66, 1962
$75

SCREWBALL, THE MAD MAD MAD GAME, 1960
Unauthorized *Mad* magazine look-alike board game was changed after *Mad* publisher William Gaines threatened to sue; a microphone was placed in front of the gap-toothed Alfred Newman look-alike on the cover, and the title was shortened.
$55 original version

SILLY SIDNEY, 1963
Based on the *Hector Heathcote* TV cartoon show (1963–64).
$85

SINK THE SHIP, ±1940
#50; S&A; 11½″ × 6½″ × 3; target game; fancy wood gun on metal base with wood wheels, six cardboard ships (each different) on wood stands, wood bullets.
$60

SPINGO AND WHIRLETTE, 1930s
Bright colored, illustrations incl wonderful man-in-the-moon character on the box apron help make this game one of Transogram's better items.
$45

STEVE SCOTT SPACE SCOUT GAME, 1952
Rare space item named after Charles Raizen's grandson Steven Scott Fadem, who is now a business man and game collector.
$100

STRATEGIC COMMAND, ±1950
This later and oversized entry into the Transogram line is a three-dimensional game based on the principles of BATTLESHIP.
$45

SUGAR BOWL, ±1950
$35

Trojan Games
111 S. 6th St., Minneapolis, MN
1930s–1940s

Games include AMERICA'S FOOTBALL, HIDE NO PEEK, and PLAY QUIZ (all ≤1939).

TRAFFIC HAZARDS, 1939
Large board game depicting the rules of the road and the pitfalls of driving.
$35

Tryne Games Mfg. Inc.
Springfield Gardens (Long Island), NY
   Tryne Products
   Tryne Sales, Inc.
   Lindenhurst (L.I.); Mineola (L.I.); New York, NY
   ±1950s, 1960s

Manufacturer of plastic puzzles and small puzzle games such as BACKFIRE, DOUBLE HI-Q, DOX, HEXED, HOO DOO, KWAZY QUILT, SPELL-O-GRAM, TAKE-OFF, TORMENTOR, and WHEEL-O-WORDS.

THIMK, 1955
Standard size board game, 16 plastic stackable checkers, four dice.
$20

Tudor Metal Products Corp.
   Tudor Toys (Trademark)
MUSICAL LOTTO, 1936
Bingo-type cards with 12 squares each, each square showing staff, cleff, and notes (key signature); sepia tone picture on reverse side makes face of composer when 12 cards are put together.
$40

The Ungame Company
190 Arovista Circle, Brea, CA
1971–Present

The company was formed in July, 1971, as "Auvid, Inc.," providing audio visual products for the health care industry. After introducing its first game, the UNGAME, and meeting with success, it began doing business as The Ungame Company in late 1972. By 1976 the company was producing only games; it took over the sale of ANTI-MONOPOLY in 1988, the same year the company name was changed to "Talicor"; it is one of the major small independent companies making games today.

"THE LOVE BOAT GAME
$15

THE SPACE SHUTTLE 101, 1981
$25

THE UNGAME
$10

United Game Co.
Brooklyn, NY
175 Fifth Ave., New York, NY
early 1900s

The United Game Co. had some connection to Parker Brothers, which is as yet unclear. What *is* known is that the games were

definitely by Parker Brothers: the style of illustration was the same, some of the games bore the Parker (Salem) ship logo, and most of the games contained a card advertising another Parker product. Games that are valued around $25 or less include HERE'S HOW (±1920), PETER CODDLES VISIT TO NEW YORK (±1910), and RUMMY (1916, the lowest value United game.)

THE GOOD OLD GAME OF DR. BUSBY, ±1920
Card game; 8½ × 6½; large cards; cover shows character with foot wrapped in bandages; same as Parker Brothers game.
$25

THE FROG WHO WOULD A WOOING GO, ±1920
Board game with excellent cover litho of frog.
$75

THE LITTLE SOLDIER, ±1900
#764; 17½ × 11½; boxbot bd with b&w center illust of soldier; cover illust shows saluting boy soldier in oversize coat in front of tent.
$75 Auc. 6'/92 $160

U.S. Playing Card Co.
Cincinnati, OH
1894-present

The name U.S. Playing Card Company was first used in 1894, as an adjunct to Russell, Morgan & Co., which was founded as a publishing company in 1867 and started making playing cards in 1881. In 1895, the USPCC began manufacturing educational card decks and formed a separate company, The Fireside Game Co., which operated until 1900. At that point there was a change of names, and Fireside became the Cincinnati Game Co., which produced new games until about 1906. Most of the 39 or so games made by these companies were packaged under different company names; only about six games were done exclusively by Fireside, and only about four were exclusive to Cincinnati; between 1895 and 1905, the USPCC did not publish any game that was not also published by either Fireside or Cincinnati. USPCC, though no longer making card games, is now the largest manufacturer of playing cards in the world.

Most USPCC, Cincinnati, and Fireside games came in hard card packs; one exception was a Cincinnati card box titled OUR NATIONAL PARKS, which had no company name on the box but contained the GAME OF YELLOWSTONE. Most titles are easy to find and are valued at around $25 to $30; military theme games, such as WHITE SQUADRON, and games depicting blacks, such as DIXIE LAND, are worth more ($75 for the former, $250 for the latter). There is no appreciable difference between games from the two companies, though collectors prefer an earlier Fireside game to a reissue of the same game by Cincinnati. In some cases, the games did change from one manufacturer to another; for example, WHITE SQUADRON by Cincinnati pictured more modern ships than the WHITE SQUADRON by Fireside. There are around forty games by the two companies, ranging from the common FLAGS to the less often seen INDIVIDUAL AND PROGRESSIVE NILOE. Games by these companies can be found easily at many antique shows, priced anywhere from $10 to $50.

Valley Novelty Works
Bloomsburg, PA
early 1900s

CAPTURE THE FORT, ±1914
#44; 8″ × 14″; boxbot bd with instr on board, spinner, playing pieces. This visually interesting game has illustrations on the outside and *inside* of two aprons; cover illust, done in black, white, and red, shows two soldiers fighting in silhouette against a background of two incoming bombs, with monoplanes and biplanes; box cover copy reads, "An exciting trip across no-mans land through barbed wire, poison gas, exploding shells, and machine gun nests." Other company names on the box were "Ottoys" and "Toycrafters."
$75

James Vick
Rochester, NY
1878–1900s

James Vick was the publisher of an illustrated monthly magazine. The first issue, in January, 1878, advertised THE GAME OF BOTANY, one of the earliest advertisments for a game. Though the game could be purchased from the publisher, it cannot be said for certain whether James Vick actually produced the game.

THE GAME OF BOTANY, ≤1878
Card game; 35 cards, each with a color illust. of a different plant, drawn "critically correct"; "in playing, the elements of science and botany are easily and thoroughly acquired"; postage prepaid retail: 50¢.
ref

Vitaplay Toy Co.
New York (possibly Long Island City), NY
1940s

Vitaplay is another company that made games by inventor Arthur Dritz and may have had a strong connection to American Toy Works and Game Makers, two other companies that produced Dritz games.

CONEY ISLAND PLAYLAND PARK, ±1940
S&A; excellent, high quality three-dimensional game has different cardboard sections that setup on wood stands, and movable cardboard parts as part of the game play: marbles, tiddley winks, ring toss, bowling, darts, Punch and Judy, and Penny Pitch.
$90

KINGS KONTEST, ±1940
#601
nva

Volume Sprayer Manufacturing Co.
Tulsa, Oklahoma
1939–≥1942

Games include HI-RO, KIC-O-LIC, HURRY HOME (1942), NUBS, and SHELL-OUT.

CONTACK, 1939
Hexagonal, tin-lined box with pressed wood pieces was the first edition of this three-sided domino tile game, later to become the classic known as TRI-OMINOES (1968). CONTACK was sold to Parker Brothers, then to Pressman.
$45 tin-lined hexagonal box
$35 cardboard hexagonal box
$15 all other versions

DISCRETION, 1942
Six cardboard cards 10 × 3, each with six dif illustrations of characters representing each of six business conditions: swell, good, fair, poor, bad, terrible; two dice, referred to as "dudecahedron" and later abbreviated "dudad"; six markers, instr sheet pasted into cover. Rare.
$45

NO-JOKE, 1941
5¾ × 3¼; 35 wood tongue depresser sticks painted black with symbols similar to card suits, instr booklet; developed by J.W. Patterson.
$20

Wallie Dorr (See under **Dorr**)

John Wanamaker
Philadelphia, PA
games: 1906

At least one game—quite an exceptional one—was sold under the name of the famous Wanamaker's department store.

SUBSTITUTE GOLF, 1906
26 × 11; wood box bottom with leatherette cover over a cotton layer; nine boards (for golf holes 1-9), each 10″ × 22″, make this one of the largest games ever produced—although the boards are played separately and not continuously. Unusual and rare.
$200

Warren Built-Rite (See **Built-Rite Toys**)

Dexter Wayne
Lansdale, PA
1950s

This virtually unknown company managed to get the license to a 1950s TV adventure show set in Africa, *Ramar of the Jungle*.

RAMAR OF THE JUNGLE, ≥1952
Based on the TV show which ran from 1952 to 1954 and starred Jon Hall, who appears on the cover.
$125

West & Lee Co.
410 Main St., Worcester, MA
1873–1875

A company linked to the earlier Snow Brothers (see listing) and spawning a spate of companies, "Successors to West and Lee," such as Noyes & Snow. Most of the games were card games in small card packs or slip-case card boxes.

AVILUDE, 1873
Card game; slipcase card pack; 64 cards with illust of bird on one card and info about the bird on companion card, illustrating four birds in each of eight catagories; slipcover illust shows birds playing the game around a tree stump; retail 50¢; forerunner of McLoughlin's AVILUDE; two or three versions: gold on black slipcase pack, retail 75¢; "tree stump" slipcover, retail 50¢; the green box was dated 1873, whereas the white box indicated "Patent applied for."
$75
$85 for white "Patent applied for" box

PORTRAIT AUTHORS, 1873
Card game; half slipcover card pack; 64 cards (illust of 4 writers in each of 8 categories, plus lengthy description cards for each writer); categories include novelists, humorists, historians, moral and religious, biographers, story writers, journalists, and poets; retail 50¢.
$40

SOCIETY, 1874
Card game; slipcover card pack; 55 cards, instr sheet; cards include green-on-grey number cards and red-on-grey and black-on-grey cards divided into 4 letters: "A, B, C, D—which may stand for Angles, Britons, Celts, and Danes, the principal components of the Anglo-Saxon race"; the game is a morality game which "symbolizes the conflict between good and evil. . . . It awakens in the mind a hatred of vice and a desire for virtue . . . teaching in particular the ruling of Providence in human affairs, the worth of Benevolence, Christianity, Education and Industry; and the evil of Sin, Selfishness, Intemperance, Debt and Indolence"; additional cards include "The Press," "Economy," "Capital," "Extravagance," "The Loafer," and "The Villain."
$95 Auc. 10/91 $98 (box damage)

TOTEM, 1873
Card game; 4½ × 3½; 36 cards "bearing neat engravings of Birds, Fowls, Wild and Domestic Animals." Each card has an appropriate inscription; instr sheet; blue box has illust of bear and quote from Longfellow: "And they painted on the grave posts/Of the graves yet unforgotten,/Each his own ancestral Totem;/Figures of the Bear and Reindeer,/Of the Turtle, Crane and Beaver."
$75

Western Publishing Co. (See **Whitman**)

Whipple & Smith
Salem, MA
1860s

A.A. Smith is credited with being the inventor of AUTHORS, the nation's most popular (and common) card game, in 1861. He joined forces with G.M. Whipple.

AUTHORS, 1861
$80

SQUAILS, 1865
S&A; large wood disks.
$85

Lisbeth Whiting
1950s

ADVENTURES OF SIR LANCELOT, 1975
Three-dimensional bldup bd with attached spinners, dials, paths, etc.; four wood pawns; based on the short-lived 1956–57 TV series; uncommon.
$70

Whitman Publishing Co.
Racine, WI
games: ±1923–±1970s

Whitman Publishing Co. started in 1916 as a subsidiary of Western Publishing, which had been in business for almost a decade. Games and jigsaw puzzles were added to the line of children's books around 1923, and the company reached its heyday in games during the 1930s. Mattel acquired Western in 1979 and the Whitman name was phased out shortly thereafter.

Whitman games often seem to be of little substance, primarily because of the company's use of thin cardboard boxes and gameboards and common implements. However, the company's aggressive licensing policy fostered the production of games bearing names such as "Blondie," "Charlie Chan," "Charlie McCarthy," "Dick Tracy," "G-Men," "Gangbusters," "Little Orphan Annie," "Popeye"— all collectible characters. The result is a wide range of values from low-end items to highly collectible licensed character games.

BLONDIE PLAYING CARD GAME, 1941
#3081; card game; 5 × 6½; 36 cards in nine sets of four make nine dif four-panel cartoons; instr in cover; excellent color illust on cards, cover shows Dagwood walking son and dog with inset of Blondie; © King Features.
$40

CAT AND WITCH, ± 1940
#3016; pin-the-tail variant; 21 × 19 linen paper board showing witch and cat flying on broomstick, town silhouette below, orange background with bright yellow moon; 24 cat tails; instr on board; cross-collectible, cats.
$45

CHARLIE CHAN CARD GAME, 1939
$50

CHARLIE McCARTHY RUMMY CARD GAME, 1938
Box cover litho; three sets of cards spelling "Mc-C-A-R-T-H-Y" plus extra "Mc" and "C."
$35

CHARLIE McCARTHY RUMMY, 1939
Card game; cards have single panel cartoon with Charlie and Edgar Bergen; suited panels form comic strip.
$35

CHARLIE McCARTHY'S FLYING HATS, 1938
$40

CORNER THE MARKET, 1938
MONOPOLY style board game.
$40

DICK TRACY PLAYING CARD GAME, 1934
#3071; card game; 36 cards consisting of 11 dif thugs, 11 the same of Tracy with inset of Junior, 13 dif jewels, instr card (instr do not indicate correct card count); one of the most uncommon covers of the DICK TRACY card games shows Tracy holding Junior by the hand; © Chester Gould.
$50
$40 1934, cover illust of Tracy with star behind him.
$30 1937, cover illust of Tracy holding flashlight; most common Tracy game.

(Courtesy of Just Kids)

DICK TRACY SUPER DETECTIVE GAME, 1941
#3083; common Tracy card game.
$35

DONALD DUCK PLAYING CARD GAME, 1941
Card game; cards feature many Walt Disney characters, one per card.
$40

EDGAR BERGEN'S CHARLIE McCARTHY RUMMY CARD GAME, 1939
(See CHARLIE McCARTHY RUMMY.)

G-MEN CLUE GAMES, ±1935
12½ × 10½; two gameboards with instr on board, metal badge, spinner, wood markers.
$50

GANG BUSTERS GAME, 1939
13 × 6½; thin cardboard board, 16 paper markers, spinner, instr in cover; striking red background cover illust shows man with tommy gun, gameboard illust shows man in jail and is dif style from box illust; game based on the radio program of Phillips H. Lord.
$70 Auc. 10/91 $82 (repaired aprons, markers missing)

HOLLYWOOD MOVIE BINGO, 1937
BINGO game with many small BINGO cards, three actors' names per card, incl Clark Gable, Boris Karloff, Al Jolson, Tracy & Hepburn, and many more.
$70

HOW GOOD ARE YOU, 1937
10½ × 7½; six party games incl quotations, categories, enigmas, etc.
$15

KENTUCKY DERBY RACING GAME, 1938
$30

LITTLE AMERICA ANTARCTIC GAME
#3075; 9½ × 12¾; thin folded gameboard, wood markers, spinner, instr on board; illust show Statue of Liberty, airplanes, people in Eskimo costumes; named on the board are Peary, Scott, Amundsen, Shackleton, Cook, and Byrd. Touted as "A thrilling trip to the South Pole." This is one of Whitman's best looking games.
$165

LITTLE ORPHAN ANNIE RUMMY CARDS, 1937
Card game; 5x6; cards have single panel cartoon with Orphan Annie characters; suited panels form comic strip.
$40

NAVIGATOR, 1938
#5020; 19½″ × 10¼″; heavy gameboard with instr on back and front, six metal sailing ships, 48 cards to direct the movement of the ships; bd bk litho; originated by C.L. Williams. This may be Whitman's largest, most substantive game.
$75

PINOCCHIO PLAYING CARD GAME, 1939
#3947; card game; 5 × 6½; 35 cards, instr card; card have red, black, and white illust of Pinocchio, Jiminy Cricket, and five other characters, plus six objects or locations such as Stromboli's wagon and school at Pleasure Island; cover shows Jiminy cricket sporting "Official Conscience" badge; © Walt Disney Productions.
$60

QUIZ KIDS RADIO QUESTION BEE, 1945
$25

RED RYDER TARGET GAME, 1939
S&A; bldup bd with 3-D stand-up section, metal shooter, wooden balls.
$125

SIXTEEN READY TO PLAY GAMES, 1931
Sixteen gameboards in book form, with punch-out pieces.
$30

SQUADRON SCRAMBLE, 1942
Card pack with 52 cards picturing 16 types of American, British, Russian, German, Italian, and Japanese aircraft; and "authorized Air Youth game," "approved by the National Aeronautic Assoc."
$50

STRATOSPHERE, 1936
#2009, S&A, 10¼ × 13¼; die-cut bldup bd with parts tray, stand-up easel target, metal catapult, metal cup, two wood balls, instr in cover; board shows moon, sun, and planets (without Pluto) with score holes, excellent graphic space cover shows round orange rocket flying through space leaving yellow and orange tail exhaust.
$75

TELEGRAMS, 1941
The colorful telegraph delivery boy against a red background makes for one of the most striking of Whitman's covers.
$70

WALT DISNEY'S DONALD DUCK PLAYING CARD GAME, 1941
See DONALD DUCK PLAYING CARD GAME

WHO IS THE THIEF, 1937
Card game; unusual die-cut cover shows card from the deck underneath.
$40

ZOOM, 1941
#3056; card game; 6½ × 5; 36 cards (9 × 4), instr sheet; cards show color illust of various international aircraft; cover is army plane.
$55

Wilder Mfg. Co.
St. Louis, MO
≤1920–1930s

Wilder produced some of the most attractive games of the 1920s and 1930s. Its games are often marked simply "YLDR."

CONSTRUCTION GAME, ±1930
#184; 12¼ × 7½; boxbot bd, small cards with segments of bridge constuction, wood markers, die; excellent cover illust of bridge under construction.
$75

FISH POND, 1920s
S&A; 9 × 7¾; cover shows youngster fishing on bank with dog and apple, fish and frog in water; board shows fish, frogs, and lily pads.
$30

FOOTBALL, ±1930
#6; S&A; 20½″ × 12½″; thick cardboard playing field attached to box bottom, die-cut with holes into which the football may land, 9″ high grandstand, wood and spring kicking device, wood football, four metal players, four wood goal posts, instr on back of grandstand.
$80

FORE, 1929
nva

HOME, ±1930
Two-sided board with the game of INDIA (PARCHEESI) on one and a European War Game on the other, showing good military graphics.
nva

JOLLY ROBBERS, 1929
S&A; target game with upright board showing five men on wall, two popguns.
$40

MOVIE-LAND KEENO, 1929
BINGO game with great cover showing caricatures of famous stars (such as Charlie Chaplin and Adolphe Menjou); eight 7 × 8¾ cards have sixteen squares on one side showing various stars, and a full-size photo on the other side picturing such stars as William Boyd and Joan Crawford; great cross-collectible movie piece.
$120

OCEAN TO OCEAN FLIGHT GAME, 1920s
#25; excellent litho cover.
$70

RADIO GAME, YLDR, ≤1927
#27; 12¼ × 17½; boxbot bd, spinner, disks, shows short wave radio.
$45

STAR FLIGHT, ≤1931, Wilder
15½ × 10¾, box bot bd, three wood markers, spinner; superb cover illust show Man-in-Moon face surrounded by "pixies" on clouds; equally brilliant board litho shows paths leading from three planets to earth, with space characters on each planet and skyscraper city on earth; the "McLoughlin-quality" litho makes this possibly the best Wilder game seen, and one of few games where both the cover and gameboard are spectacular; date ascertained by edition inscribed 1931. Rare.
$600 Auc. 11/91 $700

Wolverine Supply and Manufacturing Co.
1212 Western Avenue; 1246 Western Avenue, Pittsburgh, PA
1903–1961
Games: ≤1922 - 1961
  Wolverine Toy Co.
  Booneville, AR
  1962–1986
  Games: 1962– ±1970

Wolverine was founded by Benjamin Franklin Bain (1868–1925), a mechanical engineer, in 1903. The name Wolverine was chosen because it represented the mascot of the University of Michigan which Bain attended. Originally the company made and repaired tools and dies for local manufacturers; it also made some novelty kitchen items such as pie-turners and stove-top toasters. After Wolverine made the tools for an action sand toy for another manufacturer, the Acme Sand & Toy Co., that manufacturer went out of business, leaving Wolverine with the finished equipment. Wolverine decided to produce the toys and manufactured an all-metal gravity-action sand toy, which was the start of its now-famous "Sandy Andy" line.

Carl Church Bain, Benjamin's brother, joined the company in 1912. Benjamin Bain died in 1925, and his wife, Dora Elliott Bain, chairwoman of board, appointed Carl Bain president. By 1925 Wolverine was producing a number of games, mostly race-theme games, made out of metal gameboards with attached spinners. All the boards were two-sided, with a checkerboard on the reverse side; most were 16¼ × 16¼. Another selling point, as explained in an early catalog, was that "Playing directions are printed on each board, and cannot be lost." A separate parts box provided the necessary race cars, boats, airplanes, etc.

After only a few years Bain was replaced by James S. Lehren as president. Lehren continued to develop the game line, adding "action" games that would shoot marbles, hoops or rings. The company's peak period of game production lasted until the early 1930s. PITCH'EM, an indoor/outdoor horseshoe pitching game was the most popular game through the 1940s and '50s. From the 1950s into the 1970s the company's bagatelle games and marble games proved the most popular.

Wolverine also began manufacturing girls' housekeeping toys in the late 1920s or 1930, and the company introduced scaled appliances ("Rite Hite") in 1959. In 1962 the company name was changed to Wolverine Toy Company. James L. Lehren became president of the company in 1966 and the company was acquired by Spang and Company in 1968; its headquarters was moved to Booneville, Arkansas in 1971. Vicky Rath was appointed president of the company in 1984 and soon after began a complete change-over of the company's product line. In keeping with its new image, the company changed its name to Today's Kids in 1986. Wolverine's metal items were phased out in 1990 (the last ones being tin dishes and an ironing board) and Today's Kids features injection molded plastic toys along with rotational molded plastic items (since 1985) and blow molded plastic items (since 1987). The company's products are manufactured in Arkansas while sales, marketing, and product development are located in Dallas, Texas. The last game produced by the company was around 1970.

It isn't surprising that we can find Wolverine games in excellent condition sixty years after they were made. A 1926 catalog describes the games as "beautifully lithographed in many colors on heavy-gauge metal, and furnished with durable, water-proof lacquer. They are sanitary; can be washed when necessary. They are indestructible and will outlast any cardboard game."

The listing that follows includes nearly all the Wolverine games that were sold during the company's prime period of game production, 1922 to 1930.

ACROSS THE CHANNEL, 1926
#39
$85

AEROPLANE RACE, 1922 or 1923
#30; one of the earliest Wolverine games.
$95

CONGO BONGO, ±1930
Bagatelle game of wood and cardboard with African jungle theme.
$55

DECK DERBY, 1920s
#149A; 12 × 8½; two-piece metal board hooks together to make an 8 × 20 track, with illust in center showing game being played aboard ship; six metal two-dimensional horses similar to (or probably same as) the horses from GEE WIZ race, two metal hurdles, three wood dice; box is thin cardboard slipcase with flap on each end; box shows three images: horses racing, silhouette of ship (with title and "As Played on Ocean Liners"), and game being played on deck.
$60

FLING-A-RING, ±1930
#158
$35

GEE-WIZ, 1928 (pat. 1924)
Action toy/game; patented device uses an unseen flywheel with various protruding metal posts; as the flywheel turns (propelled by pulling a string), the revolving posts hit small ball bearings that in turn hit base of horses, propelling them along grooved track; game originated in Europe. The "popular" model is common and seems to be greatly overpriced at shows.
$50 #40: popular model, 15½" × 5¾"; retail $2.50
$90 #41: standard model, 29" × 9¾", framed in mahogany-finished wood with matching wood partitions between discs; retailed for $10(!). Rare.

GYM HORSESHOES, 1930
#155
$45

HOOP-O-LOOP, 1930
#156
$30

JUNGLE DARTS
Advertising game on a wood board.
nva

JUNIOR MOTOR RACE, 1925 (pat. 1/13/25)
#33; four metal autos
$70

JUNIOR ROUND-THE-WORLD FLYERS, 1925 (pat. 8/18/25)
#34
$70

MARBLE MARKSMEN, 1929 or 1930
#148
nva

THE MOTOR RACE, ±1922 (pat 1/13/25)
#29; 16¼ square board; six metal autos; board shows grandstand, repair pit, gas station, and the line up for the six cars, with a checkerboard on the reverse side. This was the first Wolverine game and was the model for all the metal boards that followed.
$125

NECK AND NECK, 1930
S&A; wood frame horse race device requires each of up to four players to continue jerking a string which moves a cardboard track up and back, propelling the horses forward in short jumps.
#142
$80

OLYMPIC RUNNERS, 1929 or 1930
#145
ref

PENNANT WINNER BASEBALL GAME, 1930
#157
ref

PITCH'EM, 1929 or 1930
#154; horseshoe game; box has wonderful cartoon illustration.
$45

PITCH'EM WINKS, 1929 or 1930
#152 combination horseshoes-tiddley winks
$25

ROCKETS TO THE MOON, ±1950
#149; although given #149 code which in the number sequence used by the company would place it around 1929, the item is plastic covered pinball game with modern space theme, showing Cape Canaveral which became prominent after 1947.
$25

ROUND THE WORLD FLYERS, 1925 (pat. 8/18/25)
#30; 11″ × 11″; predominantly green and light blue metal board, with illustrations in two corners of bi-planes and a blimp; this game probably replaced AEROPLANE RACE.
$85

SNAP 'N SCORE # 143A, 1929 or 1930
ref

SPEED BOAT RACE, 1926
Metal board with two built in spinners, checkerboard on reverse; retail $1.00.
$75

SPEED BOAT RACE, 1929 or 1930
#146
$65

SPOT SHOT, 1929 or 1930 (pat. 1934)
#147
ref

STRATEGY, 1924 (pat. 2/17/25)
#31; checkerboard on reverse
ref

TIPIT, 1929 or 1930
#43; 14¼″ long board, numbers on one side of blocks and letters on the other, 2 dice.
$20

TIPIT SENIOR, 1929 or 1930
#44; 15¾″ long board, numbers on side of blocks (no letters as in TIPIT #43).
ref

TRAP-A-TANK, 1920s, Wolverine
#145; 18½ × 8 thin cardboard slipcase style box, folded metal board opens to 36″; cardboard covering section of board vibrates with turning of attached handle, causing four wood tanks with metal pins for guns to move along the board; board illust is battle scene; box shows tanks climbing over wall; luck game similar in concept to NECK AND NECK, which was a skill game.
$70

Woolson Spice Co.
Huron & Jackson Streets, Toledo, OH
games: ≤1894-≥1903

Woolson Spice Co. was the maker of Lion Coffee, and one of the first companies to use game premiums to advertise extensively; most of the tiny games were available by sending in the lion heads from the Lion Coffee wrappers plus a stamp; the games usually had "Drink Lion Coffee" written somewhere on them, often on the back of every card. The company said it had 60 small card games (2⅛″ × 3⅛″) to choose from, ranging from THE SPY from 1895 to the GAME OF CHINK in 1903; most of these games are valued at around $40, though those with interesting themes, such as the two mentioned, might bring more; price depends on condition, and it is difficult to find these small, thin paper or cardboard games in very good shape. A sampling of Woolson Spice Lion Coffee premium card games includes: ASTRONOMY, PIG, and STOP.

Other Lion Coffee premiums include small, one-piece cardboard board games ranging approximately from 6″ × 6″ to 6″ × 10″. Some of these games are CIRCUS (1903), EIGHT MEN IN A ROW, FROM LOG CABIN TO WHITE HOUSE (1895), LION AND TIGER, MAYPOLE (1895), PACHESI, and QUEENS GUARD; most are valued at around $35, but they must have clean cut edges and little fading to be worth full value.

Pin-the-tail variants range from the typical DONKEY (1894), worth about $15, to the more desirable POLLY WANTS A CRACKER, from 1903, requiring the player to pin a paper cracker in the parrot's mouth; this game is valued at $40. Another premium, JACK STRAWS, is a traditional wood PICK-UP-STICKS game that came in a small envelope. Value: $30

F.A. Wright
Cincinnati, OH
≤1875-≥1888

LOGOMACHY, OR WAR OF WORDS, 1875
Card game; 2¾ × 3¾; black and white cards with letters of the alphabet; special value cards, such as the J, Q, and Z, also had b&w illustrations. Wright's LOGOMACHY may have been the first word building game using cards; it was awarded the Silver Medal (the highest premium) at the Cincinnati Industrial Exposition of 1874 for the Best New Parlor Game. The same game was issued by McLoughlin in 1889 with cards and illustrations in full color.
$60

THE GAME OF MONETA, OR MONEY MAKES MONEY, 1888
Card game; 50 cards representing U.S. money. Both the box and the 1889 Montgomery Ward catalog list this game as being "by the author of Logomachy."
nva

Wyandotte Toys (See **All Metal Product Co.**)

Willis G. Young (& Co., Inc.)
2242 Belmont Ave., Chicago, IL
1453 Winnemac Ave., Chicago, Il (1918)
1914–1917

In the short span of approximately four years Willis G. Young produced some wonderful games with exceptional illustrations. A 1918 notice in *Playthings* read, "All the patents and copyrights covering 'The Most Modern Games' . . . are for sale, the owner is on war work."

CHOCOLATE SPLASH, 1916
S&A; 7¼ × 10¾; target board stands upright; monkey-like character on a tree limb falls into a 3-D barrel when hit with a blowgun dart.
$85

FIG MILL, 1916
Bldup bd, pressed cardboard pieces; classic game of MILL (NINE MEN'S MORRIS).
$40

MOVIE INN, 1917, Willis G. Young
S&A; 10¾ × 7¼; board is part bldup and part boxbot bd, five marbles, instr on board; detailed cover illust is interesting street scene, two roadsters, movie marquis showing "The Outlaw" and "Cinderella," with prices of "children 5¢, adults 10¢."
$75

PEG AT MY HEART, 1914
S&A; 12¼ × 9¼; one-piece dart board, four darts with wood shaft, pin tip, and cardboard "feathers"; board consists of red concentric hearts on white background; nicely drawn cover shows three-generation family playing game in parlor; this may be the first game by Young.
$35

PIN-OCK'L
nva

SPEAR-EM, 1916, Willis G. Young
S&A, 12¼ × 6¾; six 6½" tall cardboard men on horseback, each man in dif colorful national military dress, representing, presumably, WWI enemies; two spears with wood shafts and cardboard tails, instr sheet; colorful artistic cover shows children playing game in backyard setting, one boy in military uniform.
$60

SUBMARINE DRAG, Willis G. Young, 1917
S&A; die-cut one-piece bldup and boxbot bd with parts tray; cardboard airplanes with attached string and hook, small cardboard subs; FISH POND variant; exceptional litho cover shows airplane dragging submarine.
$85

Zondervan Publishing House
Grand Rapids, MI
≤1900–≥1940
Manufacturers of Bible card games.

BIBLE BOYS, 1901
©1897, Helen S. Evans.
$15

BIBLE CHARACTERS, 1939
$15

Zondine Game Co.
Box 5321, Metropolitan Station, Los Angeles, CA
778 North Virgil Ave., Los Angeles 29, CA
1132 N. LaBrea Ave., Hollywood, 38, CA
1940s and 1950s

Games include BASEBALL, THE BRAIN BUILDER (an educational game for primary school; retailed for $1), HOLLYWOOD PRODUCER (with a 24 × 24 pliable plastic board, 20 special dice, and $5 million per player; retailed for $2), IMAGINATING, POT O' GOLD (with a 24 × 24 pliable plastic board and travel pouch), TAKE-N-ANTE, and TURKEY SHOOT.

GONG HEE FOT CHOY, 1948
Fortune telling game.
$20

RAMS FOOTBALL
$60

RED SKELTON'S 'I DOOD IT', ≤1947
S&A; wood "trap", six mice, two dice; retail $2
ref

TAKE IT OR LEAVE IT, 1942
20″ × 10″; two-fold gameboard with built-in spinner; many categories of questions and answers on board. Based on the radio program.
$45

WAHOO, ≤1947
$20

Zulu Toy Mfg. Co.
Battle Creek, MI
1920s

ZULU BLOWING GAME, 1927,
S&A; 24½ × 7¼; (1924 J. Arthur Redner; targets, cardboard target holder, 3 darts, two blowguns 24″ long, 1″ diam, illust booklet on the legend of the blow gun, two instr sheets; sharp arrows came in two sizes, 15″ outdoor and 12″ indoor, and could be blown through blow gun with great force; instr sheet incl rules for suggested games, a parts order list, illust of boy playing game and natives using blow guns, and info on "How to form a Zulu Blow Gun Tribe in your neighborhood."
$85

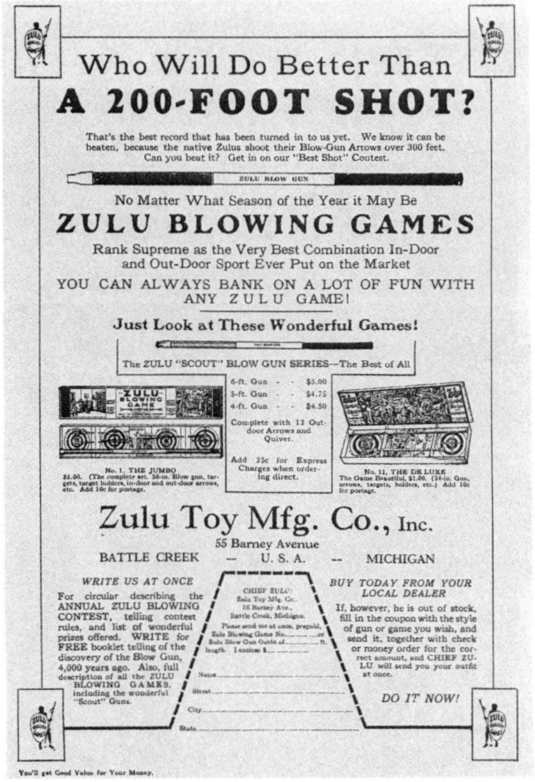

COVERED WAGON, 1927
Gameboard 25 × 19; path game on U.S. map; embossed back litho with title and illust of mule team caravan. Patent by Scholastic Publishing Co., Pittsburgh, PA.
$85

CITY OF GOLD, 1926
#200; standard size board game; good transportation theme cover.
$85

Cultural Timetable: Important Dates, 1843–1972

Appendixes

This list contains noteworthy dates in game history, as well as some of the dates of major occurrences, fads, events, and inventions that can be useful in helping determine the dates of games. In many cases, games have been based on these events, the game usually following the event almost immediately (for example, THE NEW LINDY FLYING GAME, released in 1927, the same year as Lindbergh's famous flight). In other cases, an event may be mentioned, pictured, or alluded to in the instructions or on the gameboard, box, or cards. For instance, an event as innocuous as the implementation of ZIP codes assures us that any game showing a ZIP code in an address must have been manufactured after 1962.

Illustrations used for a game may depict things or styles associated with a particular period or which could not have existed before a certain date. For example, a game showing someone on a velocipede (large-wheel bicycle) would probably be from the 1880s or into the early 1890s when they were replaced by bicycles; a game picturing the Brooklyn Bridge could obviously not be earlier than 1883, when the bridge was finished. Dates showing technical advances and innovations in printing and manufacturing are included in the list as they too can help determine the era of a game. (*Note:* Some sources show a date for an event a year or two earlier or later than other sources.)

Significant events or changes in the game industry, or important dates in the history of one of the major companies, including introduction dates of historic games, are shown for reference. Some of this information also may help in the dating of games when no patent date is available. For example, since Parker Brothers incorporated in 1901, a Parker game box that reads "Parker Brothers *Inc.*" could not be before 1901 (though the first version of the game could have been). Address changes are included where they will assist the collector in dating games; for example, an address of 30 Beekman St. on a

McLoughlin game will indicate the game was manufactured between 1861 and 1870.

The symbol (±) indicates that the event shown occurred sometime around the date listed; (≤) indicates the event occurred in or before the year shown; (≥) indicates the event occurred in or after the year shown.

Company abbreviations are: MB (Milton Bradley), McL (McLoughlin Bros.), PB (Parker Brothers), and S&R (Selchow & Righter).

The list covers the period from 1843, the year when game manufacturing took hold in the United States, to the invention of the video game in 1972.

1843	Ives publishes "Mansion of Happiness" board game; Ives publishes "Dr. Busby" card game
1844	First telegraph message (Morse code)
1845–46	Florida and Texas (1845) and Iowa (1846) become states
1846–48	U.S. war with Mexico
1848	Discovery of gold in California; Wisconsin becomes a state
1850	California becomes a state; (±) John McLoughlin publishes first game
1852	First maneuverable balloon-airship
1853	End of W. & S.B. Ives firm (descendants continue)
1858	Begin McLoughlin Bros. (24 Beekman St., NYC); "Peter Coddles" copyrighted by Gould & Lincoln
1858–59	Minnesota (1858) and Oregon (1859) become states
1860	Milton Bradley Co. created; advances in lithography lead to mass production; the era of hand-coloring games ends
1860–61	Pony Express operates between Missouri and California
1861	McL moves to 30 Beekman St.; the game "Authors" is invented; Kansas becomes a state
1861–65	Civil War
1863–67	West Virginia (1863), Nevada (1864), and Nebraska (1867) become states
1864	E.G. Selchow's association with Albert Swift begins
1866	MB patents first croquet game, establishes rules
1867	E. G. Selchow & Co. created
1869	Completion of the transcontinental railroad; celluloid invented (sometimes used for playing pieces)
1869–78	Height of the Indian wars west of the Mississippi
1870	McL moves to 71–73 Duane St.; "The long depression of the 1870s" begins, according to James Shea's 1960 book about Milton Bradley; the great Chicago fire
1872	Yellowstone becomes first U.S. national park
1876	MB "Bamboozle" board made (same as current 18 × 18 sizes); Bell patents the telephone; Custer's Last Stand at the Battle of Little Bighorn; Centennial Exposition, Philadelphia; Colorado becomes a state
1877	Edison designs the phonograph
1880	Selchow & Righter Co. created from predecessor, E.G. Selchow & Co.
1880s	Velocipedes (large front-wheeled bicycle) are the rage
1880–1920	Massive immigration of more than 20 million Europeans changes U.S. makeup and moves country from agriculture to industry
1882	Chinese Exclusion Act limits Asian immigration; first generating station (New York) supplies electric power following 1879 invention of carbon-filament bulb
1883	Geo. S. Parker Co. created; opening of "Buffalo Bill" Cody Wild West Show; opening of the Brooklyn Bridge
1884	MB Incorporates; start of Ringling Brothers circus
1885	Geo. Parker sells Ives's "Dr. Busby"; "Halma" becomes first American-invented classic; first skyscraper is built (Chicago)
1886	McL moves to 623 Broadway; Statue of Liberty, gift of France, dedicated by President Grover Cleveland
1887	Geo. Parker gets sole rights to all Ives games; first successful U.S. electric street railway (trolley) in Virginia
1888	Geo. S. Parker becomes Parker Bros.; McL makes "Reversi," which wins best new game award in 1976 as "Othello"
1889	Nellie Bly (Elizabeth Cochrane) beats "around the world in 80 days" record of Jules Verne's Phileas Fogg; Oklahoma (Indian Territory) land rush; Montana, Washington, North Dakota, and South Dakota become states
1890s	Bicycles (with equal-size wheels) reach height of popularity
1890	Ellis Island becomes port of entry for immigrants; Idaho and Wyoming become states
1891	International copyright law seeks to end plagiarization; invention of the zipper
1892	MB opens offices in New York; McL moves to 874 Broadway
1893	Columbian Exposition, Chicago; Panic of 1893
1894	MB opens offices in Kansas
1894–95	Daphne Du Maurier's "Trilby" serialized in *Harper's Monthly*
1895	Marconi invents the wireless telegraph
1896	MB opens offices in Atlanta; Utah becomes a state
1897–98	Klondike gold rush boosts development of Alaska
1898	McL moves to 890 Broadway; Spanish-American war; Dewey captures Manila; Theodore Roosevelt and the Roughriders; Cuba and the Philippines
1900	MB opens offices in San Francisco and Philadelphia; Zeppelin invents first rigid dirigible; Phoebe Snow becomes an ad gimmick for DL&W railroad
1901	PB incorporates
1902	Ping-Pong, introduced to the U.S. by Parker Brothers, begins a fad; Flinch Card Co. introduces "Flinch" (later sold to PB); (±) MB begins "4000" series numbering system
1903	MB opens offices in Boston; PB introduces "Pit" (though intro date listed as 1904); Wright Brothers' first flight (Kitty Hawk, NC); Ford Motor Co. opens first plant in Michigan; beginning of "Teddy" bear interest after Roosevelt spares one in 1902
1904	Elizabeth Magie gets patent for the "Landlord's Game"; Louisiana Purchase Exposition, St. Louis (World's Fair)
1904–5	Russo-Japanese war; Russian Revolution; Japanese power rise
1906	PB introduces "Rook"; San Francisco earthquake and fire
1907	Ideal introduces "Teddy" bear, sells first game over 50 years later; Oklahoma becomes state, eliminating Indian Territory;
1908	Bakelite (first completely synthetic plastic) invented
1909	PB production devoted entirely to jigsaw puzzles; Robert Edwin Peary reaches the North Pole
1910	Invention of neon lighting
1911–13	"Animal" dancing craze (like the "Turkey Trot") prompts game-box illustrations of clothed animals
1911	Death of Milton Bradley; Roald Amundsen reaches the South Pole

1912	*Titanic* hits iceberg and sinks; Arizona and New Mexico become states; Kewpie dolls become the rage after 1909 introduction
1913	Ford assembly line brings mass production of automobiles; American film industry established following developments after release of first commercial film in 1903; The "New York World" publishes the first crossword puzzle
1914	Panama Canal completed (begun 1904)
1915–16	Panama-Pacific and Panama-California Expositions
1917–18	U.S. in World War I; the submarine (invented in 1620) comes of age; "Ouija" craze
1919	Commercial aviation begins to develop rapidly
1920	McLoughlin Bros. ends—sold to Milton Bradley
1920s	First U.S. shopping centers
1920–33	Prohibition; rise in gangsterism
1920	Women given the right to vote; first transcontinental airmail route; first regularly scheduled radio broadcasts in U.S.
1922	J. Pressman Co. created; Alderman-Fairchild, Rochester, NY created; Mah-Jongg (under various names) becomes craze through 1925; discovery of King Tut's tomb creates fad in style through 1929; radio broadcasting accepts advertising, becomes industry
1923	Autogiro (aircraft) invented (there are two autogiro games that show no date and no maker)
1924	Elizabeth Magie gets revised patent on "Landlord's Game"; crossword puzzles become a craze
1926	First passenger service added to mail service
1927	Selchow & Righter stops jobbing, sells own games; Charles Lindbergh completes first intercontinental flight; *The Jazz Singer* brings sound to the movies
1928	Chinese Checkers, introduced by Pressman, begins a fad; Admiral Richard Byrd establishes "Little America" base in Antarctica
1929	All-Fair moves to Churchville, NY; stock market crash begins the Great Depression; Transcontinental Air Transport starts first all-passenger service
1930s	Heyday of the G-men
1930	MB opens offices in Chicago; miniature golf becomes fad after 1927 start in Tennessee; United Airlines uses eight nurses for first stewardess service; Pan Am's "China Clipper" offers first transpacific service
1931	Opening of the Empire State Building, New York City
1932	Amelia Earhart flies solo transatlantic (disappears 1937)
1933	Depression felt by MB and probably other game companies; Charles Darrow patents "Monopoly"; National Recovery Administration (NRA) established; Tennessee Valley Authority (TVA) established
1933–34	Century of Progress International Exposition, Chicago
1933–36	Games of finance help end depression for game companies
1934	Dionne quintuplets born
1935	PB buys rights to Darrow "Monopoly" and Elizabeth Magie's 1924 "Landlord's Game" patent; Works Progress Administration (WPA) established; England builds radar stations, works with U.S. on development
1936	Game companies begin recovery from Depression, issue better-constructed games, more implements
1937	Good year for large, sturdy games, multiple implements; Charlie McCarthy becomes great favorite through 1939; Amelia Earhart disappears
1939	World War II begins; first helicopter flight
1939–40	New York World's Fair
1940s	Automobile headlights are incorporated into fenders
1940	"Invention" of U.S. radar
1941	MB game line cut from 410 to 150 items; "Chinese Checkers" (taken from "Halma") is patented; U.S. enters World War II
1943	Introduction of the city number code ("New York 10, NY"), used only in larger cities until 1963 ZIP code
1945	MB comes out with "better packaging"; Franklin Roosevelt dies, Truman becomes president; World War II ends
1946	MB has banner year
1947	J. Pressman Co. becomes Pressman Toy Co.
1948	Production & Marketing Co. introduces "Scrabble"
1949	Television begins to spread throughout U.S.
1950–53	Korean War
±1950	Levitt builds America's first true suburbia
1950	Hopalong Cassidy becomes first TV character used in a game; MB "Key to Fun & Learning" logo is first used; MB identifies age range suitable for game; quiz shows become popular; first suburban mall
1952	Avalon Hill begins with games for strategy players
1953	MB's launch of TV space show games crash lands
1954	(±) Hassenfeld (later "Hasbro") enters game market; trend begins of developing games based on TV shows; Disney unleashes Davy Crockett and his coonskin cap; Civil Rights movement picks up momentum
1955	Lowell makes its first game, "Beat the Clock," which ties with Bettye-B's "Break the Bank" as first games based on TV quiz shows
1956	TV-licensed games begin trend that will revolutionize game industry—Lowell, Bettye-B, Transogram, Milton Bradley lead; first U.S. interstate highway system established; first enclosed mall
1957	*Sputnik,* the first satellite, launched
1958	Submarine *Nautilus* makes first voyage under polar ice cap; Pan Am's Boeing 707 Clipper speeds U.S. into the jet age
1959	Alaska and Hawaii become the forty-ninth and fiftieth states
1961	First manned spaceflight (*Vostok 1,* U.S.S.R.)
1962	First James Bond film, *Doctor No*
1963	Ideal makes its first game, "Mousetrap"; introduction of the ZIP code
1964	New York World's Fair; the beginning of the Beatles' popularity in the U.S.
1966–67	"Ouija" overtakes "Monopoly" in popularity Centennial edition of "Parcheesi"
1968	PB buyout by General Mills ends family ownership; Hassenfeld becomes Hasbro Industries; first manned flight to the moon
1969	First manned lunar landing
1972	Invention of the video game

APPENDIX B

Patent Numbers and Dates, 1843–1972

Many games, especially early ones, do not show dates but list patent numbers instead. By seeing where a patent number falls in the chart below, collectors can determine what year the patent was issued; the number shown next to a date indicates the first patent number issued in that year.

It is important to remember that a game may have been on the market for a few years before it was patented or that a game may have been manufactured for many years *after* the issuance of the patent (for example, the same patent number and 1936 date exists on MONOPOLY games made into the next decade). Patent numbers are issued for seventeen years.

Though the first U.S. patent was issued in 1836, this list covers the period from 1843, the year when game manufacturing took hold in the U.S., to the invention of the video game in 1972.

Date	Patent Number
1843	2,901
1844	3,395
1845	3,873
1846	4,348
1847	4,914
1848	5,409
1849	5,993
1850	6,981
1851	7,865
1852	8,622
1853	9,512
1854	10,358
1855	12,117
1856	14,009
1857	16,324
1858	19,010
1859	22,477
1860	26,642
1861	31,005
1862	34,045
1863	37,266
1864	41,047
1865	45,685
1866	51,784

Date	Patent Number
1867	60,658
1868	72,959
1869	85,503
1870	98,460
1871	110,617
1872	122,304
1873	134,504
1874	146,120
1875	158,350
1876	171,641
1877	185,813
1878	198,733
1879	211,078
1880	223,211
1881	236,137
1882	251,685
1883	269,820
1884	291,016
1885	310,163
1886	333,494
1887	355,291
1888	375,720
1889	395,305
1890	418,665
1891	443,987
1892	466,315
1893	488,976
1894	511,744
1895	531,619
1896	552,502
1897	574,369
1898	596,467
1899	616,871
1900	640,167
1901	664,827
1902	690,385
1903	717,521
1904	748,567
1905	778,834
1906	808,618
1907	839,799
1908	875,679
1909	908,436
1910	945,010
1911	980,178
1912	1,013,095
1913	1,049,326
1914	1,083,267
1915	1,123,212
1916	1,166,419
1917	1,210,389
1918	1,251,458
1919	1,290,027
1920	1,326,899
1921	1,364,063
1922	1,401,948
1923	1,440,362
1924	1,478,996
1925	1,521,590
1926	1,568,040
1927	1,612,700
1928	1,654,521
1929	1,696,897
1930	1,742,181
1931	1,787,424
1932	1,839,190
1933	1,892,663
1934	1,941,449
1935	1,985,878
1936	2,026,516
1937	2,066,309
1938	2,104,004

Date	Patent Number
1939	2,142,080
1940	2,185,170
1941	2,227,418
1942	2,268,540
1943	2,307,007
1944	2,338,081
1945	2,366,154
1946	2,391,856
1947	2,413,675
1948	2,433,824
1949	2,457,797
1950	2,492,944
1951	2,536,016
1952	2,580,379
1953	2,624,046
1954	2,664,562
1955	2,698,434

Date	Patent Number
1956	2,728,913
1957	2,775,762
1958	2,818,567
1959	2,866,973
1960	2,919,443
1961	2,966,681
1962	3,015,103
1963	3,070,801
1964	3,116,487
1965	3,163,865
1966	3,226,729
1967	3,295,143
1968	3,360,800
1969	3,419,907
1970	3,487,470
1971	3,551,909
1972	3,633,214

APPENDIX C

American Companies That Made Games

Though extensive, this list of other American companies that made games is in no way comprehensive, as games and reference material from nineteenth-century companies or from small or regional companies are constantly being uncovered.

Some companies produced only one game. Most sports games, for example, not manufactured by one of the major companies, were often a small company's only product or a sideline enterprise for a company with nongame products. There is not much information available on most of these small businesses; the city and state of the company are provided when known.

The title of the game known to have been produced by the company will be listed if known. The dates shown (if any) indicate the period the company manufactured or sold games (*not* the years the company was in business), or refer to the date of the title listed; the symbol (±) means "circa," (≤) means in or before the year shown, and (≥) indicates in or after the year shown. A number in the "Value" ($) column is the dollar value assigned to the game listed. "nva" in place of a dollar amount means "no value assigned"; "ref" means "reference."

(*Note:* if you have a game from an American company not listed in this book, or a game that is listed as "ref," please write and let us know.)

COMPANY	CITY	ST	DATES	GAME TITLES	$
Abington Press	New York	NY	1922	BIBLE GAME OF FACTS, PLACES, AND EVENTS	nva
Abraham & Strauss	New York	NY	1904	KINDERGARTEN LOTTO; paper dominoes	75
Advanced Ideas Co.	Arlington	MA	1964	FACTS-IN-FIVE	40
Adventure Games, Inc.				LET 'EM HAVE IT—OUR FIGHTING RANGERS	nva
Affinity Card Co.	Portland	OR	1913	AFFINITY	nva
C.E. Akins			1891	PARLOR QUOITS	25
Alladin			±1970s	Modern games	
Frederick J. Allen	Somerville	MA	1904	SOMERVILLE	100
Allison Mfg. Co.			1915	CHI-CHI	nva
Allstate Engineering Service				TORPEDO ATTACK	nva
Alox Manufacturing Co.	St. Louis	MO	1939	TONGO	70
America Inc.	Chicago	IL	1933	AMERICA THE NEW GAME	45
America War Game Co.	New York	NY		AMERICA IN THE WAR	50
The American Game & Puzzle Co.	New York	NY	±1930		ref
American Games & Puzzle Corp.	Portland	OR	1928	GOLPH, GAMIEST OF GAMES	nva
American Indoor Baseball Co.			1920s	AMERICAN INDOOR BASEBALL GAME	nva
American Newspaper Promotion			1938	CROSS-O-GRAMS	nva
American Publishing Corp.	Waltham	MA	1967	CREDIBILITY GAP; other current games	50
American Parlor Baseball			1903	PARLOR BASEBALL	75
American Printing Co.			1906	TEDDY BEAR (cloth board)	150
American Publishing	Hartford	CT	±1890	RAMBLES	200
American Screen Co.			1930	AMOS & ANDY ACROBATS	50
American Shuffleboard Co.	Union City	NJ		SHUFFLEBOARD	nva
American Speech Game Co.	Milwaukee	WI	1922	BETTER SPEECH, BETTER AMERICANS	40
American Toy Airship Co.	Mansfield	OH	1930	MUMBLY PEG	35
American Toys			1952	STADIUM CHECKERS	40
G.H. Anderson	Cincinnati	OH	1943	MAJOR LEAGUE BASEBALL GAME	40
Anma Card Co.	Tulsa	OK	1941	ANMA	nva

COMPANY	CITY	ST	DATES	GAME TITLES	$
D. Appleton & Co.	New York	NY	1857	THE FLOWER GAME	nva
Arba Perry	Chicago	IL	1915	KARD KELLY (KELLY POOL with cards)	35
Arnold Specialty Co.	Burbank	CA	1940	PASS 'N PUNT	40
Artcraft Paper Products	Cincinnati	OH	1954	FORE	40
Athletic Products Co.	South Bend	IN	1955	DAVE GARROWAY'S GAME OF POSSESSION	75
Atlantic Co.	Baltimore	MD	1899	NO-JUMP-O	nva
Atlantic & Pacific Tea Co.			1930s	A & P RELAY RACE (on Sunnyfield Corn Flakes Boxes)	nva
Atlas Game Co.	Milwaukee	WI	1921	NUMERICAL LOTTO	25
Autobridge, Inc.			1938	AUTOBRIDGE	25
Aydellot's Base Ball Card Co.	Detroit	MI	1910	AYDELOTT'S BASE BALL CARDS	175
B & S Inc.	New York	NY	1920s	SPINNING TRAVELER	60
B. P. Mfg. Co.			1910	WITCH BALL	45
Bakers Chocolate			1953	PANTOMIME QUIZ (premium)	50
J.S. Barcus & Co.	New York	NY		THE UNIVERSITY GAME OF LITERATURE	nva
C.W. Bardeen	Syracuse	NY	1891	OUR COUNTRY (© A.M. Edwards & Co.)	40
Wm. Bartholomae			1929	ROULETTE BASE BALL GAME	nva
Bar-Zim Toy	Jersey City	NJ	±1928	NEW YORK TO PARIS AERORACE	nva
Baseballitis Game Co.	Milwaukee	WI	1906	BASEBALLITIS	ref
Beacon Sales Corp.	Chicago	IL	±1942/1950s	TELEVISION BASEBALL	30
C.E. Begerow			1896	OUR CINDERELLA PARTY	nva
Fred.H. Behring	St. Louis	MO	1915	GOLF BUG	60
Belknap			1916	GRASSHOPPER TENNIS	65
J.C. Bell Co.	Cleveland	OH	1890	UNCLE SAM'S BASEBALL GAME	400
Bertram B. Bellows			1944	PRONUNCIATION	25
Donald E. Benge	Burbank	CA	±1970-pres	CONQUEST	nva
Berry Pink, Inc.	New York	NY		CHINKO CHECKO MARBLO	25
E. Norwood Bessling				DE-DI-DO	nva
Best Mfg. Co. Inc.	Irvington	IL	1933	SPORTMASTER	60
E.P. Best Mfg. Co.	New Haven	CT		PEEK-A-BOO; WILD INDIANS	nva
B. I. Co.			1930	STAR SHOOTER	50
Biddle Corporation	Philadelphia	PA	1910s	NEUTRAL GAME OF WAR, PEACE, AND INDEMNITY	nva
Billy & Ruth Promotion Co.	Philadelphia	PA	1954	BILLY AND RUTH (premium)	35
Bingo Card Co.	Holland	MI		BINGO, THE GREAT AMERICAN CARD GAME	nva
Blakeman & Mason					ref
Bobby Benson			1930s	H-BAR-O (premium)	35
Robert K. Bonsall	Cincinnati	OH	1898	OLD TESTAMENT CHARACTERS	nva
Joseph Borzellino & Son	Atlantic City	NJ	1930s	THE SOLDIER ON FORT	nva
The Boston Herald	Boston	MA	1920	THE GAME OF SUCCESS	60
The Boston Loan Co.	Boston	MA	≤1887	BASE BALL WITH CARDS	ref
The Bowlet Co.	Indianapolis	IN	1931	BOWLET	20
The David Bremson Co.			1961	ARNOLD PALMER'S INSIDE GOLF	50
Brevet Co. of New England	Boston	MA	±1915	BREVET	ref
Chas. A. Brewer & Sons	Chicago	IL	1925	BREWER'S GLOBE PEGGERS	50
E.L. Brewster, Inc			1957	DEKOWIT/INVENTIONS	25
Brinkman Engineering Co.	Dayton	OH		WHIRL POOL GAME	ref
D.B. Brooks & Brothers	Salem	MA	1860s	PICTURE PASSWORD (1863); others	ref
Broughton Specialty Co.	Minneapolis	MN	1942	BOMB TOKYO (POPH-ITT CEREAL CO.)	85
F.H. Brown & Co.			1894	HOSFORD'S GAME OF STATES	nva

COMPANY	CITY	ST	DATES	GAME TITLES	$
G.P. Brown & Co.	Beverly	MA	1914	GAME OF WILD BIRDS	30
Brown Mfg. Co.	Clinton	MO	1937	CHINKER CHEK	30
Brown, Taggard & Chase				GAME OF COQUETTE AND THE SUITORS	ref
William Bruce Co.	Chicago	IL	1950	ALLEY-UP	20
Brunell & Farmer Co. Inc.	Worcester	MA	1922	TWIRLO	20
W.T. Buckner	Wichita	KS	1895	NATIONAL FINANCE	ref
Buehl Book Co.	Atlanta	GA	1903	WIGGS	30
M.C. Burkel	Jersey City	NJ	±1900	JOHNNY, PIPE THE WHISTLE OUT; FORTUNE	
Burkes Adventure Games				(see Sudbury Mfg. Co.)	
Burr-Vack Co.	Chicago	IL		STEELE'S INSIDE BASEBALL	ref
E.T. Burrowes Co., Inc.	Portland	ME	1919	POOL	nva
A A Burstine Sales Organization	New York	NY	1937	KAN-U-GO	15
CBS			1934	A TRIP THROUGH COLUMBIA NETWORK STUDIOS (premium)	70
C. & P. Products Co.	New York	NY	1939	KENNEL-CLUB CARD GAME	45
C & A Sales Co.				CROWN & ANCHOR	ref
The Campfire Outfitting Co.	New York	NY		HONORS	nva
Capital Card Co.			1927	MATRIMONY CARD GAME	40
George S. Carrington Co.	Chicago	IL	1943	THE JEEP BOARD	40
C. Carlton Carroll	Troy	NY	1948	TETRADOMINO PLAYING CARDS	30
Cast Distributing Corp.				See HERALD TOY	
Caterpillar Tractor Co.				CATERPILLAR CHECKERS	30
Harvey Chalmers & Sons				BUTTON GAME (Chalmer's Pearls premium)	75
Champion Spark Plugs Co.			1930	CHAMPION ROAD RACE (premium)	65
Chaswell Co.	Chicago	IL	1952	SNAFU	30
Checkorete Co.	Baltimore	MD	1936	CHECKORETE	nva
Chessina Co.	Walnut Springs	TX		CHESSINA	nva
Cheyenne Game Co.	Adrian	MI	±1907	CHEYENNE	nva
Chicago Game Co.	Chicago	IL	1913	PANA KANAL	125
Child Improvement			1918	WONDER SPELLER	45
George A. Childs	Brattleboro	VT	1895	THE GAME OF FOOTBALL	95
N.V. Christensen	Chicago	IL	1933	AMERICA, THE NEW GAME	40
W.L.M. Clark	St. Louis	MO	1920	CLARK AUCTION BRIDGE TILES	40
Clark & Martin				NEW BASEBALL GAME	nva
Clement Toy Co.				HEXAGONS	75
Clintonville Novelty Works			±1900	GAME OF ORIENTAL AUTHORS	nva
Cloyer				TILLY THE TUNA	20
Club Aluminum Products Co.	Chicago	IL	1942	WHIRLING WORDS	25
Cluff Cover Co., Inc.	New York	NY	1930	DOUBLE CHECK	30
L.I. Cohen & Co.	Philadelphia	PA	1844	THE NATIONAL GAME OF THE STAR SPANGLED BANNER	nva
T. Cohn, Inc.	Brooklyn	NY	1920	POKERETTE MINIATURE BAGATELLE	20
Coin Card Co.	Water Valley	MS	1930	COIN CARDS (also Memphis, TN)	25
Coleman, Kerns & Williams Co.			1942	HIGH COMMAND	75
College Game Co.	Philadelphia	PA	1908	COLLEGE, THE GREATEST GAME ON EARTH	nva
Combination Card Game Co.	Atlanta	GA	1903	TRAIL	40
Commerce Game Co.	Los Angeles	CA	1925	COMMERCE	40
Commonwealth Plastics Corp.	Leominster	MA	1945	CHUCKLE FACE	35
Concord Co.	New York	NY	1930/1947	RING TOSS	20

COMPANY	CITY	ST	DATES	GAME TITLES	$
Cookson & Sullivan	San Francisco	CA	1923	PE-LING	nva
The Co-Operative Game & Nvlty Co.	Boston	MA	1909	THE BLACK SHEEP OR THE SCAPE GOAT	nva
Cooperative Recreation Service, Inc.	Delaware	OH	1950	CHINESE FRIENDS (REVERSI)	40
Cooper Bros. Co.	Springfield	MA	1944	SIGS	nva
Craig Hopkins				See HOPKINS CRAIG	
Creative Educational Society	Mankato	MN	±1950	PLA-BOARDS	25
Crosby & Nichols	Boston	MA	±1845	See WM CROSBY in Chapter 12	
Cubist Games			1956	LIVE A LITTLE	45
A.B. Cummings	Attleboro	MA	1900	FROG GOLF	50
Custom Craft Products				POT-O-GOLD	nva
John Danylerk			1961	GOLF! "THE FAIRWAYS"	nva
W.O. Dapping	Auburn	NY	1906	THE GREAT AMERICAN GAME BASE BALL	150
John J. Darala			1941	THE GAME OF AERO SHAM BATTLE	nva
Davis, Porter & Co.	Philadelphia	PA		THE HAPPY FAMILY	nva
F.A. Day & Co.	Salem	MA	1859	TIPSY PHILOSOPHERS	90
Decipher, Inc.	Norfolk	VA	1980s–1990s	THE CALIFORNIA RAISINS (1988); others	25
James L. Decker Products Co.	Culver City	CA	1947	ZOWIE HORSESHOE GAME; PUT-'N-TAKE SPIN GAME	10
Dee Jay Products			1949	DREW PEARSON'S PREDICT-A-WORD	15
The Defiance Welding Co. Toy Dept	Defiance	OH	1929	TOSS 'EM	nva
Denham & Co.	New York	NY	≤1889	BRAX	ref
Derby Games Co.	South Bend	IN	1937	DONKEY DERBY	nva
Dewey Game & Novelty Co.	Bristol	CT	±1898	DEWEY GAME	75
Dewl Plasti-Toy Corp.	New York	NY	1957	ROCK AND ROLL	10
Diamond Toy			1939	AMERICA FIRST	25
Ben Dickenson			1918	HOME TEAM BASEBALL GAME	nva
George Doan	Chicago	IL	1907	WORTHWHILE	
Domo Game Co.			1935	DOMOGOLF	100
Donaldson Bros.			1896	BICYCLE GAME	nva
Doremus-Schoen Co. Inc.			1921	BANG BIRDS	40
A.A. Dugan			1851	RAILROAD GAME	1250
G.H. Dunston	Buffalo	NY	±1904	BOTANY	nva
Duplicon Company, Inc.	Hopkinton	MA	1950's	QUBIC	20
Dynamic Design	Anaheim	CA	±1970s	Bookshelf series for adults; div. of Reiss	
E & G Novelty Co	New York	NY	1940	CROSSWORD LEXAKAN	40
E.C. Eastman	Concord	NH	±1870	THE COMMANDERS OF OUR FORCES	nva
Eclipse Game & Puzzle Co.	Chicago	IL	1940s	ECLIPSE FOOTBALL GAME	nva
The Esmond Mills	Esmond	RI		BUNNY ESMOND GAMES (premium)	35
Educating Games Co.	Newark	NJ	1920's	SRATCH (©Harry S. Bird)	45
Education Game Co.	Matteawan	NY	1895	BIBLE AUTHORS	15
Educational Game Co.	Brooklyn	NY	1890s	A TRIP THROUGH EUROPE	nva
Elbridge, Gerry & Co.	Danbury	CT	1890		ref
Elliot Mfg.	New York	NY	1881	GAMES AT THE OLD HOMESTEAD	nva
Esquire Magazine			1950's	BLIND DATE (premium)	65
Exclusive Playing Card Co.	Chicago	IL	1954	SPELLBOUND	nva
Extreme Enterprises	Lancaster	PA	1981	KAVE KEEPERS	20
Family Games			1971	THE GOD FATHER GAME; others	65
J.M. Farmer			1938	FARMER ELECTRIC MAPS (A GAME OF TOKENS)	25
Hazel L. Fauber	New York	NY	1928	THE NINE GAME BOARD	25
Feature Games			1943	BOWLO, THE CARD BOWLING GAME	nva

COMPANY	CITY	ST	DATES	GAME TITLES	$
Feher Novelty Card Co				HI SCORE BOWLING CARD GAME	20
Fenner Game Co.	Toledo	OH	1901	GAME OF BETTER UP	ref
A.K. Ferris				See WILLIS RUSSELL	
Finance Game Co.	New York	NY	1936	FINANCE	45
Fisher & Denison	New York	NY	1870	MERRY FOXES; MOORISH FORT; RAILWAY TRAFFIC	nva
Flashtold Box Corp.	Fort Wayne	IN	1931	BOL-LI-O	35
A.B. Floyd	Buffalo	NY	1890	WAR, OR AMERICAN GENERALS AND THEIR BATTLES	125
Forker Mfg. Co.	Oil City	PA	1888	GAME OF GEOGRAPHY	nva
Fortune Games			1960	MANDALAY	25
Fowler & Wells	New York	NY	1883	THE PHRENOLOGICAL CHARACTER GAME	ref
C.S. Francis & Co.	New York	NY	±1850	MULTIPLICATION MERRILY MATCHED	nva
H.M. Francis			1861	NEW GAME OF AESOP	nva
Maurice L. Freedman Co.	Providence	RI	1940s	WARFARE NAVAL COMBAT	20
J.F. Friedel Co.	Syracuse	NY	±1930	SIEGE	25
F.B. Frye	Waltham	MA	1890	THE NATIONAL TEMPERANCE GAME	ref
Full-O-Fun Co.	Brockton	MA	±1930	LET'S GO GOLFUN	20
Fulton Specialty Co.	Elizabeth	NJ	1921	THE WIZARD	100
Fun Educational Co.					
Gabriel-Nealey Co.	Washington	DC	1942	ONINO	45
Game Creations	New York	NY	1946	ELOPING	40
Game Designers Workshop	Bloomington	IL	1973–pres.	Modern board games and role playing games	
Gameophiles Unlimited	Berkeley Heights	NJ	±1970s	Modern strategy games	
Gamescience	Gulfport	MS	1960s–pres.	Modern strategy games	
Gamut of Games	New York	NY	1970s	Modern strategy game; div. of Reiss	
The Gangler-Gentry Co.	Cantonsville	MD	±1950	QUAD	20
Gardner & Co			1955	PHIL SILVER'S YOU'LL NEVER GET RICH; (other TV-related)	100
W.W. Gavitt Printing & Publishing Co.	Topeka	KS	1903	GAVITT'S STOCK EXCHANGE	30
L.B. Gaylor	Stamford	CT	1919	THE GAME OF PASSO	nva
Gem Publishing	Cleveland	OH	1922/23	TREASURE ISLAND	40
Gem Publishing Co.			1960s	BORIS KARLOFF GAME; other character games	
Gibbs Mfg. Co.	Canton	OH	1930s	PUTT-IN-PLAY	nva
Gibson Game Co.			1915	LITTLE SHOPPERS	250
B.R. Gilmour & Co.	New York	NY	1910	EGG ROLLING	45
Ginasta Corp. of America				GINASTA	20
Girl Scouts			1929	TRUPE	50
Michael Glenn Productions	Romulus	MI	1985	OUR TOWN TRIVIA	15
The Glessner Co.	Findlay	OH		AMERICAN TOURS	nva
Gnirol Game Co.	Plymouth	MA	1920	GNIROL AND THE PILGRIM'S PARTY	70
C.D. Gocanower	Phoenix	AZ	±1940	KIDDIE KARDS	10
Gold Mine Card Co.	Fenton	MI		A GOLD MINE	nva
D.O. Goodrich	Boston	MA	1859	PRESIDENTIAL QUARTETS	nva
E.J. Goodrich	Oberlin	OH	±1900	GAME OF FORTY-TWO	
The Gorham Press	South Norwalk	CT	±1940	THE NAVY GAME	15
Gould & Lincoln	Boston	MA	1858	PETER CODDLE'S TRIP TO NEW YORK	nva
J. Jay Gould	Boston	MA	1876	WHO DO YOU LOVE BEST	nva
Grand Rapids Label Co.	Grand Rapids	MI	1925	POLLY, THE CHILDREN'S PET	nva

COMPANY	CITY	ST	DATES	GAME TITLES	$
Gray's Portland Business College	Portland	ME	±1910	DRIVER OR PARLOR GOLF (premium) (© J.W. Kelley)	45
Grebnelle Game Co.	Philadelphia	PA	1914	CHAMPIONSHIP BASE BALL PARLOR GAME	nva
Greibel Games	Seattle	WA	1920	KNOW YOUR OWN UNITED STATES	nva
Grid Games	Huntington Beach	CA	±1970s	Modern strategy games	
Carl W. Grimm			1927	MUSICAL CASION	nva
Groovy Games Inc.	Aspen	CO	1977	NEW YORK SCENE	25
G. Romain Grow & Co.			1890	OUR FRIENDS IN FUR	nva
Gulf			±1960	GO-GULF GAME (premium)	25
Hackbarth Enterprises	Fayetteville	NY	1938	NUKENO	nva
Hamilton Sales (Distrib.)	Pomona	CA	1939	SOLITARY CHECKERS (© Jerry Tyler)	20
C.E. Hammett Jr.	Newport	RI	1877	WORD MAKING & WORD TAKING	65
C.S. Hammond & Co., Inc.	New York	NY	1925	GEOGRAPHICAL CROSSWORD GAME; MA JONG	nva
W.H. Harper			1943	SALVO (game booklet)	15
Harrison Game Co.	Syracuse	NY	1920s	PLAY BALL	50
S. Hart & Co.					ref
Harter Publishing Co.	Cleveland	OH	1930	DIVISION	20
The Hatch Litho Co.	New York	NY	≤1889	WILLIAMS POPULAR INDOOR GAME	ref
Hayes Novelty	Springfield	MA	1920s	LINK A LINK	20
Hecker H-O			1933	FORCE HO! (premium)	30
Paul F. Henning			1955	BULLS 'N' BEARS	25
Herald Toy Prod. Co.	New York	NY	1954	ARTHUR GODFREY'S PAR-TEE GOLF	75
P.M. Hillard	Westerly	RI	1892	PEEK-A-BOO	nva
Hoffman & Knickerbocker	Albany	NY	1854; 55	LITTLE CORPORA; AMERICAN EAGLE	nva
Hoffman Lion Mills Co.	New York	NY	±1930	HOFFMAN'S ROPE KWOIT	15
A.J.F. Hoffman Novelty Co.	San Francisco	CA	1914	EDUCATIONAL MUSIC GAME	25
Hoffmann's				NIPSY	nva
Holland Crafts Inc.	Holland	NY	±1920	SPRINT	65
Hollywood Game Co.	Hollywood	CA	1928	HOLLYWOOD BURLESQUE	30
Holt Games Inc.	Selma	AL	1950	LET'S PLAY FOOTBALL; LET'S PLAY BASEBALL	nva
Holt-Folt-Howard Co.	Chicago	IL	1905	THE CAPTURE OF MR. RAFFLES	nva
Hoosier Basketball Co.	Princeton	IN	1950	DRIBBLING AROUND BASKET BALL	30
Hopkins Syndicate, Inc.	Chicago	IL	1940s	FAX	40
O-D Hopkins	New York	NY	1922	BI-JINX	nva
J.W. Hosford				See F.H. BROWN & CO.	
House of Ideas			±1960	3-RING CIRCUS CARD GAME	10
Alfred F. Howe	Chicago	IL	1892	CITIES OF OUR COUNTRY	nva
J.W. Howell	Grafton	PA	1894	THE GAME OF PRONOUNCIT	nva
Hoyles Games				HOYLES (premium for Mueller's)	20
Huntex Co.	Worcester	MA	1899	NEW STAR GAME 35 OR HUNTEX	nva
Hypergames Co.	Richmond	VA	±1970s	Modern strategy games	
Ideal Book Builders	Chicago	IL	1912	FUNNYFACE GAME; THE JOLLY FACES GAME	35
Indiana Game Co.			1939	BO McMILLIN'S INDOOR FOOTBALL GAME	40
Intercollegiate Football Inc.	St. Paul	MN	1935	AMERICAN FOOTBALL GAME	35
Inter Paper Goods Co.			1925	RADIO	45
Interstate School Service	New York	NY	±1920s	AMERICAN HISTORY IN PICTURES	nva
I.P.C. Universal Corp.			1914	THE PEANUT RACE (also C.W. Marsh Co.)	40

COMPANY	CITY	ST	DATES	GAME TITLES	$
Jackbilt				See ROCHESTER FOLDING BOX CO.	
Jack-Pot Dice	Milwaukee	WI	1948	ROLL-EM JACK-POT DICE	10
Kaye Jacobel Assoc	Yonkers	NY	±1950	TRI TAC TOE	25
The Japino Co.	Detroit	MI		JAPINO	25
Jay Bee Games Inc.	New York	NY	1943	FLIP-A-RING	15
Jayline Mfg. Co.	Philadelphia	PA	1943	RATION BOARD GAME	60
The Jenlon Co.	Boston	MA	1929	HONK-HONK-HONK	25
JHSNY				See SINGER, Part 3	
Jockette Co.	Cincinnati	OH		JOCKETTE	35
Alex L. Johnson	Phoenix	AZ	1951	DOUBLE CROSS	20
Johnson & Johnson Co.			1937	SNOW WHITE GAME (Tek tooth brush premium)	40
Johnson Store Equipment Co.	Elgin	IL	1920s	BAMBINO	75
Neil R. Jones			1946	INTERPLANETARY (Board only)	40
Roland W. Jones				A MUSICAL GAME	nva
C.H. Joslin	New York	NY	±1870	AMUSETTE	nva
Jotto			±1954	JOTTO (sold to Selchow & Righter)	20
JS				See JOSEPH SCHNEIDER or JOHN SANDS, Part 3	
The Junior Games Co., Inc.	Baltimore	MD	1921	GOLF JUNIOR	40
Kam-Ra Card Co.	Hollywood	CA	1928	KAM-RA	nva
Kaysons Novelty Co.	Brooklyn	NY	±1950	OLD MAID	20
Keiler Corp.	Brooklyn	NY	±1950	SPIN-A-WORD	20
J.W. Keller			±1890s	HOUNDS & HARES	nva
Kelloggs	Battle Creek	MI		JUNGLE JUMP UP GAME; other cereal premiums	50
Kenton Hardware Co.	Kenton	OH	±1950	GENE AUTRY'S BANDIT TRAIL GAME	200
E.W. Keyes	Boston	MA	1887	NEEDLE GUN GAME	nva
Kim Game Co.	Lancaster	PA	±1890		
King-Larson-McMahon	Chicago	IL	1942	BATTLE CHECKERS	80
The Klax Co.	New Haven	CT	1920	VICTORY	60
Koplow Games			1974	ORGANIZED CRIME; others	30
Kraeg Games	St. Louis	MO	1945	TOSS WORDS	10
Owens Krass, Inc.	Rochester	NY	1949	SARK CROSSWORD CARDS	15
Frank Lackner & Co.	Aurora	IL	1894	THE GAME OF PRESIDENTS & HISTORICAL EVENTS	nva
Wm. Chauncy Langdon	New Orleans	LA	1846	THE GAME OF ENGLISH ROYAL BLOOD	nva
Larue Sales Inc.	Lynn	MA		HIT THAT LINE	nva
L.E. Lawrence			1891	LOLO (PARLOR CROQUET)	65
Lawson Co.			1942	JUNIOR BOMBSIGHT GAME	nva
Lawson Card Co.	Boston	MA		LAWSON'S PATENT BASEBALL PLAYING CARDS	150
The Lederer Co.	New York	NY	1933	MAGIC RACE	30
Wingert Leefers	Cedar Rapids	IA	1920	THE POPULAR ADVERTISING GAME NAPOLEON	75
Lee and Shepard	Boston	MA	±1840s	OLD PAMPHEEZLE AND HIS COMICAL FRIENDS	nva
John Bunyan Lemon	Greenfield	MA	1919	LEMON'S BIBLE GAME	25
Lemor Novelty Co.	Brooklyn	NY	1920S	KIDS-ON-BRIDGE; TIT FOR TAT INDOOR HOCKEY	nva
Leonard, Burditt & Co.	Boston	MA		CLASSIC WONDERS	nva
Leonard Mfg. Co.	Grand Rapids	MI	±1900; ±1910	COMBINOLA; SNOOK	nva

COMPANY	CITY	ST	DATES	GAME TITLES	$
Albert H. Lewis	Los Angeles	CA	1917	THE SAVING GAME (Distrib. by System Thrift Book Co.)	40
Wayne W. Light Co.	New York	NY	1940	FOOTBALL AS YOU LIKE IT	45
Lilco Enterprises Inc.	New York	NY	1958	BRAND IMAGE (Advertising game)	85
Literati Game Co.	Foxcraft	ME	1901	PAINTERS & SCULPTORS	ref
Lith-o-Ware Products, Inc	Cicero	IL	1954	LAS VEGAS WILD	25
Little Teacher Games Co.	San Francisco	CA			
Loew's			1959	BEN HUR; CHARIOT RACE	35
Oswald B. Lord	New York	NY	1935	THE POLITICS GAME (sold to Parker Bros.)	40
Lord Calvert Coffee				LORD CALVERT GAME (premium)	30
Los Angeles Soap				WHITE KING GAME (premium)	30
A.E. Lyman & Son	Northampton	MA	±1875	LYMAN'S IMPROVED AMERICAN TIVOLI GAME	nva
L.H. Mace & Co.	New York	NY	1891	THE NEW GAME OF RED, WHITE AND BLUE	nva
Pasquale "Pat" H. Maffeo	New Haven	CT	1945	DOUBLE-0 BOWLING	15
Magnetic Novelty Corp.	New York	NY		MAGNETIC SPELL GAME	nva
Charles Magnus	New York	NY	±1859	THE MASQUERADE GAME	nva
Mahco Line Novelties				POP GAME OF MONTE CARLO	nva
Mah-Jongg Sales Co. of America	San Francisco	CA	1923	MAH-JONGG	nva
Minuteman Novelty Games Co.	Lexington	MA	±1920	KRISS KROSS/KROSS WONSA (envelope game)	25
C.W. Marsh				See I.P.C. UNIVERSAL	
Marx, Hess & Lee Inc.			1933	THE FOUR DAREDEVILS	70
Howard Mason	Natick	MA	1922	ASTRONOMY	nva
Mason & Parker Mfg. Co.	Winchedon	MA	±1920	TEN PINS	nva
The Maxim Games Co.	New York	NY	1945/6	TALLYIT; ADDIT	20
Mayfair Games		IL	1970s–pres.	Modern board games and role playing games	
Ralph Mayhew			±1930	WHIRL-A-WORD	15
McDonald			1958	THE BIG BOARD	45
Elizabeth McDowell & F. Mellor			1917	ALLIE-PATRIOT GAME	nva
McGill & Delany			1886	OUR NATIONAL BALL GAME	nva
James McGowan Associates	New York	NY	1937	Guilty	25
Mego			±1970s	OBSESSION; many others	
Walter Meyner	New York	NY	±1920	THE GAME OF BATTLE	ref
Edw. Mikkelsen	Chicago	IL	±1900	OWL GAME BOARD (carrom)	75
E.E. Miles	So. Lancaster	MA	1896	EUREKA BIBLE GAME	nva
Miniature Game Co.	Philadelphia	PA	1940s	POCKET GOLF; AMERICAN SWEEPSTAKES	25
Modern Makers Inc.	Utica	NY	±1926	HORSES (issued by All-Fair)	65
Moh-Sah Co.	Chicago	IL	1899	ORTHOEPY	nva
Robert Morey	New Haven	CT	1938	PRIVILEGE	65
Morgantown Game Co.	Morgantown	WV	1955	ART LEWIS FOOTBALL GAME	nva
V.E. Morrill			1914	NEUTRAL	75
Howard Mullin			1962	SAIL AWAY	35
Municipal Service Corp.	Los Angeles	CA	1932	HOWARD H. JONES COLLEGIATE FOOTBALL GAME	nva
Murray-Way Games Co.	San Francisco	CA	1925	THE MURRAY-WAY STATES GAME	35
Musicraft Industries	Richmond	VA	1963	PLAYS THE BEATS	25
Mystoplane			1940s	FLYING TARGET GAMe	35
National Biscuit Co.			1936	TRAVELING TO WHEATSWORTH CASTLE (premium)	45
The National Game & Nvlty Co.	Baltimore	MD	1944	JIGTOONS CARTOON PUZZLE GAME	35

COMPANY	CITY	ST	DATES	GAME TITLES	$
National Games Co. Inc.			1950s	PLAY BALL	15
National Golf Service Co., Inc.	New York	NY	1926	PAR GOLF CARD GAME	nva
National Refining Co.	Cleveland	OH	1919	EN-AR-CO WHITE ROSE GASOLINE (premium)	40
Erich Naumann	Glendale	NY	1930s	AIR ATTACK	250
L.H. Nelson Co.	Portland	ME	1908	TRAFFIC; ANGLE-PLAY	ref
The Nemo Card Co.	Sudbury	OH	1904		
New Haven Toy, Game + Nvlty Co.	New Haven	CT	1894	HUB-CHECKERS	135
Northern Signal Co.	Milwaukee	WI	1948	SPECULATION (also Electroline Products Corp.)	ref
Novelty Novelties	New York	NY		MAGNETIC PICK UP STICKS	15
The Numerica Co.	Utica	NY	1894	GAME OF NUMERICA	50
Oakley & Mason	New York	NY		THE HOUSE OF WASHINGTON . . . PALACE OF SANTA CLAUS	nva
Optimus Printing Co.	New York	NY	1904	TRUSTS AND BUSTS	40
Orange Judd Co.	New York	NY	1879	PEDESTRIANISM	nva
R.H. Osbrink			1933	MARBLE T-A-N-G-O	85
B.F. Oshei Co.	Buffalo	NY	±1950	TOP SPIN	nva
Charles Overly	Harvard	MA	1958	THE GREAT GAME OF VISITING WILLIAMSBURG, VA.	15
Pacific Game Co.	No. Hollywood	CA	±1940; 1967	GRAVITATION; THE MILL	20
Pajaro Card Co.		TX		PAJARO	nva
Pan American Toy Co.	Kansas City	MO		BASEBALL	nva
Panic Card Co.	Topeka	KS	1903	GAME OF PANIC (Also Detroit, MI)	50
Pantone Co.	New York	NY	1943	BOMBARDO	20
V.S.W. Parkhurst	New York	NY	1852	THE GAME OF UNCLE TOM AND LITTLE EVA	nva
Pastime Games Co.	Chicago	IL	1930	BASEBALL (envelope; premium?)	15
E.M. Patrick Eng. Prov. (?)			1881	FROM NEW YORK TO SAN FRANCISCO (gamebrd only)	150
Paul Educational Games	Wyoming	OH	±1922	HEROES OF AMERICA	25
Henry J. Peck	Boston	MA	1910	THE GREAT AMERICAN GAME BASEBALL	ref
Peerless Playthings	Ridgefield Park	NJ		MAGNETIC FUNNY FACE	20
Pente Games	Stillwater	OK	1977	PENTE	20
Pepper Lane Industries	Ramsey	NJ	1984	MIAMI VICE; (Division of Colorforms)	20
Arba Perry				See ARBA	
David M. Pfaelzer & Co.	Chicago	IL	±1920	COMBINATION (GEO. L. LEWIS SERIES)	nva
Philadelphia Game Mfg. Co.	Philadelphia	PA	1912	MAJOR LEAGUE BASE BALL GAME	nva
F.C. Phillips	Stoughton	MA	±1900	COLORED NUMBER GAME	45
John Phillips			±1930	DEUCE (tennis card game)	50
D.S. Pillsbury (or Pilksbury)	New York	NY	1875	GEOGRAPHICAL GAME OF THE OLD WORLD	80
The Piso Co.	Warren	PA	±1900	TWELVE MEN MORRICE	35
Pittsburgh Game & Novelty	Pittsburgh	PA	1916	LET U.S. HAVE PEACE	80
Planter's Peanuts			1930	PLANTERS' PEANUT PARTY (premium)	75
Plas-Trix Co.			1954	SCRABBLE POCKET PUZZLE	nva
Play Equipment Co.	Los Angeles	CA	1939	BAFFEL	25
Playgames, Inc.	Newark	NJ		AMERICAN VARSITY FOOTBALL	nva
Playtime House	Rochester	NY	±1930	ALL AMERICAN, A SOAP BOX DERBY GAME	nva
Plaza Mfg. Co.			±1937	FIDDLESTIX; MATCHET	15
Pleasantime				See PACIFIC GAME CO.	
Pleasantville Games				See PACIFIC GAMES CO.	

COMPANY	CITY	ST	DATES	GAME TITLES	$
Polaris Co.			±1940	POLARIS	25
Polygon Corp.			1947	PONY EXPRESS	60
Popular Game Co.	New York	NY	1911	INSIDE BASE BALL	nva
Porter & Coates	Philadelphia	PA	1872	AUTHORS	nva
George Vincent Post	Cincinnati	OH	1927	MONTE CARLO WHIPPET DERBY	250
Proctor Amusement Co.	No. Cambridge	MA	±1920	THE CHAMPIONSHIP GAME OF BASEBALL	nva
Progressive Research Co.	Port Jervis	NY	±1955	ALL STAR SPORTS BASEBALL GAME	15
Psychic Baseball Corp	New York	NY	±1928	PSYCHIC BASEBALL	ref
Pung Chow Co., Inc.	New York	NY	1923	PUNG CHOW	15
Pyro Plastics Corp.	Union	NJ	1950	CATAPULT SPEEDWAY	20
Quadro Games Co.	Milwaukee	WI	1928	QUADRO	nva
Quiztick Mfg.			1943	QUIZTICK	25
Radio Games Co.	Peoria	IL	±1925	GAME OF RADIO (card game)	40
Radio Questionnaire Corp.			1928	RADIO QUESTIONNAIRE	25
Rainshine Game Co.	Joplin	MO	1930s–1940s		
Ranger Steel Products Corp.	New York	NY	1940s	TOWN & COUNTRY TRAFFIC	150
Rappaport Bros. Inc.	Chicago	IL	±1940	QUIZ KIDS ELECTRIC QUIZZER	35
The Rayo Card Co.	New York	NY	1907	RAYO	25
Read & White Game Co.	Bloomington	IL	1904	TRIX	20
Reco Toy and Game				See ATHLETIC	
Recreational Games, Inc.	Northbrook	IL	±1950	PHILADELPHIA LAWYER (Cracker barrel gameboard)	50
Reed & Associates			±1950	SHAZAM (Captain Marvel premium)	40
Rexall				STREAMLINED TRAIN GAME (premium)	175
R.W. Reynolds			1905	DIN	20
RGI/ATHOL	New York	NY	1960s–1970s	Modern sports, strategy, and war games	
Rhode Island Game Co.	Providence	RI	1898	UNCLE SAM AT WAR WITH SPAIN	300
Richardson & Co.	New York	NY	1867	MARTELLE	nva
Rippon			1935	PETER RABBIT'S BUNNY HUNT	30
Ritt Bros. & Co.	Philadelphia	PA	±1950	SKRIMAGE	45
T. Francis Roark & Co.	Providence	RI	1900	FLUTTER	70
Rochester Folding Box Co.	Rochester	NY	±1940	NIP-N-TUK	35
Roller Derby	Chicago	IL	±1940	ROLLER DERBY	50
Roll-O Mfg. Co., Inc.	Geneva	NY	1920s	ROLL-O: GOLF; JR BASEBALL; MOTOR SPEEDWAY	
G. Romain Grow & Co.	St. Paul	MN	1890	OUR FRIENDS IN FUR	75
A.I. Root Co.				See Shepard Toy	
Rosenwald-Milius Co.				RADIO FLASH ROSENWALD	125
Walter L. Rothschild	New Rochelle	NY	1919	ZIMBA	40
R.T.A. Co.	New York	NY	1933	NRA GAME OF PROSPERITY	60
Willis Russell Card Co.		NJ	1905	ROULETTE CARDS	30
Rust Craft	Boston	MA		RUSTOP GAME	nva
Ruthameto Novelty Co.	Chicago	IL	±1991	RUTHAMENTO PARLOR GAME	ref
S&W Fine Foods			1938	HAPPY MARRIAGE GAME (premium)	30
Sackett & Wilhelms Litho. Co.	New York	NY	1890s	GAME OF NEGOMI	30
The Sammy Card Co.	Atlanta	GA	±1934	SAMMY	nva
Sathas Store Co.			1918	PARIS TO BERLIN	85
E. Saugus		MA		SKITTLES	35
Savo Mfg. Co.	Chicago	IL		THE GAME OF HIDDEN NOLEDGE	nva
Walter Schaefer	Philadelphia	PA	1939	PALS KARTOON CARDS	65
Schapter			1950s	KING OF THE HILL GAME	15

COMPANY	CITY	ST	DATES	GAME TITLES	$
John M. Schealer	Boyertown	PA	1948	PUN-FUN	10
Scholastic Publishing Co., Inc.	Pittsburgh	PA	1927	ARBO, THE GAME OF TREE FAMILIES	20
Scientific Game & Novelty Co.	St. Louis	MO	±1910	SKIRMISH	30
Screen Patch Co.	Philadelphia	PA	±1950	DROP TIT TAT TOE	20
Sensational Toy Mfg.	Linden	NJ	±1931	CARDINAL POINTS FOXY GAME	ref
Neville Seymour			1930	WICKET GOLF	25
Shackman				Maker mostly of wood old game-puzzle repros	
Shakespeare Club of Camden			1897	A STUDY OF SHAKESPEARE	30
Shepard Toy Co.			1940s	THE MAGIC BLACKBOARD (Also A.I. Root Co.)	20
Wm., Shepherd & Co.	St. Joseph	MO		SHEPHERD'S NATIONAL GAME OF FINANCE	nva
Sherms Creations				PUZZLE PEG; other solitaire puzzles	
Shulman & Sons			1925	SAFETY CITY	40
Siritama Co.	New York	NY	1950s	THE MONEY GAME	20
Skor-Mor Corp.	Carpenteria	CA	±1970s	Modern strategy games; bookshelf	
John Smarkola	Philadelphia	PA	±1925	SPEEDWAY MOTOR RACE	50
Edward Smith Mfg. Co.	Highland Park	IL	1935	AFTER-DINNER	20
Frank J. Smith			1909	NORTH POLE	ref
Karl Smith	Louisville	KY	1937	SKYSCRAPER	nva
Norman C. Smith	Columbus	OH	1936	I-GOT-IT	15
Snap Ball Co.				IN & OUT GAME	20
South Bend Toy Co.	South Bend	IN	1900	THE UNIVERSAL COMPANION GAME BOARD	100
Charles Sowden			1895	ANAGRAMS & LOTTO	nva
A.G. Spalding & Bros.	Chicago	IL	≤1887	OUR NATIONAL BALL GAME (also 241 Broadway, NY)	ref
Spare Time Corp.	Minneapolis	MN	1940s	SPARE TIME BOWLING (Franchised 1947 to Trojan)	20
J.W. Spear				English maker of games for U.S. market	
W.H. Spencer				A FLORA GAME	nva
SPI (Simulations Publications) Inc.	New York	NY	1960s–1980s	Modern war and sci-fi games	
Sprague Wholesale Co.	Chicago	IL	1904	THE MAKERS OF HISTORY GAME	30
Springfield Games Corp.	Springfield	MO	±1925	SAFETY FIRST GAME WITH TEN COMMANDMENTS	25
Springfield Photo Mount Co.	Springfield	MA	±1930 (?)	SPELLING & ANAGRAMS	15
Stafford Products Co.	Webster Groves	MO	1945	FOX & GEESE	45
Standard Oil			1937	RED CROWN GAME (premium)	40
Standard Playing Card Co.	Chicago	IL	1910	CHANTECLER	35
Starex Novelty Co. Inc.			1931	SALVO	20
Star Publishing Co.			1892	GAME OF WORLD'S FAIR	nva
Stars on Stripes Games Co.	Pittsburgh	PA	1941	STARS ON STRIPE FOOTBALL	70
Statis-Pro Games	Waterloo	IA	±1970s	Modern sports games (bought by Avalon Hill)	
Statler Mfg. Co.	Baltimore	MD	±1930	U.S. GEOGRAPHICAL LOTTO	20
The Sterling Co. Ltd.	New Orleans	LA	1900	POLITICS; PICKWICK CARD DOMINOES	nva
Frederick A. Stokes Co.	New York	NY	1933	WHO'S THE GENIUS (Dr. Seuss Cover)	70
Straits Mfg.	Detroit	MI	1939	MILL	20
Strat Game Co.			1915	STRAT	150
The Strathmore Co.	Aurora	IL	1944; 1950	SEA BATTLE; MAGIC SLATES	15
Strato-Matic	Glen Head	NY	1960s–pres.	Modern sports games	
Strato-Various Products	Utica	MI	±1970s	Modern strategy games	

COMPANY	CITY	ST	DATES	GAME TITLES	$
Sudbury Mfg. Co.	Sudbury	MA	1948	SPAN-IT	50
The Sweethearts Co.	Columbus	OH	±1910	SWEETHEARTS	25
The System Thrift Book Co.	Los Angeles	CA	1917	THE SAVING GAME	45
The Target Co.	Chicago	IL	1938	TARGET (card game)	25
Tek Tooth Brush				See JOHNSON & JOHNSON	
Robert Teller Sons & Dorner	New York	NY	1939	OUTLAW RUMMY	40
Texall Corp	San Antonio	TX	1950	GRACIE ALLEN'S GAB	45
Third Millennia, Inc.	Philadelphia	MS	±1970s	Modern war/fantasy games	
Thomas Sales Co.	Fort Worth	TX	1936	THE NEW GAME INFLATION	nva
John H. Tingley	New York	NY	1864	COURTSHIP & MARRIAGE	125
Toddy, Inc.	New York	NY	1933	Games with jigsaw puzzle gameboard	50
Top-Notch			1951	COPS & ROBBERS	40
T-P Card Co.	Green Bay	WI	1939	SILVER STRIKE	nva
Traps Mfg. Co.	Seattle	WA	±1910	GAME OF TRAPS	50
Trips Card Co.	Albany	NY	±1920	TRIPS	35
TSR (Tactical Studies Rules)	Lake Geneva	WI	1970s–pres.	Modern role-playing game; DUNGEONS & DRAGONS	
Tuco Workshops (Distrib.)	Lockport	NY	±1940	TAGALONG JOE (© W.G.S.)	40
Tung Tju Co.			1923	TUNG TJU	25
The Tur-Boy Co.	St. Louis	MO	±1920	BASE BALL CARD GAME	ref
Twining Game Co.	Ann Arbor	MI	1950s		ref
Ullman Mfg. Co.	New York	NY	±1925	WILD WEST	50
Wm. P. Ulrich	Spokane	WA	1941	STAR BASE BALL GAME	nva
Unique Items Co.	New York	NY	1941	CHESS CHECKERS CHEK-MATE	15
United Toy & Novelty Co.			1938	BALL BINGO	15
U.S. Publishing House			1884	GASKELL'S POPULAR HISTORICAL GAME	nva
Van Wagenen & Co.			1943	DEFENSE; PURSUIT	nva
Victory Game Co.	New York	NY	1942	VICTORY RUMMY	60
Victory Games	New York	NY	1980s–pres.	Modern war and role-playing, div. of Avalon Hill	
Vincent & McDonald Co. Inc.	Gloversville	NY	1910s	LIBERTY GUN WITH GAME	70
The Waddell Co. Inc.	Greenfield	OH	±1920	PYRAMID PEG (30″ × 30″ table board)	80
Wagaman Bros.	Lititz	PA	1949	WHO'S SANTA (Barney's premium)	40
J.M. Waggaman	Washington	DC	1930s	GREEN'S HIGHROAD TO HEALTH & HAPPINESS (premium)	40
Wah Chuck Card Co.	San Francisco	CA	1923	WAH CHUCK	35
Wa Hoo Sales Co.	Pontiac	MI	1953	WA-HOO	30
Waner Baseball Games Inc.	Pittsburgh	PA	±1928	WANER'S BASEBALL GAME	ref
J.H. Warder			1927	TU-TEE (forerunner of COOTIE)	nva
Warner & Co.	Northampton	MA	±1878	CITADELLE	nva
Warner Mfg Co.	Bennington	VT		MAJOR BOWES' AMATEUR HOUR GAME	80
Watkins Mfg. Co.	Milford	CT	1937	BLIND PEG	15
Wealth Unlimited			1936	WEATLH	35
Samuel Weller			1844	THE PICKWICK CARDS	nva
Wescott Bros.	Seneca Falls	NY	±1910	FISH POND	50
West Coast Game Co.	Pasadena	CA	1934	JAN KEN PO	nva
Westinghouse Electric & Mfg. Co.			1940	BLONDIE GOES TO LEISURELAND GAME (premium)	65
Wff 'n Proof			1960s	maker of five number-cube strategy games	
W.G.S.				See TUCO WORKSHOPS	
J.W. Wheeler			1893	MUSICAL HITS	50
White & Williams Game Co.	Hillside	NJ	1943	TEST YOUR GRIDIRON SKILL	40

COMPANY	CITY	ST	DATES	GAME TITLES	$
W.H.O.			1924	LINCOLN'S LOG CABIN	35
Wilkens Thompson Co.	Malden	MA	1905	CHINA (board game)	nva
Egerton R. Williams			±1890	EGERTON WILLIAMS BASE BALL GAME	1500
A. Williams & Co.	Boston	MA	1857	TRIP TO PARIS; THE GAME OF REBELLION	nva
J.B. Williams			1939	DR. HAGEN'S IQ (premium)	20
Roger Q. Williams Inc.	Brooklyn	NY	±1931	FAMOUS FLYERS RACE AROUND THE WORLD	nva
H.S. Windle Mfg. Co.	Philadelphia	PA	±1914	THE GREAT ALLIED WAR GAME	250
The Wing National Game Co.	St. Augustine	FL	1898	OUR NAVY	175
The Wits Co.	Bloomsbury	PA	1922	WITS	60
W.J.Z. Publ. Co.	New York	NY	1938	PROFESSOR WIZ PARTY BOOK	10
Wonder Co.			1933	LITTLE ORPHAN ANNIE TREASURE HUNT	75
Word-O-Rama	New York	NY	1958	WORD-O-RAMA	15
Henry O. Wurth	Schenectady	NY	1926	STAR BASKETBALL	65
Yankee Navy Card Co.	Tacoma	WA	±1910	THE YANKEE NAVY GAME	nva
C.L. Zimmer Co.	Cleveland	OH	≤1892	A GAME OF BASE-BALL	ref
Lou Zocchi	Biloxi	MS	±1970s–pres	Modern strategy games	
Zone Co.	Delray	FL	1940s	GEE-GEE CANASTA (spelling cubes)	15
Grover C. Zweifel	Tulsa	OK	1932	ZWEIFEL CARD GOLF	nva

Glossary

Collectors use a common terminology to describe types of games and their components and to help clarify the condition of a game. This basic vocabulary is especially useful when cataloging a collection or describing games advertised for sale. Suggested abbreviations are given in parentheses where applicable.

Action Game: A game in which some object, such as a spinning top or rolling marble, affects play but is not under the control of the player, so the outcome is based on pure luck. See also **Skill-and-Action Game**, an action game that requires a player's dexterity.

Apron: The side of a game box; often mistakenly referred to as the "flap." If aprons are torn or separated at the

Gamebox aprons of (from top to bottom): LEAPING LENA, MR. BUG GOES TO TOWN, BLACKOUT, LOTTO, MOVING PICTURE GAME, AUTO RACING GAME, FLIVVER GAME, GAME OF INDIA, FLAGSHIP AIRFREIGHT.

corners of the box, the game is said to have **split aprons;** a box with all aprons missing or with aprons split and folded under is said to be **flat.**

Block Spinner: Lithographed paper spinner mounted over a wooden block, normally about 3″ × 3″; found in games from the 1880s and 1890s.

Board: (See **Gameboard**)

Board Back (Bd Bk): The back or underside of a gameboard. The board back may have a textured or embossed pattern (Bd Bk Emb). A lithographed sheet may be pasted on the board back (Bd Bk Litho), showing the name of the game and often having the same illustration as on the box cover.

Board game: Any game which is played on a gameboard.

Bookshelf Game: Folding box game that can be stored upright and, on the hinged side, would look like two books. In the United States this form of packaging was begun around 1875 by McLoughlin Bros., and was repopularized in the 1960s by 3M (a company whose game line was later bought by Avalon Hill). The earliest bookshelf games had no embossed or titled cover on the "spine"; the gameboard was on the outside of the "book cover" and the playing pieces were stored inside. By 1880 most bookshelf games had a book-like spine, one game outside and two games inside, and the folded gameboard fit into a slipcover.

Bottom Box Ad (Botbox Ad): An advertisement found on the *outside* bottom of the box, usually advertising a game different from the one in the box; found usually on pre-1900 card games. Many modern games now have instructions or a summary of play on the outside bottom of the box.

Box Bottom Board (BoxBotBd): A lithographed sheet affixed to the inside of the box bottom, used as the gameboard and not removable from the box.

Box Wrap: The patterned paper covering the entire box top and bottom of the box, including the aprons; the lithographed sheet depicting the game was then pasted on top of the box wrap. After around 1910, the box wrap was eliminated and the litho sheet was wrapped around the entire box cover, while the box bottom was plain coated cardboard.

Build-up (Bldup): The cardboard section(s) in a game box that forms a support tray or platform for the gameboard and/or the implements; sometimes the end of the build-up folds down, then flat, then up again to provide a tray for the implements. Normally just a structural piece, the build-up should be noted when it is illustrated (referred to as a **Printed Build-up** or Prntd Bldup) or, less commonly when it is used as the gameboard (**Build-up Board** or Bldup bd).

Card Game: Any game in which cards are the primary focus of play. (A game with gameboard and cards is a "board game" with cards as implements.) Early card games usually came in small boxes, about 6″ × 5″, with a separate box bottom and box top. Card games by such companies as Cincinnati and Fireside and traditional playing cards were packaged either in single-deck boxes or in soft boxes called **card packs** that opened at either end.

Card Pack: (See **Card Game**)

Chance Cards: Cards used in a board game that determine a player's forfeit or gain. These cards are usually plentiful, and missing some cards will not affect the game's outcome. Often the game's instructions refer to a "pack" without indicating exactly how many cards the game contains.

Checkerboard-style: A game that uses a grid-pattern gameboard on which players can move in various directions on any one turn. Winning may depend on a player's reaching the other side of the board, or trapping or eliminating the opponent. (Examples: CHECKERS, CHESS, OTHELLO)

Circuit Game: A game in which players move clockwise around the perimeter of the gameboard, continuing around the board until the criteria for winning have been met. Also referred to as "Monopoly-style game." (MONOPOLY is a trademark of Parker Brothers.)

Coated Stock: Box paper or cards with a shiny protective finish. Almost all game boxes and gameboards after 1860 used coated stock and can therefore be cleaned without rubbing off the design or illustration. Descriptions should state if a game does *not* have coated stock.

Combination Game: A game box that offers a multitude of games, often with different games being designed to be played on the same gameboard.

Components: The complete contents of a game. (See also **Implements**).

Condition (Cond): The state of being of a game and its components. The condition of the box cover usually is not as good as that of the gameboard. Tears, punctures, dings, creases, warping, missing paper, edge wear, fading or discoloration, ink marks, soiling, water stains, taping, or sewing detract from condition. General terminology for condition includes:

Mint: pristine condition; as good as new; box unmarked and contents unused; very few pre–World War II games can be described accurately as Mint; newer games that were shrink-wrapped should have wrapping intact, and components should still be sealed if originally packaged that way.

Near Mint (Nr Mint): implements unwrapped; game may have been played; very minor wear on box edges; no markings or discoloration, though game box or components may show minor sign of age; very few pre–World War II games can be described accurately as Near Mint.

Excellent (Ex): game has been used and shows some imperfections or mild wear, but overall litho is good and clean; one split apron may be okay.

Very Good (VG): box shows some wear but litho intact, colors faded, cards worn or bent, gameboard rough at edges or along center fold.

Good (G): game shows general wear and minor damage such as tears, creases, discoloration, stray marks, or tiny litho piece missing.

Fair (F): game shows heavy use, rough edges, split aprons, soiling, minor tears in litho, but box is still reasonably firm and majority of cover litho is intact.

Poor (P): box nearly crushed or badly warped, aprons torn and sections missing, pieces of litho missing, heavy soiling, discoloration, stray marks.

Flat: Most or all aprons missing or torn off. (This is not a category and should be used in conjunction with one of the above classifications referring to condition of the lithography; for example, "Box flat but litho Ex.")

Conundrums: Technically defined as "riddles or baffling problems," the term "conundrums" was often used to describe early card games that employed a fill-in-the-blank question-and-answer form of play. (See also **Mad-Libs**).

Copy: The written words (as well as individual code numbers and letters) that appear on box covers and gameboards. (See also **Second-line Copy**) (*Note*: For clarity, the term "photocopy" should be used rather than "copy" when referring to sets of instructions and catalogs that have been duplicated from the original.)

Crease: A line made from the wrinkling or buckling of the paper on a game box, board, or card. A corner crease is a crease that runs one to three inches from the corner of a box cover toward the center; this is usually caused by the placement of a smaller game on top of a larger one so that the weight of the upper game, which is not supported by the sides of the box below, presses down on the middle of the box cover.

Dexterity Game: (See **Skill-and-Action Game**)

Dice: Small cubes with "pips" (small colored indentations) on each face, each face having a different number of pips, with the pips of opposite faces always totaling seven. Early dice were usually made of bone, sometimes ivory, and often were very tiny; wooden dice were also used. In a descriptive game listing, "special dice" means that one or more sides of each die was blank or had a special symbol instead of pips. Many early manufacturers provided teetotums instead of dice because dice were seen as gambling devices and therefore "tools of the devil." Because the personal effects of soldiers killed during the Civil War were sent back to the families (and the families would not approve of dice), soldiers often buried dice before going into battle, making Civil War battlefields a great repository of early American dice.

Die: Singular of "dice." (In listing implements, "one die" is redundant; "a die" is correct.)

Die-Cast: Three-dimensional heavy metal pieces that have been manufactured from a mold.

Die-cut: Machine-made cuts in cardboard; "die-cut pieces" refers to playing pieces cut out of the build-up or parts sheet, and "die-cut gameboard" refers to sections or holes cut out of the board. **Unpunched** signifies die-cut pieces that are still attached to the surrounding cardboard.

Dimensions: The measurements of a game, always stated with the horizontal figure given first. Depth of a game box usually is not noted unless it exceeds two inches. The box and gameboard dimensions are given separately, unless the board is a standard one-fold board that opens to the same length and twice the height of the dimensions of the game box. In other words, if a game box is 14″ (width) by 9″ (height), the gameboard would be a one-fold board approximately 14″ × 18″ unfolded unless otherwise stated. Board dimensions are indicated if the gameboard unfolds to 18″ × 14″ or if the fold is on the short side of the board which makes it open into a 28″ × 9″ board (as some horse-race games do).

Ding: A small dent in a gameboard or box, less than a puncture.

Edge: The portion of the box cover where the top and the aprons meet; usually the first part of a game to show signs of use and wear.

Electric Questioner: Style of battery-operated game, usually a question and-answer game, in which various thin cardboard sheets with small holes in them are placed over a metallic build-up, requiring a player using two built-in wires to touch the correct two holes (corresponding to a question and the appropriate answer or to two matching items); a small bulb lights or a buzzer rings when a correct match is made, thereby completing an electrical circuit. The name comes from the title of one of the earliest games of this type, made by the Knapp Electric Company.

Embossing (Emb): Raised lettering, illustration, or pattern sometimes found on the box wrap or wraparound litho, and on some wooden game pieces such as tiles used for Anagrams. The Embossing Company of Albany, New York, produced many styles of embossed games, especially from the 1920s through the 1940s.

Fish Pond Variant: Any game that employs the same principle as the games of FISH POND—that is, where a string and/or pole with a hook on the end is used to pick up objects from the board or table, each object having a different point value; the objects are usually cardboard fish but can also be cardboard submarines (as in Willis G. Young's SUBMARINE DRAG RACE), wood blocks, or even airplanes (as in Parker Brothers' WE game).

Flap: The portion of an envelope that seals it; many advertising games and premiums were distributed in envelopes, and usually the flap is now missing or torn. Box aprons are often mistakenly called "flaps."

Flat: (See **Condition**)

Gameboard (Board or Bd): The playing surface of a board game; usually litho-covered cardboard but sometimes wood or metal or, more rarely, cloth, felt, and even paper. In listings, the type of gameboard should be described if it is other than a one-fold cardboard gameboard. The vertical or horizontal orientation of a gameboard is indicated by giving the horizontal dimension first (See **Dimensions**). Types of gameboards include: one-piece (nonfolding) boards that are removable from the box, non-removable box bottom boards (See **Box Bottom Board**), nonremovable build-up boards (see **Build-up**), two-fold (three section) boards, and the uncommon three-fold (four section) boards. Special gameboards need to be described individually—for example, the boards for some large pre-1900 Parker Brothers' games, such as BATTLE OF WATERLOO and the Corey Game Company's 1941 game BLOCKADE, in which the box bottom and the build-up are one piece. Other special boards include split-fold boards that have a portion of gameboard cut to allow for multiple folds (found more often in modern war and simulation games and in bookshelf

games), box cover boards (where the game box houses only the components and the game is actually played right on the box cover), and cereal pack boards (where the board is cut from the back of a box of cereal).

Generic game: A game in the public domain, not trademarked or owned by any one company. (For example, TIDDLEY WINKS and TIC-TAC-TOE.)

Graphics: The "look" or design of a box cover, gameboard, or card, based on the illustration, the type style used, the paper, and the use of color; the term is often used interchangeably with "Lithography." (See **Lithography**)

Implements (Imps): The contents of a game, other than the gameboard and instructions, such as playing pieces, cards, play money, spinner, dice, and dice cup. Implements, sometimes called "utensils," were usually packed under the build-up or in a tray in the box bottom, or they would come in a separate **Implements Box** or **Parts Box**. All the items sold with the game—the implements plus the gameboard and instructions and any advertising inserts—make up the **components**.

Insert: Any advertisement or manufacturer's/publisher's notice included with the game but separate from the instructions. Common inserts include cards or small brochures advertising other games in the company's line; less common were promotional endorsements for the game or explanatory notes from the manufacturer (such as notes during wartime that explained changes in playing pieces or colors due to a shortage of materials).

Instructions (Instr): Directions for playing the game. Though often called "rules," rules are actually laws governing play or procedural steps detailed within the instructions. A description of a game should indicate whether the instructions are printed inside the box cover (Instr in cvr), on the gameboard, on the box cover, or on a single or folded sheet (instr sheet). Instructions of more than one folded sheet (five pages) up to sixteen pages are referred to as an "instruction booklet" (instr bklt); instructions of more than sixteen pages, such as those found in modern tactical or electronic games, or games requiring a lot of assembly, are referred to as "instruction manuals." Some games had instructions included in a story booklet or question-and-answer book.

Litho: Short for "lithography" or "lithograph."

Lithography or **Lithograph** (Litho): Though the latter is defined as a "print" and the former as a "process," the term "litho" has come to mean the mechanically printed or photographically reproduced image that covers the game box and gameboard. The advent of the lithographic process was the most important factor leading to the mass production of games. Prior to the refinement of the lithographic process around 1860, most games were hand-colored. **Graphics** refers to the design or artwork, "lithography" to the process of reproduction, including color reproduction, though both words are often used interchangeably. A **litho sheet** is a designed and printed paper that is pasted onto the cardboard gameboard or on top of the box wrap; a **wraparound litho** is a sheet that covers the entire outside box cover, including the aprons, thereby eliminating the need for the box wrap.

Mad-Libs: Games employing a booklet in which a story is written with blank spaces in place of many of the words, the idea being to supply words before knowing the story, so that when the story is read with the inappropriate words inserted the results are humorous; usually the game came with small, thin cards with words on them; the cards were chosen at random and used to fill in the blanks in the story. One of the earliest types of game, best exemplified by the many PETER CODDLES games; though usually noncompetitive (no winner), some later games indicated that the player who chose (by luck of the draw) the most appropriate word cards was the winner. Sometimes referred to as "conundrums" in the nineteenth century; current terminology comes from the pencil-and-paper game MAD-LIBS, first published in 1958 and now a registered trademark of Price/Stern/Sloan Publishers, Inc.

Marker: (See **Playing Pieces**)

Mint: (See **Condition**)

Movement Cards (Mvmt cds): Small cards (usually about half the size of a playing card) that, along with dice or spinner, govern movement along a path or track on a gameboard.

Parcheesi-style: Type of game in which a player moves each playing piece (usually four) clockwise around the gameboard once and then along a path to the center of the board. (PARCHEESI is a trademark of Hasbro-Bradley.)

Parts Box: Small box containing the implements for a game when the gameboard was sold unboxed; also called **Implements Box** and **Utensils Box.**

Path Game: A game in which players move their playing piece or pieces in one direction along adjacent spaces that make up a meandering trail, beginning at "Start," and ending at "Finish," the space where the first player to arrive is the winner. (Examples: CANDYLAND; UNCLE WIGGILY)

Pawn: (See **Playing Pieces**)

Pencil-and-paper game: Any game playable with just pencil and paper, such as BATTLESHIP and TIC-TAC-TOE; some manufactured games are based on pencil-and-paper games, once called "slate" games.

Pin-the-Tail Variant: Any game like PIN THE TAIL ON THE DONKEY in which blindfolded players pin objects onto a large linen or paper gameboard affixed to a wall.

Playing Pieces (pieces): Small objects, often called "men," used to represent a player's position on the gameboard. Though the terms ascribed to various playing pieces are frequently used interchangeably, the suggested terminology for four specific types of playing pieces is as follows:

Disks: small, flat, circular pieces (usually made of ivory, ivoroid, bone, celluloid, Bakelite, plastic, or cardboard), all the same shape but sometimes of different sizes (for example, the large, flat "tiddle" and the smaller "wink" in TIDDLEY WINKS), sometimes referred to as **counters.** (See **Markers**)

Markers: small circular wood pieces of the same shape about one- quarter of an inch high with flat top and bottom, being all of one color when there is no need to distinguish ownership (for example, BINGO markers), or of different colors when designed to differentiate between players; also called **counters.**

Pawns: figural pieces narrow at the top and broad at the bottom, usually made of wood or plastic, which use different colors to distinguish between players; based on the pawns used in chess. (Example: CLUE). Nineteenth century wood playing pieces that were cut or "turned" on a lathe were often referred to as "turned men."

Tokens: playing pieces, usually metal, designed and shaped into different figures, where shape is normally used to differentiate ownership (for example, in MONOPOLY), but where color may differentiate ownership and shape may indicate value differences (for example, in CONFLICT).

Proprietary game: A game owned by a particular company and not in the public domain (for example, MONOPOLY, PARCHEESI, SCRABBLE).

Reproduction (Repro): A copy of the original. (See also **Copy.**) Few repros of original games exist, so the collector normally does not have to fear buying a fake (however, new color laser technology may change that); in the later 1900s, Milton Bradley reproduced approximately five classic card games from the late 1800s, including AUTHORS, and Schackman issued reproductions of some games and puzzles, including a variation of Snyder Brothers' 1904 game TROLLEY, called TRAINS; there are also reproductions on the market of specific catalogs from Bliss, Milton Bradley, Horsman, and Parker Brothers; all the repros were clearly marked as such.

Rules: (See **Instructions**)

Second-line Copy: The subtitle or secondary title of a game. For example (in italic), HOP OFF, *THE NEW AIRPLANE GAME* or EXCUSE ME, *A GAME OF MANNERS FOR CHILDREN*. The alternate title of a game (usually found only on nineteenth Century games) may also be considered as second-line copy. For example, LOGOMACHY OR *WAR OF WORDS*. Most brief listings of games, such as for-sale lists, do not include the second-line copy.

Sewn: The term used to refer to box aprons that have been attached to the box cover with thread or yarn (before the advent of tape).

Shrink-Wrap: The thin plastic film or covering completely encasing newer games; also, the process of wrapping in which the film, when heated, shrinks and adheres firmly to the product.

Skill-and-Action Game (S&A): A boxed game requiring the player to engage in a specific physical activity, including games in which something is thrown, tossed, tiddled, shot, spun, rolled, slid, balanced, carried, hooked, and so forth. The most common skill-and-action games are ring toss, tiddley winks, indoor target games, skittles (bowling games), and some marble games. (Games with tops are usually just **action games**, since the player has no control over the movement or direction of the top.) Often called **dexterity games**, S&A games usually require (and help develop) eye-hand coordination.

Skittles: An indoor bowling game with pins, usually painted wood or cardboard with lithographed figures, such as soldiers. Also called **Nine Pins** and **Ten Pins**, depending on the number of figures.

Slipcase: The jacket-style box cover, open on one end, that slipped over a folded wooden gameboard; slipcases were used almost exclusively by McLoughlin Brothers for its three-in-one games of the 1870s and 1880s.

Spinner: A device used instead of dice that dictates a player's move; it usually consists of a metal arrow attached to a small, square card with sections divided into pie shapes on which numbers or directions are written; early spinners were sometimes affixed to the gameboard (especially a build-up board), pasted on a wood base (called a **block spinner**), or made with a small, heavy metal base that was placed directly on the gameboard; often referred to in early games as an **indicator**. (See also **teetotum**)

Swath: A small strip or piece of lithography torn from the game box or gameboard, usually the result of the removal of a price sticker; unless stated, a swath is approximately the size of a nickel ("small swath" = size of a dime; "large swath" = size of a quarter).

Teetotum,: An early game device shaped like a top and used to determine the number of spaces or moves a player was allowed. Teetotums served the same purpose as dice but were used in their stead, as dice were considered gambling devices and "tools of the devil." Many teetotums had a wooden shaft that was inserted into a hexagonal piece of cardboard with six numbers.

Tiddle: The larger disk in a game of TIDDLEY WINKS; to snap the large tiddle against your smaller disk, the **wink**, was the procedure "to tiddle your wink."

Token: (See **Playing Pieces**)

Track Game: Type of game in which a player moves a playing piece in one direction once around the outer edge of the gameboard, as in various auto race and horse race games, a player winning usually after reaching the space from which the player started.

Turned men: (See **Playing pieces**)

Unpunched: Die-cut pieces or sections (usually on a parts sheets or the gameboard) that have not been separated from the surrounding board.

Wink: The smaller disk in a game of TIDDLEY WINKS. (See also **tiddle**)

Xenogameophobe: A collector opposed to the acquisition of games not manufactured in his or her country.

Suggested Reading

Special Books with Information on Games

Anderson, Brian, and Iona and Robert Opie. *The Treasures of Childhood*. New York: Arcade Publishing, 1989. Oversized, coffee-table book with brilliantly reproduced photographs, primarily showing English games, toys, and books.

DiNoto, Andrea (Ed.). *The Encyclopedia of Collectibles*, volume F-H. Alexandria, VA: Time-Life Books, 1978. The section on games, written by Lee Dennis, contains historical background and some of the best color photos to appear in print (some a full page), including Ives's MANSION OF HAPPINESS and THE NATIONAL GAME OF THE AMERICAN EAGLE, McLoughlin's DISTRICT MESSENGER BOY, GAME OF GOLF, HIDE AND SEEK, MAN IN THE MOON, RIVAL POLICEMEN, and TELEGRAPH BOY, Parker's PING PONG, SIEGE OF HAVANA, TRAIN FOR BOSTON, and WAR OF NATIONS, Bradley's AUTO RACE and FLIVVER GAME, and George Child's GAME OF FOOTBALL (1895).

Frederick, Filis. *Design and Sell Toys, Games, & Crafts*. Radnor, PA: Chilton Book Co., 1977. Includes historical articles on BLOCKHEAD, MANCALA, Milton Bradley, Charles Darrow, MONOPOLY, Alexander Randolph, Herb Schaper, SCRABBLE, and TWIXT but perpetuates the myths of COOTIE and MONOPOLY.

Hake, Ted. *Hakes' Guide to TV Collectibles*. Radnor, PA: Wallace-Homestead, 1990. Includes TV games listed under their respective shows, plus chapter on "Game Show Games," including BREAK THE BANK, NAME THAT TUNE, WHAT'S MY LINE, and nine others.

Made for New York: Antique Toys From The Lawrence Scripps Wilkinson Collection. New York: New-York Historical Society, 1986. Exhibit catalog including a brief social commentary on games, a "select index of toy manufacturers," and photographs of BRINGING UP FATHER, CHIROMAGICA, DISTRICT MESSENGER BOY, FLYING THE UNITED STATES AIR MAIL, FOXY GRANDPA, HOP SCOTCH TIDDLEDY WINKS, MAIL EXPRESS AND ACCOMMODATIONS, and NEWPORT YACHT RACE.

McClinton, Katharine Morrison. *Antiques of American Childhood*. New York: Clarkson N. Potter, 1970. A classic work, now out of print, containing a detailed history of early game manufacturing in the United States, lists of pre-1900 Milton Bradley and Parker Brothers' games, and photos of Ives's MANSION OF HAPPINESS, Bradley's CHECKERED GAME OF LIFE, and Parker's BANKING, CHIVALRY, CHRISTIAN ENDEAVOR, INNOCENCE ABROAD, THE RACE FOR THE CUP, and WATERLOO.

Petretti, Allan. *Petretti's Coca Cola Collectibles Price Guide*. Hackensack, NJ: Nostalgia Publications, 1991. Extensive, revised 1989 hard-cover book on Coke collectibles, including games such as BINGO, BO LYN'S FLIP FOOTBALL, HOUSEHOLD WORDS, SHANGHAI, and CHINESE CHECKERS and a PARCHEESI variant, both with "Coca-Cola" insignias, plus Milton Bradley games marked "Compliments ,of the Coca-Cola Company," such as BROADSIDES and WINKO BASEBALL.

Slocum, Jerry, and Jack Botermans. *Puzzles Old and New*. Seattle: University of Washington Press, 1986. Excellent book on mechanical, dexterity, and paper puzzles, including those made by the Embossing Co., McLoughlin Brothers, Parker Brothers, Pressman, Selchow & Righter, and other game companies.

Toys and Games. Alexandria, VA: Time-Life Books, 1991. Six pages of this beautifully illustrated book are devoted to board, card, and action games, and two to marble games, with a brief history and photos of more than 40 games by Ives, McLoughlin, Reed, S&R, and others; most of the photo captions, however, do not clearly identify the companies.

Tumbusch, Tom. *Illustrated Radio Premium Catalog and Price Guide*. Tomart Publications, 1989. Includes radio premiums that were games, usually found in or on the back of cereal boxes.

Whitton, Blair. *Bliss Toys and Dollhouses*. New York: Dover Publications, 1979. Includes reproduction of the 1911 Bliss catalog, showing numerous wooden marble, ring-toss, beanbag, and target games.

———. *Paper Toys of the World*. Cumberland, MD: Hobby House Press, 1986. Shows pages from McLoughlin, Bradley, and Parker catalogs.

Books on Games

Bell, R C. *Board and Table Games from Many Civilizations 1*. New York: Oxford University Press, 1969 (2nd ed.). This revised reprint of Bell's 1960 book is a classic, historical study of the origin of ancient games and their infusion into modern, Western culture; games are categorized according to method of gameplay (race games, war games, games of position, etc.) bibliographic source is included for each entry; covers all classic games, including BACKGAMMON, CHECKERS, CHESS, FOX AND GEESE, GO, GO-MOKU, GOOSE, LUDO, MA-JONG, MANCALA, NINE MEN'S MORRIS, PACHISI, PATOLLI, and WARI.

———. *Board and Table Games from Many Civilizations 2*. New York, 1969. This classic work supplements the previous volume (above), including additional games by game-play classification in the same six chapters from the first book, and adding four new chapters: "Games with Numbers," "Card Games Requiring Boards," "Games Requiring Manual Dexterity," and "Gaming-Counters."

———. *The Boardgame Book*. Los Angeles, CA: The Knapp Press, 1979. Oversized, lavishly illustrated book contains photos of actual game boards, mostly ancient and classic games such as GO, GOOSE, HALMA, NINE MEN'S MORRIS, PACHISI, and SENAT, plus UP TO KLONDYKE (probably American ±1898) and J. Pressman's CHINESE CHECKERS; comes with four separate large sheets with eight full-size gameboard illustrations.

———. *Discovering Old Board Games*. Aylesbury, Bucks., England: Shire Publications, 1980. Second edition of 1973 book covers origins and rules of mostly ancient and historic strategy games, including FOX AND GEESE, GO, LUDO, NINE MEN'S MORRIS, PACHISI, REVERSI, SENAT, SHUT THE BOX, and games from specific countries.

The Book of Classic Board Games. Palo Alto, CA: Klutz Press, 1990. This 10″ × 10″ book on how to play such historic games as MANCALA and NINE MEN'S MORRIS (and other classic games slightly altered or renamed) was cited for its design and the quality of the original illustrations of its gameboards, which lay flat so readers can play the games with the attached stone-style markers and dice.

Botermans, Jack, and Tony Burrett, Pieter van Delft, and Carla van Splunteren. *The World of Games.* New York: Facts on File, Inc., 1989. History and rules for many ancient and classic games or the world, including GO, HALMA, NINE MEN'S MORRIS, SENAT, TIC-TAC-TOE, and WARI.

Costello, Matthew J. *The Greatest Games of All Time.* New York: John Wiley & Son, 1991. The games people have played, from the games of the Pharaohs to Nintendo, and the stories of the games' inventors and players, with more than 80 illustrations, including those of games you can play.

Dennis, Lee. *Antique American Games, 1840–1940.* Elkins Park, PA: Warman Publishing Co., 1986. First-of-its-kind price guide with more than 600 photographs, 49 in color; prices are out of date, but the book will never be; contains brief historical and collecting information.

Diagram Group. *The Way to Play.* New York: Paddington Press, 1975, and Bantam Books, 1977. Histories, rules, and drawings of many board and card games, many ancient and classic, including GO and HALMA, and proprietary games such as CLUEDO (CLUE), DIPLOMACY, MONOPOLY, and SCRABBLE.

Diagram Visual Information Ltd. *Rules of the Game: Board and Tile Games.* New York: Paddington Press, 1974, and Crown Publishers, 1977. Histories and rules of classic games, including FOX AND GEESE, GAME OF GOOSE, LUDO, NINE MEN'S MORRIS, PACHISI, and SNAKES AND LADDERS.

Gibson, Walter. *Family Games America Plays.* Garden City, NY: Doubleday, 1970. An excellent book by the man who created "The Shadow" for radio, offering strategies and standard and optional rules for many games, including AUTHORS, BATTLESHIP, FLINCH, FOX AND GEESE, GO TO THE HEAD OF THE CLASS, HALMA, JACKSTRAWS, MAH-JONGG, MONOPOLY, PARCHEESI, PIT, RACK-O, REVERSI, ROOK, SCRABBLE, STRATEGO, and TIDDLYWINKS.

Grunfeld, Frederic V. *Games of the World.* New York: Plenary Publications International, 1975. Excellent book covering history and rules of many games of the world, including CAROMS, CHINESE CHECKERS, FOX AND GEESE, GO, GOOSE, LOTTO, PACHISI, SENET, SNAKES AND LADDERS, SHUT THE BOX, and WARI, with instructions for making the gameboards.

Leeming, Joseph. *Games to Make and Play at Home.* New York: D. Appleton-Century Co., 1943. This book of various indoor and outdoor games includes rules for AMERICAN BAGATELLE, THE DONKEY'S TAIL (PIN-THE-TAIL-ON-THE-DONKEY, FIVE-IN-A-ROW or GOBAN (GOBANG), FOX AND GEESE, HALMA, HANGMAN, THE GAME OF INDIA, JACKSTRAWS (PICK UP STICKS), LETTERS AND WORDS (ANAGRAMS), MILL, NINE MEN'S MORRIS or MERELLES, SALVO, TENPINS, and numerous toss games, indoor golf and croquet games, and classic card games.

Leggett, Jeanette Miller. "Illustrated Games in the United States". Scranton, PA: thesis for Maywood (PA) College, 1990. A scholarly examination of the style and type of illustration used on games manufactured in the U.S.

Levy, Richard C., and Ronald O. Weingartner. *Inside Santa's Workshop.* New York: Henry Holt & Co., 1990. This insider's look at the relationship between the "external" game-inventing community and the major game manufacturing companies profiles 75 leading inventors; the book will be released in paperback under the Fireside label with the proposed title *From Workshop to Toystore.*

Love, Brian. *Great Board Games.* New York: Macmillan, 1979. The best of the coffee-table books for the American collector has histories, rules, cardboard playing markers, and large, beautifully reproduced color illustrations of 43 games, 31 of which are American, including ACROSS THE CONTINENT, EDDIE CANTOR'S "TELL IT TO THE JUDGE," BING CROSBY'S CALL ME LUCKY, DEPARTMENT STORE, HOPALONG CASSIDY, INNOCENCE ABROAD, THE LONE RANGER, LOUISA, MANSION OF HAPPINESS, MICKEY MOUSE LUDO, NELLY BLY, RADIO GAME FOR LITTLE FOLKS, A TRIP WITH PHOEBE SNOW, and HENDRIK VAN LOON'S WIDE WORLD GAME.

———. *Play the Game.* Los Angeles, CA: Reed Books, 1979. Oversize book similar in quality and style to his *Great Board Games.*

Meyer, Jerome S. *The Big Fun Book.* New York: Greenberg, Publishers, Inc., 1940. Contains hundreds of pencil-and-paper and parlor games, some of which Meyer made into various boxed party games, such as MENTAL WHOOPEE (1936, Simon & Schuster).

Murray, Harold J. *History of Boardgames Other than Chess.* New York: Oxford University Press, 1952. Considered the classic work of its time, this scholarly book covers early games classified by style of paly (games of alignment and configuration, war games, hunt games, race games, etc.) and includes a chapter on the origin and world distribution of board games and an index of more than 700 game titles.

Orbanes, Philip. *The Monopoly Companion.* Boston: Bob Adams, Inc., 1988. History, strategies, and trivia for MONOPOLY.

Peek, Steven. *Gameplan: The Game Inventor's Handbook.* White Hall, VA: Betterway Publications, 1987. A primer for prospective inventors who want to design, manufacture, and market games.

Piggott, John, and Richard Sharp. *The Book of Games.* New York: Galahad Books, 1977. Alphabetical lisitng of many games, with histories, rules, and drawings, including FOX AND GEESE, GO, HALMA, LUDO, MAH-JONGG, MANCALA, MASTERMIND, REVERSI, SCRABBLE, SNAKES AND LADDERS, SNAP, the game of SNIP, SNAP SNOREM, TICK-TACK-TOE, and TIDDLYWINKS.

Polizzi, Rick, and Fred Schaefer. *Spin Again: Boardgames from the Fifties and Sixties.* San Francisco: Chronicle Books, 1991. Coffee-table nostalgia book with 170 photos includes brief histories of companies to accompany the firm's most notable game; chapters by theme include children's games, space, sports, television, western, and games for girls/games for boys.

Rinker, Harry L. *Collector's Guide to Toys, Games, and Puzzles.* Radnor, PA: Wallace-Homestead Book Co., 1991. A guide to collecting that includes a brief history of games, an analysis of market trends, lists of resources, and other information of use to game enthusiasts; peppered with pictures of games throughout.

Sackson, Sid. *A Gamut of Games.* New York: Random House, 1969. Games to play (some classics and some newer games by the author), and short reviews of games in print; includes copy of Elizabeth Magie's 1904 patent for MONOPOLY.

Shea, James, Jr. (as told to Charles Mercer). *It's All in the Game.* New York: G.P. Putnam, 1960. The only book that covers the entire history of a game company; a must for collectors.

Slizewski, Tom. *Game Collectors Guide, Vol. 1.* Thornton, CO: Panzer Press, 1989; price guide lists values for hundreds of war games (and others).

Whitehouse, F.R.B. *The Games of Georgian and Victorian Days.* Hertfordshire, England: Priory Press, 1971. Revised 1951 book details history of games and European manufacturers from about 1750 to 1860; includes classics of GOOSE, MAH-JONGG, NINE MEN'S MORRIS, and PARCHEESI.

Wood, Clement, and Gloria Goddard (Eds.). *The Complete Book of Games.* Garden City, NY: Doubleday & Co and Country Life Press, 1940.

Resources

Antique Shows and Flea Markets

There are so many antiques and collectibles shows and flea markets across the country that it would be impossible to list even a respectable sampling of the best. The shows listed here have been recommended by the many game collectors who shop them; since most of the collectors who reported come from the country's Northeast, the majority of the listings are from that region.

The advertisements and articles in the newspapers and magazines catering to collectors will give you current information about antiques shows. Naturally, you'll want to check your own newspapers for local shows.

The All-American Collectors Show: Glendale, CA; (818) 980-5025; two days, indoor.

Allentown Toy Show: Allentown, PA; tel. Bob Bostoff, (516) 791-4858; indoor.

Antique and Collectors' Revival: San Mateo, CA; tel. (707) 942-5079; two days, indoor.

Antique Toy & Doll World Shows: St. Charles, IL; 3 times a year; P.O. Box 34509, Chicago, IL 60634; one of the best of the Midwest shows for games.

Atlanta Antique Toy, Train, & Doll Show: Atlanta, GA; tel. (415) 221-2788.

Atlantique: Atlantic City, NJ; Brimfield Associates Inc., P.O. Box 1800, Ocean City, NJ 08226, tel. 800-526-2724; 2 days, once a year, usually March, indoor; pricey, but for quantity *and* quality of games this could be the country's best show.

The Big "E" Collectibles Show: Springfield, MA; two-day indoor antiques and collectibles show twice a year (Halloween weekend and in April) at the Eastern States Exposition grounds; lots of merchandise, some games, good values; Maven Co., Inc., P.O. Box 1538, Waterbury, CT 06721; tel. (203) 758-3880.

Brimfield Shows: Brimfield, MA; one week, 3 times a year, outdoor; 22 shows opening field after field with hundreds and hundreds of dealers; one of the largest and best shows in the country for games, with some good bargains. Major promoters (all Brimfield, MA 01010) include Mays: Richard May, Route 20, P.O. Box 416, tel. (413) 245-9271; J&J: Route 20, (413) 245-3436; and Heart-O-The-Mart: Pam Moriarty, P.O. Box 26, tel. (413) 245-9556.

Farmington Antiques Weekend: Farmington, CT; Revival Promotions, Box 388, Grafton, MA 01519; 2 days, twice a year, outdoor.

Hartford Papermania: Hillcrest Promotions, PO Box 152, Wethersfield, CT 06109; tel. (203) 563-9975; indoors, 2 days, Jan. and Aug.

Liberty Fair Antiques and Collectibles Expo: Liberty State Park, Jersey City, NJ; Stella Shows, 163 Terrace St., Haworth, NJ 07641; tel. (201) 384-0010; Sunday, once a year, usually June, indoor and out; a good show in a spectacular setting in and around a restored train station on the Hudson overlooking lower Manhattan and the Statue of Liberty.

Manhattan Antiques and Collectibles Triple Pier Expo: NYC; Stella Shows, 163 Terrace St., Haworth, NJ 07641; tel. (201) 384-0010; two days, twice a year, indoor at the Hudson River passenger ship terminals.

Midwest Collectors Toy Assoc. Antique & Collectible Toy & Doll Show: Dayton, OH; April & October; P.O. Box 403 N.D. Station, Dayton, OH 45404, tel. (513) 233-8381.

Philadelphia International Toy Show: Trevose, PA; tel. Bob Bostoff, (516) 791-4858; indoor.

Renninger's Extravaganza: Kutztown, PA; Renningers Promotions, 27 Bensinger Dr., Schuylkill Haven, PA 17972; tel. (717) 385-0104; every Saturday plus three special weekends per year, mostly outdoor.

Renninger's No.1: Adamstown, PA; every Sunday; see "Renninger's Extravaganza."

Associations and Clubs

There are numerous clubs, national and local, for game players, from war-gamers to SCRABBLE players to aficionados of particular strategy games such as GO and OTHELLO. The organizations listed below are those which might be of interest to game collectors.

American Game Collectors Association (AGCA): 4628 S.E. Barlow Drive, Bartlesville, OK 74006. Founded in 1985, dedicated to the collection and preservation of American games, and to research on American games and game companies. Though the focus is on commercially produced games manufactured in the U.S. through World War II, members come from all disciplines and include collectors of television games, '70s and '80s character collectibles, jigsaw puzzles, mechanical puzzles, marbles, architectural blocks, tops, yoyos, paper ephemera, and other memorabilia. The AGCA maintains an archive, consisting of company histories, game and toy catalogs, instructions for games, and other material. The organization has held an annual convention since its founding. Membership is $25 per year ($30 overseas) and includes subscriptions to *Game Times* and *Game Researchers' Notes*.

Antique Toy Collectors of America: 1621 Monk Rd., Gladwyne, PA 19035. The ATCA, in its research into toys and toy companies, often collects information on games along the way, and sometimes publishes reproductions of early game catalogs. Prospective members must be sponsored by current members.

52 Plus Joker: Bill Coomer, 1024 So. Benton, Cape Jirardeau, MO 63701. This organization has members who collect card games, as well as those who specialize in playing cards. Membership is $15 per year and includes the quarterly newsletter "Clear The Decks" and an invitation to the club's annual convention and auction.

Gamers Alliance: P.O. Box 197, East Meadow, NY 11554. This international network of game players and collectors conducts all business by phone and mail; there are no meetings. The *Gamers Alliance Report* is its quarterly publication which offers reviews of new games, and news and views on the hobby and game industry; the focus is on post-WWII games, especially strategy, sport, and simulation games. A search service helps locate games for members. Annual catalogs are distributed free and list games available for sale or trade (no prices are given, so members must ask for the current price or negotiate the best price). There is a master catalog which covers primarily conflict simulation games, a sports catalog, and a catalog of TV-related collectibles. Annual membership is $25.

Marble Collectors' Society of America: P.O. Box 222, Trumbull, CT 06611. Some members collect games which use marbles. Membership in this educational, non-profit organization entitles you to regular newsletters for an annual contribution of $12.

Auction Houses

Included here are several auction houses which typically offer some games in each auction. Price is the cost of annual catalog subscription; do *not* send any money without confirming catalog costs with the auction house.

Auction houses such as Sotheby's (1334 York Avenue, New York, NY 10021, tel. [212] 472-8424), and others periodically hold toy auctions which include games. Local and regional auction houses may be a better source of inexpensive items.

Hake's Americana and Collectibles: P.O. Box 1444, York, PA 17405; tel. (717) 848-1333; four to six catalogs per year; four catalogs = $20.

New England Auction Gallery: P.O. Box 2273BB, W. Peabody, MA 01960; tel. (508) 535-3140; fully illustrated color catalog auctioning toys, games, and character collectibles; 4 catalogs/yr. (with prices realized) = $30.

Noel Barrett Antiques and Auctions: P.O. Box 1001, Carversville, PA 18913; tel. (215) 295-5109; toy auctions sometimes containing games; catalog prices average between $18 and $25 postpaid per auction.

Lloyd Ralston Gallery: 173 Post Road, Fairfield, CT 06430; tel. (203) 255-1233; three to four auctions per yr., mostly toys and trains, some games; $18 per catalog.

Skinner Inc.: 357 Main Street, Bolton, MA 01740; tel. (508) 779-6241; ask for Mim Ewing. Toy and doll auction late spring and late Fall; $14 catalog by mail.

Mail-Order Games

Shop owners, collectors and dealers who sell games by mail and/or publish mail-order catalogs are listed below. *Always* send a self-addressed stamped envelope with your inquiries; if telephoning, please take note of time zone differences, as some telephone numbers shown are home numbers.

The Big Game Hunter, 620 Park Ave, #202, Rochester, NY 14607; tel. (716) 442-8998; collector, dealer, and mail order.

Darrow's Fun Antiques, 309 E. 61st Street, New York, 10021; tel. (212) 838-0730; shop; game locating service.

Robert DeCenzo, 18 Barber Rd., Framingham, MA 01701; tel. (508) 879-8541; dealer & mail order.

Paul Fink, Box 266, Kent, CT 06757; tel. (203) 927-4001; collector, dealer, and mail order.

Gamers Alliance (see "Associations")

Just Kids Nostalgia, 326 Main Street, Huntington, NY 11743; tel. (516) 423-8449; shop; approximately 3 catalogs per year, 50-75 pages, all items photographed, $3 per catalog.

Robert LaFerriere, 40 Harrington Rd., N. Kingston, RI 02852; tel, (401) 884-5013; periodic mail listings.

Games People Play, 1105 Mass. Ave., Cambridge, MA 02138; tel. (508) 492-0711; shop & mail order.

Debby and Marty Krim, PO Box 2273BB, W. Peabody, MA 01960; tel. (508) 535-3140; collector, dealer, and mail order.

The Load of Mischief, Peter Barrett, 1250 Yosemite Ave., San Jose, CA 95126; tel. (408) 279-1628; shop & mail order.

Lloyd Ralston Gallery, 173 Post Road, Fairfield, CT 06430; tel. (203) 255-1233; shop & mail order.

Of Dice and Men, 161 Belmont St., Carbondale, PA 18407; tel. (717) 282-3503; inquire re cost of periodic listing of '50s & '60s games.

Schneider's, 3217 Pinewyn Circle, Lancaster, PA 17601; tel. (717) 285-3200; dealer & mail order.

John & Mildred Spear, 1545 Lititz Rd., Manheim, PA 17545; tel. (717) 898-0494; mail listing for pre-1940 games.

Sunsmith House Antiques, Rt. 6A, RR 2, Brewster, MA 02631; mail listing includes pre-1940 games.

Wizard of Os, 57 Lakeshore Drive, Marlboro, MA 01752; Tel. (508) 481-1087; dealer & mail order.

Museums

Museums with games on permanent exhibit, archival material, or periodic exhibits.

Essex Institute, 132 Essex Street, Salem, MA 01970; tel. (508) 744-3390.

Museum and Archive of Games, University of Waterloo, BMH Room 1016, Ontario, Canada N2L3G1; tel. (519) 888-4424.

Margaret Woodbury Strong Museum, One Manhattan Square, Rochester, NY 14607; tel. (716) 263-2700.

Washington Dolls House and Toy Museum, 5236 44th Street NW, Washington, DC 20015.

Museums with major toy collections often have games. Local museums around the country may also have material worth noting (if you know of such museums, please let us know). Other museums with archival research material or which sometimes hold special game exhibits include:

American Antiquarian Society, 185 Salisbury St., Worcester, MA 01609; tel. (508) 755-5221.

Children's Museum of Indianapolis, Box 3000, Indianapolis, IN 46206; tel. (317) 924-5431.

Children's Museum of Manhattan, 314 W. 54th St., NY 10019; tel. (212) 765-5904.

Connecticut Valley Historical Museum, 194 State St., Springfield, MA 01103; tel. (413) 732-3080.

Museum of the City of New York, 5th Ave. & 103rd St., New York, NY; tel. (212) 534-1672.

Periodicals Specializing in Games

Every game collector, game enthusiast, or game player should have a subscription to *at least* one of these publications.

Games. Subscriptions: P.O. Box 55483, Boulder, Colorado 80323-5483; Editorial: 19 W. 21st St., New York, NY 10010; bi-monthly magazine covers pencil puzzles, picture puzzles, features, contests, and new games for the game player; each issue has a page of pop-out puzzles printed on perforated pieces of proper paper; six issues per year, $15.

Game Times. The American Game Collectors Association, 4628 S.E. Barlow Drive, Bartlesville, OK 74006. General publication on games and game companies, on building, maintaining, and cataloging a game collection, and on events of interest to collectors; focus is on pre-WWII games; contains classifieds. Published approximately three times a year. Subscription available only with AGCA membership ($25/yr.); back issues available at member and non-member prices.

Game Researcher's Notes. The American Game Collectors Association, 4628 S.E. Barlow Drive, Bartlesville, OK 74006. Published approximately three times a year. Specialized publication provides specific information on game companies and the games they made. Subscription available only with association membership ($25/yr.); back issues available at member and non-member prices.

Gamers Alliance Report. Gamers Alliance, P.O. Box 197, East Meadow, NY 11554; quarterly publication for members of Gamers Alliance (annual membership is $20; see "Clubs"); edited by H.M. Levy; contains detailed reviews of current games plus news about post-war games, gamers conventions, resources.

Name of the Game. Box 721, Plainville, CT 06062; tel. 203 793-2383; bimonthly, $20 (six issues); edited by William Longstreet; focus on contemporary collectibles, esp. TV and film-related including games, informative articles and classifieds.

Strategy Plus. Lamerton House, 27 High Street, Ealing, London W5 5DF, England; monthly magazine, £25; focus on computer, simulation and strategy games of the U.S. and Europe.

World Game Review. 3367-I North Chatham Road, Ellicott City, MD 21043; published by Michael Keller two to four times a year, $8 for four issues; articles on new games, mental puzzles, reviews, resource information.

Index to Game Titles

Subject Index

Makers of games are listed alphabetically in Part Three and Appendix C; those listings are not included in this index.